MODERN SYNTHETIC REACTIONS

THE ORGANIC CHEMISTRY
MONOGRAPH SERIES

ORGANIC REACTION MECHANISMS
Ronald Breslow
Columbia University

MODERN SYNTHETIC REACTIONS
Herbert House
Massachusetts Institute of Technology

INTRODUCTION TO STEREOCHEMISTRY
Kurt Mislow
Princeton University

■ EDITOR'S FOREWORD

AS THE SCIENCE of organic chemistry continues to expand, a need has become apparent for teaching materials which can supplement the usual undergraduate organic chemistry textbook. A good undergraduate will want to go beyond his textbook by independent reading in areas of interest to him, and many teachers find that they personally want to give more emphasis to certain aspects of organic chemistry than is done in an otherwise excellent text. In order to help satisfy this need we have initiated a series of short monographs, usually in paperback form, which examine important topics in organic chemistry in more depth than is possible in comprehensive textbooks. These books are intended to supplement, not supplant, the ordinary introductory text, and they will also be useful in intermediate level courses. If they have any general characteristic, it is their tendency to concentrate on established facts rather than shaky generalizations, bringing the student to current research frontiers and pointing out gaps in our knowledge.

The first volume of this series, *Modern Synthetic Reactions* by Professor Herbert O. House, is in many ways typical. The usual undergraduate textbook presents synthetic reactions with very little real indication of the advantages and limitations of each method. The interested student will want to know more about which oxidation method is really best for a particular purpose, for instance, and in this monograph Professor House presents the needed critical discussion of a variety of important synthetic procedures together with literature references as a further guide for the student. However, this particular book is also ideally suited for use as the textbook in an advanced course on synthetic methods, and it will probably be widely employed by practicing synthetic chemists. For these latter reasons, and because the present monograph is longer than typical members of the series will be, it has been published only in a hardcover edition.

The editor hopes that these books will serve the important teaching purpose for which they are designed. We welcome all suggestions which will help us to provide a truly useful series.

RONALD BRESLOW

New York, New York
October 1964

MODERN SYNTHETIC REACTIONS

HERBERT O. HOUSE MASSACHUSETTS INSTITUTE OF TECHNOLOGY

W. A. BENJAMIN, INC. ■ New York, Amsterdam

1965

MODERN SYNTHETIC REACTIONS

Library of Congress Catalog Card Number 64–25245
Manufactured in the United States of America

*The final manuscript was put into production on March 19, 1964
This volume was published on January 28, 1965; second
printing with corrections December, 1965.*

W. A. BENJAMIN, INC. *New York, New York 10016*

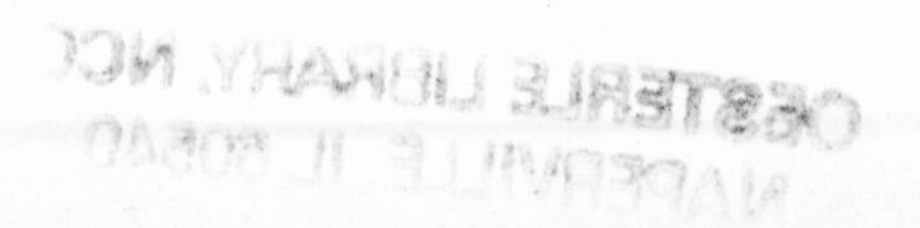

■ PREFACE*

THIS BOOK was written for advanced undergraduate and beginning graduate students of organic chemistry as a survey of certain reactions that currently enjoy widespread application to the synthesis of organic compounds in the laboratory. It was not my intention either to survey all of the important synthetic methods or to offer an exhaustive survey of those reactions which have been included. The Diels-Alder reaction, reactions of organometallic compounds, acylations at oxygen and nitrogen atoms, and elimination reactions leading to the formation of double and triple bonds are examples of important synthetic reactions which have received little, if any, mention. Nevertheless, I believe students will find that the assortment of reactions included have wide applicability to the practical solution of synthetic problems, and I can only hope that someone else, engaged in the training of students, will be sufficiently indignant about my omission of certain reactions to write a second volume which includes them.

The chapters have been written to survey reactions as they are currently used in the organic laboratory; accordingly, many of the references included refer to recent detailed descriptions of the applications of these reactions. In many cases examples have been taken from *Organic Syntheses* because of the detailed

* Written in collaboration with Joseph Ciabattoni, Theodore W. Craig, David B. Ledlie, George M. Rubottom, and Barry M. Trost.

descriptions of experimental procedure which these preparations offer. In general, I have chosen not to trace the historical development of reactions and experimental procedures. However, these references may usually be found in the articles cited. Also, students of organic chemistry today are already burdened with the necessity to assimilate an immense body of factual knowledge, and I believe they should not also be required to concern themselves with which chemist should be allotted priority for discovering a particular reaction or procedure.

Discussions of the mechanisms of the various reactions included have been limited for the most part to statements and expressions of opinion, with leading references. Except for discussions of the stereochemical consequences of the various reactions, I have not reviewed the evidence that has led to the reaction mechanisms proposed since this is not the purpose of this book. In reading the mechanisms suggested, the student will do well to bear in mind that the evidence on which these proposals have been made is often tenuous and the mechanisms proposed may be shown to be partially or totally incorrect as additional evidence is accumulated.

Since the task of citing references to all of the synthetically important modifications of a reaction is impossible for one person to accomplish, I have asked a number of people in this country to offer suggestions of other material that might be included. I am indebted to Drs. W. G. Dauben, C. H. DePuy, E. L. Eliel, D. S. Heywood, K. B. Wiberg, and Mr. P. Starcher for offering suggestions relevant to certain portions of the manuscript, and I am particularly grateful to Drs. A. W. Burgstahler, R. K. Hill, R. E. Ireland, W. S. Johnson, G. Poos, and Mr. G. Mitchell for reading the entire manuscript and offering many helpful suggestions. The burden of preparing the manuscript and index as well as locating references, checking references, and proofreading the manuscript in various stages of preparation was lightened considerably by my five collaborators: Messrs. Joseph Ciabattoni, Theodore W. Craig, David B. Ledlie, George M. Rubottom, and Barry M. Trost, all of whom are currently graduate students at the Massachusetts Institute of Technology. Finally, I am most grateful to Miss G. C. Martin, who typed the entire manuscript.

HERBERT O. HOUSE

Cambridge, Massachusetts
February 24, 1964

CONTENTS

1

· CATALYTIC HYDROGENATION

OF THE MANY REACTIONS AVAILABLE for the reduction of organic compounds, catalytic hydrogenation—the reaction of a compound with hydrogen in the presence of a catalyst—offers the advantages of widespread applicability and experimental simplicity to a unique degree.[1] Catalytic hydrogenation is usually effected in the laboratory by stirring or shaking a solution of the compound to be reduced with a heterogeneous catalyst under an atmosphere of hydrogen gas. The progress of the reduction may be followed readily by measuring the uptake of hydrogen, and the crude reduction product is usually isolated simply by filtration of the catalyst followed by evaporation of the solvent.

(1) (a) H. Adkins and R. L. Shriner in H. Gilman (ed.), *Organic Chemistry, An Advanced Treatise*, Vol. 1, 2d ed., Wiley, New York, 1943, pp. 779–832; (b) G. Schiller in E. Müller (ed.), *Methoden der organischen Chemie* (*Houben-Weyl*), Vol. 4, Part 2, Georg Thieme Verlag, Stuttgart, Germany, 1955, pp. 283–332; (c) K. Wimmer, *ibid*., pp. 163–192; (d) V. I. Komarewsky, C. H. Riesz, and F. L. Morritz in A. Weissberger (ed.), *Technique of Organic Chemistry*, Vol. 2, 2d ed., Wiley-Interscience, New York, 1956, pp. 94–164; (e) F. J. McQuillin in A. Wiessberger (ed.), *Technique of Organic Chemistry*, Vol. II, Wiley-Interscience, New York, 1963, pp. 497–580.

Catalysts, Solvents, and Equipment

The selection of the solvent, reaction temperature, and hydrogen pressure for a given hydrogenation is dependent on the catalyst chosen. It is convenient to divide the common hydrogenation catalysts into the group of certain noble metal catalysts as well as active grades of Raney nickel, which are generally used with low (1 to 4 atm or 0 to 60 psi) hydrogen pressures and at relatively low (0 to 100°) temperatures; and the group of less active catalysts, which are normally used at higher (100 to 300 atm or 1500 to 4500 psi) hydrogen pressures and may require higher (25 to 300°) reaction temperatures.

The noble metal catalysts frequently used for low-pressure hydrogenations contain platinum, palladium, or rhodium. Whereas reductions over platinum frequently employ finely divided metallic platinum obtained by the reduction of platinum oxide (PtO_2)[2] in the hydrogenation apparatus, the palladium[3] and rhodium[4] catalysts are usually deposits of the metal on the surface of an inert support such as carbon, alumina, barium sulfate, calcium carbonate, or strontium carbonate. The activity of a catalyst on an inert support is normally diminished as the support is changed from carbon to barium sulfate to calcium or strontium carbonate. Also, the activity of a given catalyst is generally increased by changing from a neutral, nonpolar solvent to a polar, acidic solvent. Solvents frequently employed for low-pressure hydrogenation include ethyl acetate, ethanol, water, acetic acid, and acetic acid plus perchloric acid. Obviously, the acidic solvents cannot be employed with catalysts that are supported on metal carbonates. Diagrams of typical laboratory equipment used for low-pressure catalytic hydrogenations are provided in Figure 1-1a and b. The apparatus illustrated in Figure 1-1a utilizes a hydrogen pressure of 1 atm, and the hydrogen uptake is measured as the change in volume of the hydrogen gas in the system. Some workers prefer a modification of this apparatus in which the suspension of the catalyst in the reaction solution is shaken rather than stirred.

(2) R. Adams, V. Voorhees, and R. L. Shriner, *Org. Syn.*, **Coll. Vol. 1,** 463 (1944).

(3) (a) E. R. Alexander and A. C. Cope, *Org. Syn.*, **Coll. Vol. 3,** 385 (1955); (b) R. Mozingo, *ibid.*, 685 (1955).

(4) Palladium, platinum, rhodium, and ruthenium catalysts are commercially available from Engelhard Industries, Inc., Chemical Division, 113 Astor St., Newark 14, New Jersey.

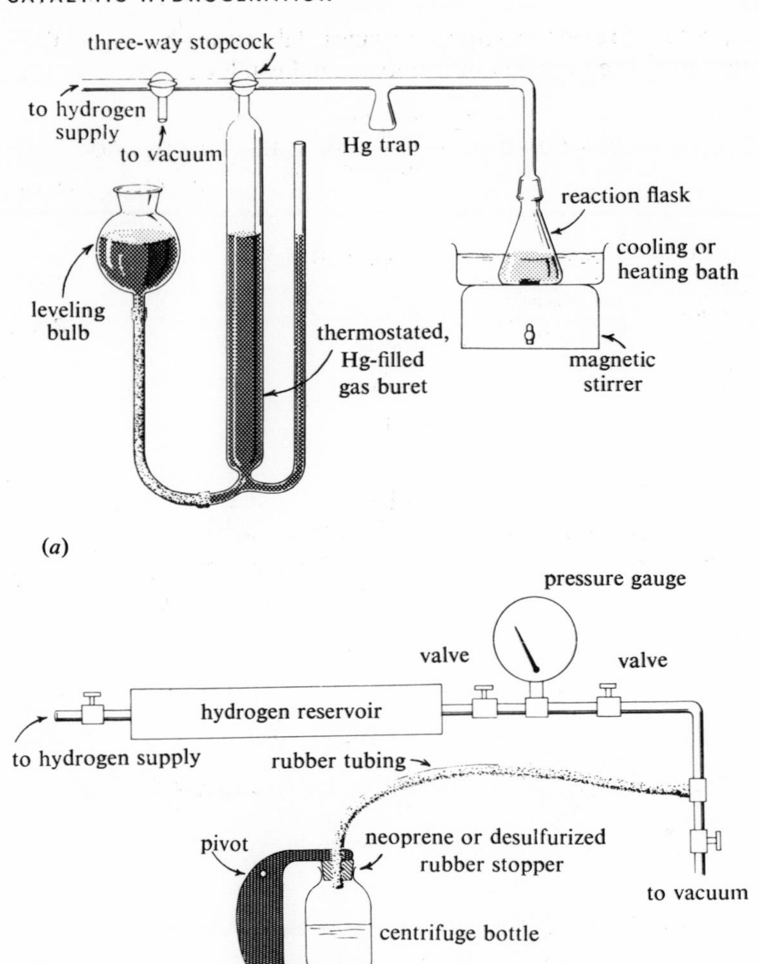

FIGURE 1-1.
Apparatus for low-pressure catalytic hydrogenation.

Apparatus of this type is often used to obtain a quantitative measure of the number of reducible functions in a compound of unknown structure. Figure 1-1b represents apparatus[5] usually used with 2 to 4 atm hydrogen pressure, the hydrogen uptake being measured by observing the pressure change within the system. The following

(5) R. Adams and V. Voorhees, *Org. Syn.*, **Coll. Vol. 1,** 61 (1944).

equations provide examples of typical laboratory hydrogenations that have been effected over noble metal catalysts.

$$C_6H_5—CH{=}CH—CO—C_6H_5 \xrightarrow[CH_3CO_2C_2H_5,\ 25°]{H_2(3\ atm),\ Pt(from\ PtO_2)} C_6H_5—CH_2CH_2—CO—C_6H_5$$

(81–95%) (*Ref. 6*)

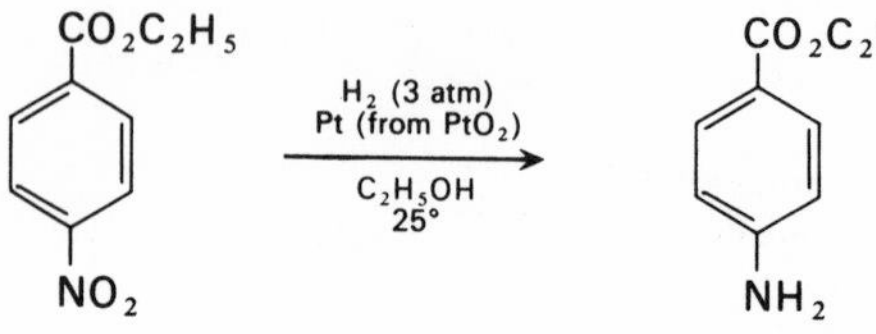

$CO_2C_2H_5$ / NO_2 (benzene ring) $\xrightarrow[C_2H_5OH,\ 25°]{H_2\ (3\ atm),\ Pt\ (from\ PtO_2)}$ $CO_2C_2H_5$ / NH_2 (benzene ring)

(91–100%) (*Ref. 7*)

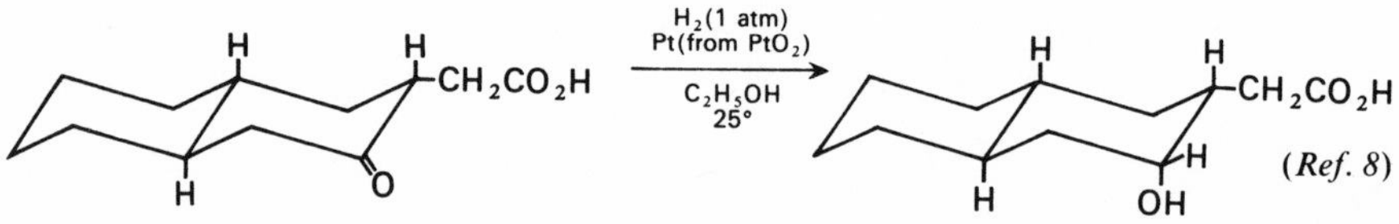

H, H, CH_2CO_2H, H, O $\xrightarrow[C_2H_5OH,\ 25°]{H_2(1\ atm),\ Pt(from\ PtO_2)}$ H, H, CH_2CO_2H, H, H, OH

(74%) (*Ref. 8*)

$(CH_3)_3C$, H, O $\xrightarrow[CH_3CO_2H,\ HCl,\ 25°]{H_2(4\ atm),\ Pt(from\ PtO_2)}$ $(CH_3)_3C$, H, OH, H + $(CH_3)_3C$, H, H, OH

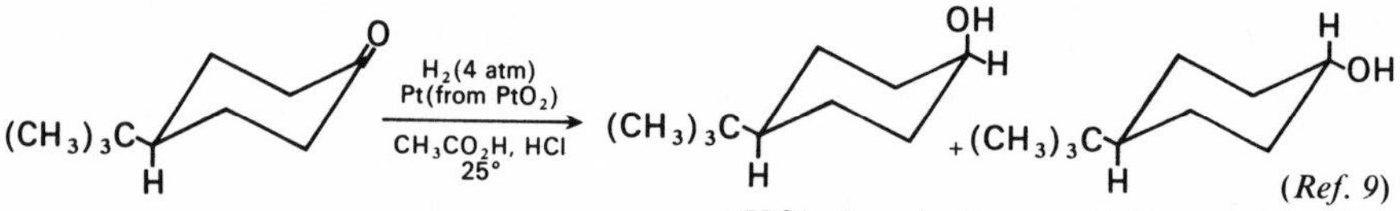

(78% of product) (22% of product) (*Ref. 9*)

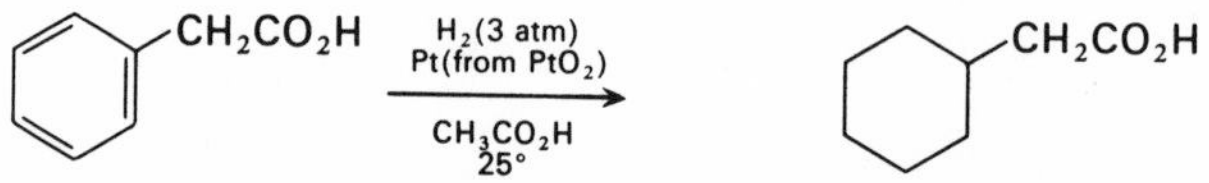

CH_2CO_2H (benzene ring) $\xrightarrow[CH_3CO_2H,\ 25°]{H_2(3\ atm),\ Pt(from\ PtO_2)}$ CH_2CO_2H (cyclohexane ring)

(100%) (*Ref. 10*)

(6) (a) R. Adams, J. W. Kern, and R. L. Shriner, *Org. Syn.*, **Col. Vol. 1,** 101 (1944); see also (b) E. C. Horning, J. Koo, M. S. Fish, and G. N. Walker, *Org. Syn.*, **Coll. Vol. 4,** 408 (1963).

(7) R. Adams and F. L. Cohen, *Org. Syn.*, **Coll. Vol. 1,** 240 (1944).

(8) W. S. Johnson and co-workers, *J. Am. Chem. Soc.*, **83**, 606 (1961).

(9) (a) E. L. Eliel and R. S. Ro, *ibid.*, **79**, 5992 (1957); see also (b) R. J. Wicker, *J. Chem. Soc.*, **1956**, 2165; (c) for a discussion of reaction conditions useful in the reduction of ketones, see E. Breitner, E. Roginski, and P. N. Rylander, *J. Org. Chem.*, **24**, 1855 (1959).

(10) R. Adams and J. R. Marshall, *J. Am. Chem. Soc.*, **50**, 1970 (1928).

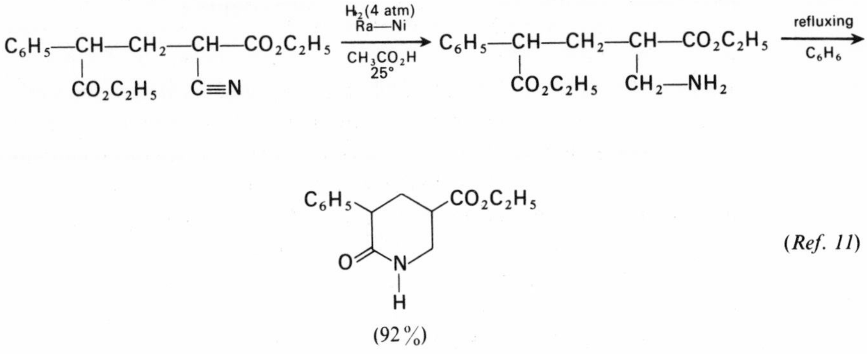

(*Ref. 11*)

A recent modification of the usual low-pressure catalytic hydrogenation technique utilizes the reaction of various metal salts with either sodium borohydride or a trialkyl- or triarylsilane to generate the hydrogenation catalyst.[12] Salts of rhodium, platinum, and palladium are reduced to the finely divided free metals, which may be used directly as catalysts or, preferably, adsorbed on carbon prior to use.[12a] Reaction of excess sodium borohydride with an acid added to the reaction mixture provides a source of hydrogen,

$$H_2PtCl_6 + NaBH_4 + C(\text{powder}) \xrightarrow[25^\circ]{C_2H_5OH} \text{Pt on C}$$

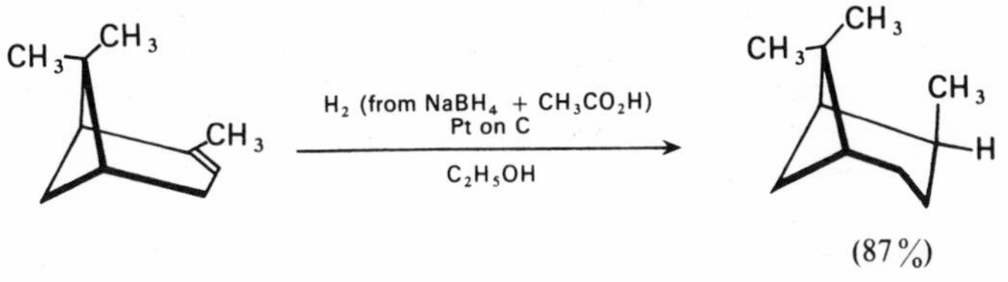

(*Ref. 12a*)

(11) (a) R. K. Hill, C. E. Glassick, and L. J. Fliedner, *ibid.*, **81**, 737 (1959); see also (b) H. J. Dauben, Jr., H. J. Ringold, R. H. Wade, and A. G. Anderson, Jr., *ibid.*, **73**, 2359 (1951).

(12) (a) H. C. Brown and C. A. Brown, *J. Am. Chem. Soc.*, **84**, 1493–1495, 2827, 2829 (1962); (b) H. C. Brown and K. Sivasankaran, *ibid.*, **84**, 2828 (1962); (c) H. C. Brown, K. Sivasankaran, and C. A. Brown, *J. Org. Chem.*, **28**, 214 (1963); (d) R. W. Bott, C. Eaborn, E. R. A. Peeling, and D. E. Webster, *Proc. Chem. Soc.*, **1962**, 337; (e) R. Paul, P. Buisson, and N. Joseph, *Ind. Eng. Chem.*, **44**, 1006 (1952); (f) H. C. Brown and C. A. Brown, *J. Am. Chem. Soc.*, **85**, 1003, 1005 (1963).

permitting the direct hydrogenation of easily reducible functions (nitro groups and unhindered olefins). This procedure, illustrated in the preceding equations, offers the advantage of simplicity. However, it suffers from the fact that the final hydrogenated product must be separated into a number of components in the reaction mixture and that any functional groups present which are reduced by sodium borohydride (see Chapter 2) will also be altered by the reduction procedure. A hydrogenation catalyst, thought to be nickel boride,[12e,12f] has similarly been prepared by the reduction of various nickel salts with sodium or potassium borohydride. This catalyst is reported[12e,12f] to be more reactive than commercially available Raney nickel.

For hydrogenations at relatively high hydrogen pressures (100 to 300 atm), the common catalysts are Raney nickel, copper chromite, and ruthenium[4] supported on carbon or alumina. Raney nickel (abbreviated Ra-Ni)[13] is a porous form of metallic nickel, obtained by reaction of a nickel-aluminum alloy with aqueous sodium hydroxide.[14] Copper chromite (abbreviated $CuCr_2O_4$)[15] is a mixture of copper and chromium oxides. Depending on the physical properties of the compound to be reduced, the

(13) (a) R. Schröter in *Newer Methods of Preparative Organic Chemistry*, Wiley-Interscience, New York, 1948, pp. 61–101; (b) Raney nickel catalyst of ordinary activity, designated W-2, can be purchased or prepared as described by R. Mozingo, *Org. Syn.*, **Coll. Vol. 3,** 181 (1955); more active grades of Raney nickel, designated W-3 to W-7, which are effective at lower hydrogen pressures, may also be prepared: see (c) H. R. Billica and H. Adkins, *ibid.*, 176 (1955), and (d) X. A. Dominguez, I. C. Lopez, and R. Franco, *J. Org. Chem.*, **26**, 1625 (1961); (e) nickel catalysts are commercially available from the Raney Catalyst Co., Inc., Chattanooga, Tennessee, and from Girdler Catalysts, Chemical Products Division, Chemetron Corp., Louisville, Kentucky.

(14) The reduction of organic compounds by reaction with the Raney alloy and aqueous alkali has also been used: for examples, see (a) D. Papa, E. Schwenk, and B. Whitman, *J. Org. Chem.*, **7**, 587 (1942); (b) D. Papa, E. Schwenk, and H. F. Ginsberg, *ibid.*, **16**, 253 (1951); (c) E. Schwenk, D. Papa. H. Hankin, and H. Ginsberg, *Org. Syn.*, **Coll. Vol. 3,** 742 (1955). This procedure may involve, at least in part, a low-pressure catalytic hydrogenation in which the hydrogen liberated from reaction of the aluminum with the aqueous alkali is adsorbed on the surface of the newly formed Raney nickel catalyst; however, certain of the reductions performed by this procedure resemble more closely the subsequently discussed dissolving metal reductions (see Chapter 3).

(15) (a) C. Grundman in *Newer Methods of Preparative Organic Chemistry*, Wiley-Interscience, New York, 1948, pp. 103–123; (b) W. A. Lazier and H. R. Arnold, *Org. Syn.*, **Coll. Vol. 2,** 142 (1943); (c) commercially available from Girdler Catalysts, Chemical Products Division, Chemetron Corp., Louisville, Kentucky.

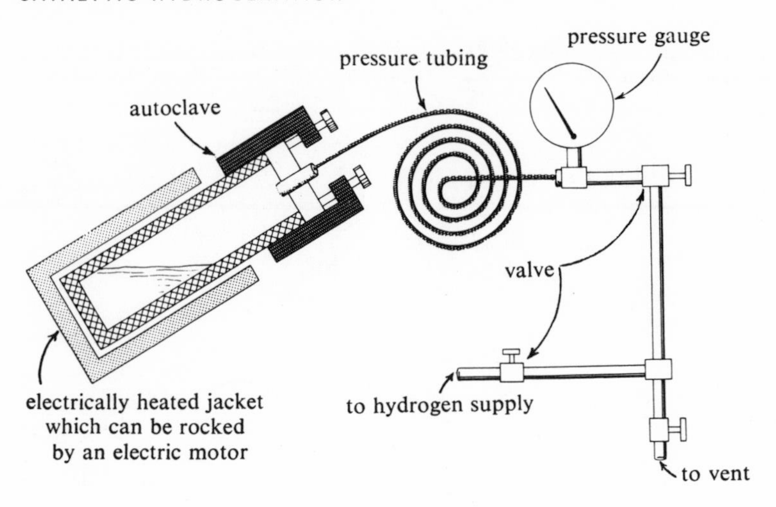

FIGURE 1-2.

Apparatus for high-pressure catalytic hydrogenation.

high-pressure hydrogenations may be performed with or without a solvent. The solvents usually employed with these catalysts are ethanol, water, cyclohexane, or methylcyclohexane. Strongly acidic solvents or reactants cannot be used with nickel or copper chromite because these catalysts will dissolve. Figure 1-2 illustrates a typical autoclave used in the laboratory for high-pressure hydrogenations. The uptake of hydrogen in this apparatus is followed by observing the change in pressure. The total volume of liquid placed in such an apparatus should never exceed one-half the total volume of the autoclave, in order to allow room for the liquid to expand as it is heated. Typical examples of high-pressure laboratory hydrogenations are described by the following equations.

[2-naphthol, OH] $\xrightarrow[C_2H_5OH,\ 90°]{H_2\text{(275 atm)},\ \text{Ra—Ni}}$ [5,6,7,8-tetrahydro-2-naphthol, OH] (86%) + [1,2,3,4-tetrahydro-2-naphthol, OH] (7%) (*Ref. 16*)

(16) H. Adkins and G. Krsek, *J. Am. Chem. Soc.*, **70**, 412 (1948). If the reaction mixture is alkaline during the hydrogenation, the alcohol rather than the phenol becomes the major product [G. Stork, *ibid.*, **69**, 576 (1947)].

$$C_2H_5O_2C—(CH_2)_4—CO_2C_2H_5 \xrightarrow[\text{no solvent, } 255°]{H_2(200\text{ atm}),\ CuCr_2O_4} HO—CH_2—(CH_2)_4—CH_2—OH \quad (85–90\%)$$ (*Ref. 17*)

$$m\text{-}O_2NC_6H_4CH(OCH_3)_2 \xrightarrow[CH_3OH,\ 40–70°]{H_2(67\text{ atm}),\ Ra—Ni} m\text{-}H_2NC_6H_4CH(OCH_3)_2 \quad (67–78\%)$$ (*Ref. 18*)

$$(CH_2)_8\text{-ring } C{=}O / CH—OH \xrightarrow[C_2H_5OH,\ 150°]{H_2(135\text{ atm}),\ CuCr_2O_4} (CH_2)_8\text{-ring } (H)C(OH)—C(H)(OH)\ (48–52\%) + (CH_2)_8\text{-ring } (OH)C(H)—C(H)(OH)\ (27–32\%)$$ (*Ref. 19*)

The rate of a given hydrogenation may be increased by increasing the hydrogen pressure,[20] by increasing the amount of catalyst employed,[6a] or by increasing the temperature. However, many compounds can be reduced either by low-pressure or by high-pressure hydrogenation. The selection of the reaction conditions in such cases is usually determined by the quantity of material to be reduced. The type of low-pressure hydrogenation apparatus illustrated in Figure 1-1a is normally useful for reduction of quantities ranging from 10 mg to 25 g, whereas the apparatus shown in Figure 1-1b is most often used with 10- to 100-g quantities. The high-pressure equipment (Figure 1-2) available in most organic laboratories permits the reduction of 10- to 1000-g quantities.

Reduction of Functional Groups

From the equations previously used to illustrate reaction conditions, it is apparent that a variety of functional groups can be

(17) (a) W. A. Lazier, J. W. Hill, and W. J. Amend, *Org. Syn.*, **Coll. Vol. 2,** 325 (1943); (b) for a discussion and review of this reaction, see H. Adkins, *Org. Reactions*, **8**, 1 (1954).

(18) R. N. Icke, C. E. Redemann, B. B. Wisegarver, and G. A. Alles, *Org. Syn.*, **Coll. Vol. 3,** 59 (1955).

(19) A. T. Blomquist and A. Goldstein, *Org. Syn.*, **Coll. Vol. 4,** 216 (1963).

(20) For example, see C. F. H. Allen and J. VanAllan, *Org. Syn.*, **Coll. Vol. 3,** 63 (1955).

reduced by catalytic hydrogenation. In Table 1-1 the common functional groups are listed in approximate order of decreasing ease of catalytic hydrogenation. This order should not be considered inflexible since special structural features in the compound

TABLE 1-1 ▪

Approximate Order of Reactivity of Functional Groups in Catalytic Hydrogenation

Functional group	Reduction product(s)	Comments
R—CO—Cl	R—CHO	Most easily reduced
$R—NO_2$	$R—NH_2$	
R—C≡C—R	$(H)(R)C{=}C(H)(R)$ (cis)	
R—CHO	$R—CH_2OH$	With Pt catalyst, reduction is accelerated by ferrous ion
R—CH=CH—R	$R—CH_2CH_2—R$	Ease of reduction is decreased by the presence of additional substituents
R—CO—R	R—CHOH—R	
$C_6H_5CH_2OR$	$C_6H_5CH_3$ + ROH	
R—C≡N	$R—CH_2NH_2$	
naphthalene	tetralin	Also partial reduction of other polycyclic aromatic systems
R—CO—O—R′	$R—CH_2OH$ + R′—OH	Pt and Pd catalysts fail to effect these reductions
R—CO—NH—R	$R—CH_2NH—R$	
benzene	cyclohexane	Least easily reduced
$R—CO_2^{\ominus}Na^{\oplus}$		Inert

being reduced or changes in catalyst or reaction conditions sometimes result in interchanging the ease of reduction of functional groups having similar reactivity. However, it is almost always possible to selectively reduce functional groups found near the top of Table 1-1 in the presence of functional groups listed at the bottom of the table, and it is rarely possible to selectively reduce the functional groups listed at the bottom in the presence of the more reactive functions listed at the top. For example, the reduction of an unsaturated ester or ketone to an unsaturated alcohol is normally accomplished with metal hydride reducing agents (Chapter 2) and not by catalytic hydrogenation, whereas reduction of an unsaturated ester or ketone to a saturated ester or ketone is readily achieved by catalytic hydrogenation. The platinum, palladium, and nickel catalysts are most often used for the reduction of isolated carbon-carbon double bonds; the platinum, copper chromite, and ruthenium catalysts are most often used to reduce carbonyl groups;[9c] and the platinum, nickel, and rhodium catalysts are most often used to reduce aromatic systems.

It will be noted in Table 1-1 that catalytic hydrogenation may serve either to saturate a multiple bond (e.g., C=C or C=O) or to cleave certain types of single bonds. The cleavage of a single bond by catalytic hydrogenation, termed hydrogenolysis, is normally found with allylic or benzylic amines or alcohols having the structural units $-\overset{|}{C}=\overset{|}{C}-CH_2-O-$ or $-\overset{|}{C}=\overset{|}{C}-CH_2-\overset{|}{N}-$ and with compounds containing C—halogen and C—S single bonds. Hydrogenolysis is also observed with N—N, N—O, and O—O single bonds as well as with C—C single bonds of small rings.[21] The occurrence of hydrogenolysis may be considered either desirable or objectionable, depending on the goal of a given reaction. The hydrogenation of the aryl ester **[1]** to benzyl alcohol is difficult to realize, because of further reaction to form toluene, and requires

$$\underset{\textbf{[1]}}{C_6H_5CO_2C_2H_5} \xrightarrow[\substack{C_2H_5OH \\ 200\text{–}250^\circ}]{\substack{H_2(200\ atm) \\ CuCr_2O_4}} \underset{C_2H_5OH}{[C_6H_5CH_2OH] + } \xrightarrow{\text{hydrogenolysis}} \underset{H_2O}{C_6H_5CH_3 +}$$

the use of excess catalyst and lower reaction temperatures.[22] However, the comparable reduction of the keto acid salt **[2]** offers a

(21) J. Newham, *Chem. Rev.*, **63**, 123 (1963).

(22) R. Mozingo and K. Folkers, *J. Am. Chem. Soc.*, **70**, 229 (1948).

useful procedure for the removal of the ketone function. The ready hydrogenolysis of benzyl ethers and amines[24] has prompted the

$$\underset{[2]}{CH_3O\text{—}C_6H_4\text{—}COCH_2CH_2CO_2Na} \xrightarrow[H_2O,\ 200°]{H_2(150\ atm),\ CuCr_2O_4} \underset{(88\%)}{CH_3O\text{—}C_6H_4\text{—}(CH_2)_3CO_2Na}$$

(*Ref. 23*)

extensive use of the benzyl group as a protecting group that can be removed under mild, nonhydrolytic conditions. The last step in Bowman's ketone synthesis is illustrated by the hydrogenolysis of the benzyl ester **[3]**; the hydrogenolysis of the benzyl urethane **[4]** illustrates the use of the carbobenzyloxy blocking group in peptide synthesis.

$$\underset{[3]}{[CH_3(CH_2)_6CO][CH_3(CH_2)_7]C(CO_2CH_2C_6H_5)_2} \xrightarrow[C_2H_5OH,\ CH_3CO_2C_2H_5,\ 25\text{–}30°]{H_2(1\ atm),\ 10\%\ Pd\ on\ C} \left[[CH_3(CH_2)_6CO][CH_3(CH_2)_7]C(COOH)_2 + 2\ C_6H_5CH_3\right]$$

$$\xrightarrow{heat} \underset{(91\%)}{CH_3(CH_2)_6CO\text{—}CH_2(CH_2)_7CH_3} + 2\ CO_2$$

(*Ref. 24b*)

$$\underset{[4]}{HO_2C\text{—}CH_2CH_2\text{—}CH(NH\text{—}CO\text{—}OCH_2C_6H_5)\text{—}CONHCH_2CO_2C_2H_5} \xrightarrow[C_2H_5OH,\ CH_3CO_2H]{H_2(1\ atm),\ Pt(from\ PtO_2)}$$

$$\left[HO_2C\text{—}CH_2CH_2\text{—}CH(NH\text{—}CO\text{—}OH)\text{—}CONHCH_2CO_2C_2H_5 + C_6H_5CH_3\right]$$

$$\longrightarrow CO_2 + \underset{(80\%)}{{}^{\ominus}O_2CCH_2CH_2\text{—}CH(\overset{\oplus}{N}H_3)\text{—}CONHCH_2CO_2C_2H_5}$$

(*Ref. 24a*)

(23) (a) H. O. House and R. J. McCaully, *J. Org. Chem.*, **24**, 725 (1959); see also L. F. Fieser and W. H. Daudt, *J. Am. Chem. Soc.*, **63**, 782 (1941); (b) for the hydrogenolysis of aryl *p*-toluenesulfonic esters to form aromatic hydrocarbons, see G. W. Kenner and M. A. Murray, *J. Chem. Soc.*, **1949**, S 178.

(24) (a) W. H. Hartung and R. Simonoff, *Org. Reactions*, **7**, 263 (1953); (b) R. E. Bowman, *J. Chem. Soc.*, **1950**, 325.

The relative ease of cleavage of benzyl groups, namely,

$$C_6H_5CH_2—\overset{|}{\underset{|}{N}}{}^{\oplus}— > C_6H_5CH_2—O— > C_6H_5CH_2—\overset{|}{N}—,$$

is illustrated in the following equation.

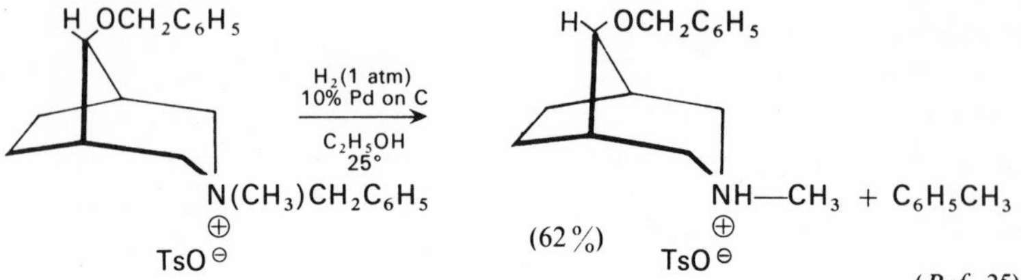

H OCH$_2$C$_6$H$_5$ ... N(CH$_3$)CH$_2$C$_6$H$_5$ ⊕ TsO⊖ $\xrightarrow[\substack{C_2H_5OH \\ 25°}]{\substack{H_2(1\ atm) \\ 10\%\ Pd\ on\ C}}$ H OCH$_2$C$_6$H$_5$ ... NH—CH$_3$ ⊕ TsO⊖ (62%) + C$_6$H$_5$CH$_3$

(*Ref.* 25)

The hydrogenolysis of allyl alcohols, ethers, and esters is less often synthetically useful because the rate of cleavage is often similar to the rate of reduction of the carbon-carbon double bond, leading to mixtures of products.

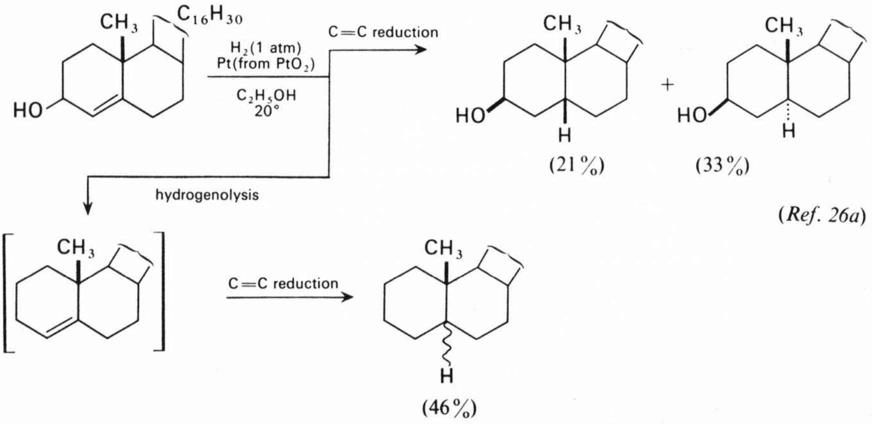

CH$_3$ C$_{16}$H$_{30}$ HO $\xrightarrow[\substack{C_2H_5OH \\ 20°}]{\substack{H_2(1\ atm) \\ Pt(from\ PtO_2)}}$ C=C reduction → CH$_3$ HO H (21%) + CH$_3$ HO H (33%)

hydrogenolysis ↓

[CH$_3$] C=C reduction → CH$_3$ H (46%)

(*Ref.* 26*a*)

(25) H. O. House, P. P. Wickham, and H. C. Müller, *J. Am. Chem. Soc.*, **84**, 3139 (1962).

(26) (a) M. C. Dart and H. B. Henbest, *J. Chem. Soc.*, **1960,** 3563; these authors found that the presence of alkaline inorganic salts in the reaction mixture decreased the amount of hydrogenolysis and produced more saturated alcohol where the hydrogen has added *cis* to the hydroxyl function; (b) the use of alkali with platinum and palladium catalysts to minimize the hydrogenolysis of benzyl alcohols has been reported by W. Theilacker and H. G. Drössler, *Chem. Ber.*, **87**, 1676 (1954).

Either palladium-on-carbon or copper chromite catalyst is usually employed for the hydrogenolysis of benzyl groups, since with these catalysts competing reduction of the aromatic ring occurs only very slowly. Rhodium and ruthenium catalysts have been found most effective when one wishes to minimize hydrogenolysis[27,28] during the reduction of an aromatic ring. The following example is illustrative:

HO O CH$_3$ → H_2(3 atm), 5% Rh on Al_2O_3, C_2H_5OH, 50° → HO OH CH CH$_3$ (78%) (*Ref.* 28)

Although the ready hydrogenolysis of carbon-halogen bonds offers a useful method for removing halogen from a molecule (e.g., reduction of [**5**]), the ease of the cleavage often prevents the use of catalytic hydrogenation when one desires to retain a halogen atom in a reduction product. The Rosenmund reduction of acid

CH$_3$ N Cl [**5**] → H_2(2 atm), Pd on C, CH_3CO_2Na, CH_3CO_2H, 55–70° → CH$_3$ N (81–87%) (*Ref.* 29*a*)

chlorides (such as [**6**]) to aldehydes illustrates the ease of carbon-halogen cleavage. In this synthesis, a mixture, called a catalyst poison, is usually added to reduce the activity of the hydrogenation catalyst.

(27) (a) A. W. Burgstahler and Z. J. Bithos, *Org. Syn.*, **42**, 62 (1962); (b) J. H. Stocker, *J. Org. Chem.*, **27**, 2288 (1962); (c) A. E. Barkdoll, D. C. England, H. W. Gray, W. Kirk, Jr., and G. M. Whitman, *J. Am. Chem. Soc.*, **75**, 1156 (1953); (d) G. E. Ham and W. P. Coker, *J. Org. Chem.*, **29**, 194 (1964).

(28) I. A. Kaye and R. S. Matthews, *ibid.*, **28**, 325 (1963).

(29) (a) F. W. Neumann, N. B. Sommer, C. E. Kaslow, and R. L. Shriner, *Org. Syn.*, **Coll. Vol. 3,** 519 (1955); (b) for the use of hydrogen and Raney nickel catalyst with methanolic potassium hydroxide for the hydrogenolysis of aryl halides, see H. Kämmerer, L. Horner, and H. Beck, *Chem. Ber.*, **91**, 1376 (1958); (c) M. G. Reinecke, *J. Org. Chem.*, **29**, 299 (1964); (d) D. A. Denton, F. J. McQuillin, and P. L. Simpson, *J. Chem. Soc.*, **1965**, 5535.

[6] 2-naphthoyl chloride (CO—Cl) $\xrightarrow[\text{sulfur-quinoline poison, refluxing xylene}]{H_2\text{(passed through the solution), Pd on } BaSO_4}$ 2-naphthaldehyde (CHO) (74–81%) + HCl

(*Ref. 30*)

A variety of substances are poisons for hydrogenation catalysts,[31] the most commonly encountered being mercury, divalent sulfur compounds, and, to a lesser degree, amines. These poisons are believed to function by being preferentially bonded to the catalyst surface, preventing bonding between the catalyst surface and the molecule to be reduced. Although carbon-sulfur bonds are liable to hydrogenolysis, the bond cleavage cannot be performed in the manner of a normal catalytic hydrogenation because both the reactants and the products are powerful catalyst poisons. However, the problem has been circumvented by allowing divalent sulfur compounds to react with the hydrogen adsorbed on a large (tenfold) excess of Raney nickel.[32] This process, Raney nickel desulfurization, is illustrated in the following equation.

CH_3-octalone $\xrightarrow[BF_3 \cdot O(C_2H_5)_2,\ 0°]{CH_2\text{—}SH / CH_2\text{—}SH}$ dithioketal (S, S) (99%)

(*Ref. 33*)

$\xrightarrow{\text{Ra—Ni (7 g/ 1 g dithioketal)},\ C_2H_5OH,\ \text{reflux}}$ CH_3-octalin (61%)

(30) (a) E. B. Hershberg and J. Cason, *Org. Syn.*, **Coll. Vol. 3,** 627 (1955); (b) see also E. Mosettig and R. Mozingo, *Org. Reactions*, **4**, 362 (1948); (c) the use of thiourea as a poison for the Rosenmund reduction has been recommended: see C. Weygand and W. Meusel, *Ber.*, **76**, 503 (1943); (d) in at least one instance a successful Rosenmund reduction was effected at 30–35° in the absence of a catalyst poison: see W. S. Johnson, D. G. Martin, R. Pappo, S. D. Darling, and R. A. Clement, *Proc. Chem. Soc.*, **1957**, 58.

(31) For examples, see L. Horner, H. Reuter, and E. Herrmann, *Ann. Chem.*, **660**, 1 (1962).

(32) (a) G. R. Pettit and E. E. van Tamelen, *Org. Reactions*, **12**, 356 (1962); (b) H. Hauptmann and W. F. Walter, *Chem. Rev.*, **62**, 347 (1962); (c) for a review of syntheses involving the desulfurization and reduction of thiophene intermediates, see Y. L. Gol'dfarb, S. Z. Taits, and L. I. Belen'kii, *Tetrahedron*, **19**, 1851 (1963).

(33) F. Sondheimer and D. Rosenthal, *J. Am. Chem. Soc.*, **80**, 3995 (1958).

Whereas this procedure offers an extremely mild method for the reduction of an aldehyde or ketone to a methyl or methylene group, it becomes much less attractive for large-scale reductions because of the quantities of Raney nickel that must be employed.[34]

The reduction of nitriles to primary amines is complicated by the equilibria illustrated in the accompanying equations, which lead to the production of secondary amines as by-products. With noble metal catalysts this difficulty may be avoided by performing the hydrogenation in an acidic solvent or in acetic anhydride, a practice which serves to remove the primary amine from these equilibria as its salt or as its acetamide derivative. Either of these procedures, both of which have also been used for the reduction of oximes, converts the amine to a substance that is no longer a

$$R{-}C{\equiv}N \xrightarrow{H_2} R{-}CH{=}NH \xrightarrow{H_2} R{-}CH_2{-}NH_2$$

$$R{-}CH_2{-}NH_2 + R{-}CH{=}NH \rightleftharpoons R{-}CH_2NH{-}\underset{NH_2}{\underset{|}{CH}}{-}R \rightleftharpoons R{-}CH_2{-}N{=}CH{-}R + NH_3$$

$$R{-}CH_2{-}N{=}CH{-}R \xrightarrow{H_2} R{-}CH_2{-}NH{-}CH_2{-}R$$

catalyst poison. For the high-pressure hydrogenation of nitriles over Raney nickel, where an acidic solvent cannot be used, an

$$N{\equiv}C{-}(CH_2)_3{-}\underset{HON}{\underset{\|}{C}}{-}COOH \xrightarrow[CH_3COOH,\ 25°]{H_2(3\ atm),\ Pt(from\ PtO_2)} H_2N{-}(CH_2)_4{-}\underset{NH_2}{\underset{|}{CH}}{-}COOH$$

(43% as hydrochloride) *(Ref. 35)*

excess of ammonia is added to the reaction mixture to displace the equilibrium responsible for secondary-amine formation.

(34) Alternative methods for the reduction of dithioketals include the reaction with hydrazine and base reported by V. Georgian, R. Harrisson, and N. Gubisch, *J. Am. Chem. Soc.*, **81**, 5834 (1959); also reduction with sodium and liquid ammonia has been used; for example, see R. E. Ireland, T. I. Wrigley, and W. G. Young, *ibid.*, **80**, 4604 (1958).

(35) (a) A. F. Ferris, G. S. Johnson, F. E. Gould, and H. K. Latourette, *J. Org. Chem.*, **25**, 492 (1960); (b) the use of a rhodium catalyst for the reduction of nitriles to amines has been recommended: see M. Freifelder, *J. Am. Chem. Soc.*, **82**, 2386 (1960).

$$C_6H_5CH_2\text{—}C{\equiv}N \xrightarrow[\text{excess } NH_3,\ \text{no solvent},\ 120\text{–}130^\circ]{H_2(130\ \text{atm}),\ \text{Ra—Ni}} C_6H_5CH_2CH_2\text{—}NH_2\ (83\text{–}87\%)$$ (*Ref.* 36)

Similar reaction conditions have been used for the conversion of a ketone to an amine. In this process, called reductive alkylation,[37] a mixture of a ketone (e.g., **[7]**) and ammonia or a primary or secondary amine (e.g., **[8]**) is hydrogenated over a Raney nickel or platinum catalyst. The product is presumably formed by preferential reduction of an intermediate imine (e.g., **[9]**).

$$\underset{[7]}{CH_3COCH_3} + \underset{[8]}{H_2N\text{—}CH_2CH_2\text{—}OH} \xrightarrow[C_2H_5OH,\ 25^\circ]{H_2(2\ \text{atm}),\ \text{Pt(from } PtO_2)} \underset{[9]}{[(CH_3)_2C{=}N\text{—}CH_2CH_2OH]}$$

$$\longrightarrow (CH_3)_2CHNHCH_2CH_2OH\ (94\text{–}95\%)$$ (*Ref.* 38)

Mechanism and Stereochemistry

The early studies by Linstead and co-workers[39] of the hydrogenation of phenanthrene and diphenic acid derivatives (e.g., **[10]**) over platinum led to the concept that the less hindered side of an

H₂(2–3 atm), Pt(from PtO₂), C₂H₅OH; **[10]** → (both isomers) + (*Ref.* 39)

catalyst surface; catalyst; **[11]** → **[12]** → **[13]**

(36) J. C. Robinson, Jr. and H. R. Snyder, *Org. Syn.*, **Coll. Vol. 3,** 720 (1955).

(37) W. S. Emerson, *Org. Reactions*, **4**, 174 (1948).

(38) E. M. Hancock and A. C. Cope, *Org. Syn.*, **Coll. Vol. 3,** 501 (1955).

(39) (a) R. P. Linstead, W. E. Doering, S. B. Davis, P. Levine, and R. R. Whetstone, *J. Am. Chem. Soc.*, **64**, 1985, 1991, 2003, 2007, 2009, 2014, 2022 (1942); (b) see also L. F. Fieser and M. Fieser, *Steroids*, Reinhold, New York, 1959, pp. 271–274.

unsaturated molecule is adsorbed on the catalyst surface. The adsorption was thought to be followed by the simultaneous transfer of two or more hydrogen atoms from the catalyst to the adsorbed molecule and subsequent desorption of the reduced molecule, as illustrated in the sequence **[11]** → **[12]** → **[13]**. This concept has led to the useful generalization that catalytic hydrogenation of a multiple bond results in the *cis* addition of two hydrogen atoms from the less hindered side of the multiple bond. Two of the many examples of the utility of this generalization are illustrated below: the hydrogenation of disubstituted acetylenes (e.g., **[14]**) to *cis*-olefins over a palladium catalyst partially poisoned with lead acetate (Lindlar catalyst)[40] or quinoline,[41] and the reduction of the ketone **[15]** from the less hindered side.

$$CH_3O_2C(CH_2)_3—C{\equiv}C—(CH_2)_3CO_2CH_3 \xrightarrow[\text{quinoline, } CH_3OH,\ 25^\circ]{H_2\text{(1 atm)}, \text{ 5\% Pd on } BaSO_4}$$

[14]

$$\text{cis-}CH_3O_2C(CH_2)_3(H)C{=}C(H)(CH_2)_3CO_2CH_3$$

(97%)

(*Ref. 41*)

$$[15] \xrightarrow[CH_3CO_2H,\ 20^\circ]{H_2\text{(1 atm)}, \text{ Pt (from } PtO_2)}$$

[15]

(83% of product) + (17% of product)

(*Ref. 9b*)

However, studies of the isomerization of olefins over hydrogenation catalysts, of hydrogen-deuterium exchange, and of the stereochemistry of catalytic hydrogenation have established that the transfer of hydrogen atoms to an adsorbed molecule must occur in a stepwise manner.[42] The commonly accepted mechanism for

(40) H. Lindlar, *Helv. Chim. Acta*, **35**, 446 (1952).

(41) D. J. Cram and N. L. Allinger, *J. Am. Chem. Soc.*, **78**, 2518 (1956).

(42) (a) R. L. Burwell, Jr., *Chem. Rev.*, **57**, 895 (1957); for more recent work with leading references, see (b) J. F. Sauvage, R. H. Baker, and A. S. Hussey, *J. Am. Chem. Soc.*, **83**, 3874 (1961); (c) G. V. Smith and R. L. Burwell, Jr., *ibid.*, **84**, 925 (1962); (d) S. Siegel and B. Dmuchovsky, *ibid.*, **84**, 3132 (1962); (e) S. Siegel, G. V. Smith, B. Dmuchovsky, D. Dubbell, and W. Halpern, *ibid.*, **84**, 3136

this process, postulated by Horiuti and Polanyi,[43] involves the series of accompanying equilibria which implicate both π-bonded

H_2 + catalyst surface ⇌ H H

$>C_1=C_2-C_3-$ (H)

[18] ⇌ [16]

[17]

$-C_1-C_2-C_3-$ (H H H) + catalyst surface

$-C_1-C_2=C_3-$ (H) + H H

intermediates, such as **[16]** and **[17]** (or comparable intermediates where both carbon atoms are bonded to the catalyst surface), and a half-hydrogenated intermediate **[18]**. More recently, evidence has been obtained for yet another mechanism, which involves the formation of a π-allyl intermediate **[19]** from the catalyst and the compound being reduced.[44] The intervention of such intermediates

$-C_1=C_2-C_3-$ (H) + H ⇌ [19] ⇌ $-C_1-C_2=C_3-$ (H) + H

[16] [19] [17]

(1962); (f) F. J. McQuillin, W. O. Ord, and P. L. Simpson, *J. Chem. Soc.*, **1963**, 5996.

(43) I. Horiuti and M. Polanyi, *Trans. Faraday Soc.*, **30**, 1164 (1934).

(44) (a) F. G. Gault, J. J. Rooney, and C. Kemball, *J. Catalysis*, **1**, 255 (1962); (b) W. R. Moore, *J. Am. Chem. Soc.*, **84**, 3788 (1962).

serves to explain the facts that olefins are isomerized on hydrogenation catalysts; that reaction of an olefin with deuterium and a catalyst leads to a mixture of reduction products, including molecules that contain more and fewer than two deuterium atoms per molecule; and that the net result of the catalytic hydrogenation of certain olefins (e.g., **[20]**) is not the expected *cis* addition of two

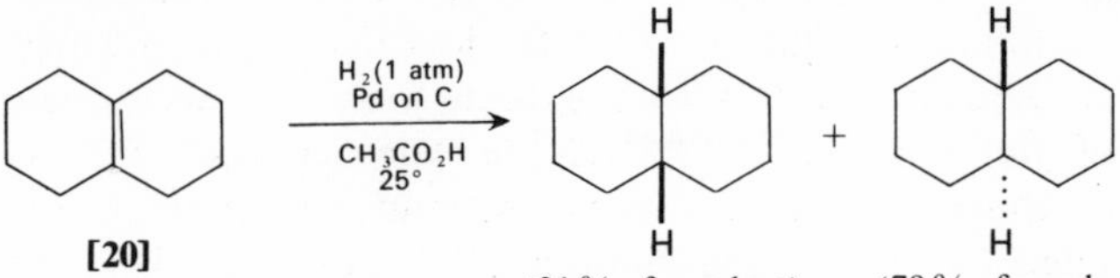

H_2(1 atm), Pd on C, CH_3CO_2H, 25° (*Ref. 42b*)

[20] (21% of product) (79% of product)

hydrogen atoms. As the foregoing discussion would predict, the *cis* addition of hydrogen from the less hindered side of a double bond has been found to be favored by the use of relatively high hydrogen pressures[45] and relatively small quantities of catalyst.[46] Furthermore, platinum catalysts have been found superior to palladium catalysts[45] if a net *cis* addition of hydrogen from the less hindered side of the unsaturated molecule is desired.

One possible course for the hydrogenolysis of benzyl and allyl groups can also be pictured as involving an intermediate π-allyl system **[21]**, as illustrated. Such a sequence would predict that

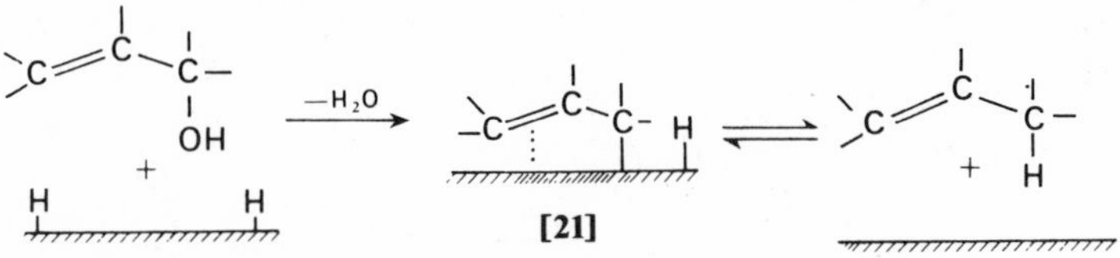

$-H_2O$

[21]

hydrogenolysis at an asymmetric center would occur with retention of configuration, as has been reported[47a] for the alcohol **[22]** over Raney nickel. However, the hydrogenolysis of other bonds

(45) S. Siegel and G. V. Smith, *J. Am. Chem. Soc.*, **82**, 6082, 6087 (1960).

(46) (a) H. O. House, R. G. Carlson, H. Müller, A. W. Noltes, and C. D. Slater, *ibid.*, **84**, 2614 (1962); (b) R. L. Augustine, *J. Org. Chem.*, **28**, 152 (1963).

(47) (a) W. A. Bonner, J. A. Zderic, and G. A. Casaletto, *J. Am. Chem. Soc.*, **74**, 5086 (1952); (b) W. A. Bonner and J. A. Zderic, *ibid.*, **78**, 3218 (1956); (c) S. Mitsui and S. Imaizumi, *Bull. Chem. Soc. Japan*, **34**, 774 (1961); (d) S. Mitsui, Y. Senda, and K. Konno, *Chem. Ind.* (*London*), **1963**, 1354.

C_6H_5, $CO_2C_2H_5$, CH_3, OH on C (optically active) **[22]** $\xrightarrow[\text{C}_2\text{H}_5\text{OH, reflux}]{\text{Ra—Ni (excess)}}$ C_6H_5, $CO_2C_2H_5$, CH_3, H on C (optically active with partial retention of configuration) (*Ref. 47a*)

over Raney nickel has been observed[47b] to occur with racemization or inversion of configuration, and the hydrogenolysis of benzyl ethers over palladium catalysts has been found to occur with inversion of configuration.[47c,47d] Even the hydrogenolysis of C—O bonds over Raney nickel may occur without retention of configuration since the illustrated equilibrium between **[21]** and the product may isomerize the initially formed reduction product to a more stable isomer. Such a result has been observed with the two cholestane derivatives **[23]** and **[24]**, both of which gave the hydrocarbon **[25]** with Raney nickel in boiling ethanol. However, the product **[26]** was produced from the alcohol **[23]** by hydrogenolysis with retention of configuration at lower temperatures. This hydrocarbon **[26]** was isomerized to the more stable isomer **[25]** by Raney nickel in refluxing ethanol.[48]

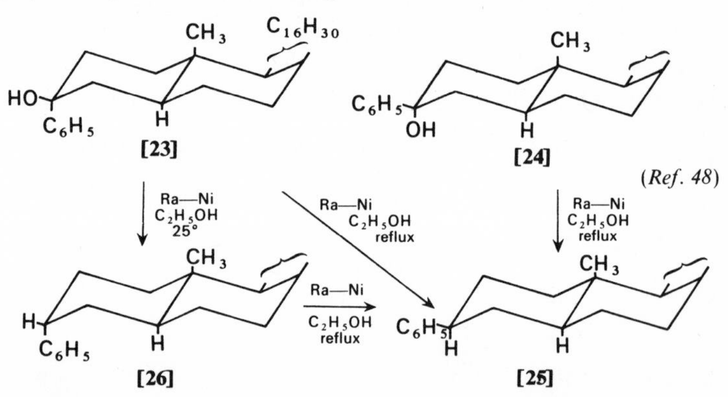

The presence of acids or bases in the reaction mixtures employed for catalytic hydrogenation has been reported to alter the rate and steric course of many reductions. Although there is clear evidence[26,49] that acid accelerates the hydrogenolysis of C—O bonds, the effect of acid on the stereochemistry of the hydrogenolysis is apparently unknown. For reductions of cyclohexanone

(48) E. W. Garbisch, Jr., *J. Org. Chem.*, **27**, 3363 (1962).

(49) F. J. McQuillin and W. O. Ord., *J. Chem. Soc.*, **1959**, 2902, 3169.

derivatives, the modified von Auwers-Skita rule[9b,50] has led to the expectation that hydrogenation in neutral or basic media will produce predominantly equatorial alcohols, whereas axial alcohols are the major products from reduction in acidic solution. However, there is reason[9b] to believe that much of the earlier work on which this rule is based suffered from both inadequate product analysis and isomerization of initially formed products. As a result, it is unwise to consider this rule a reliable criterion for stereochemical assignments.

Both the ease and the stereochemical course of hydrogenations of α, β-unsaturated ketones are influenced by the presence of acid or base in the reaction mixture.[46b,49–52] For example, reduction of the unsaturated ketone **[27]** gave the product compositions indicated in the following equations. It must be noted that this

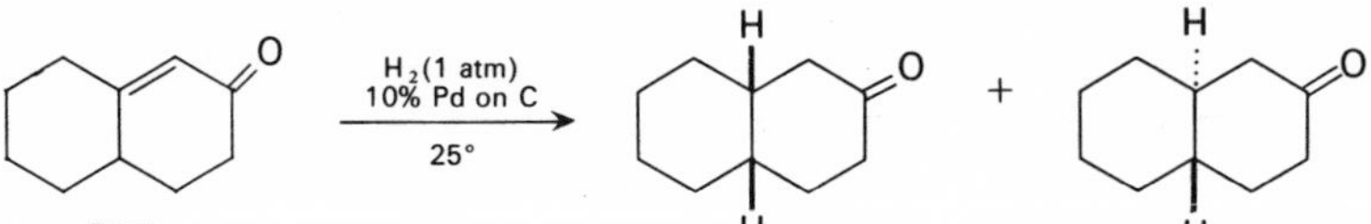

[27] $\xrightarrow[25^\circ]{H_2\text{(1 atm)}, \text{ 10\% Pd on C}}$ (H, H) + (H, H)

solvent	*product composition*		(*Ref. 52*)
C_2H_5OH	53%	47%	
C_2H_5OH, H_2O, HCl	93%	7%	

example is clearly contradictory to the earlier generalization[51] that hydrogenation in neutral or alkaline medium favors the production of a *cis*-fused ring system in comparable cases. The

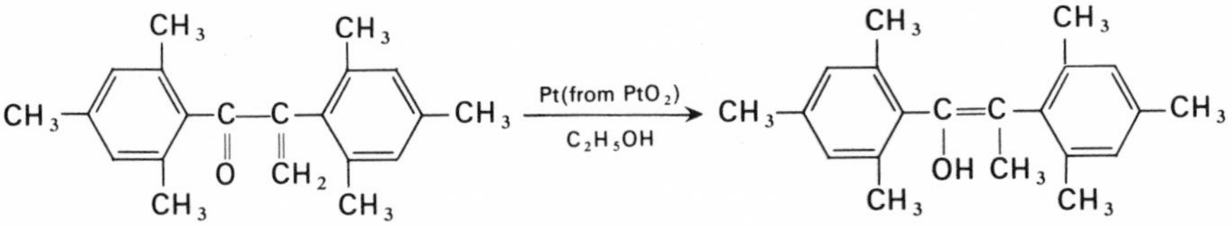

[28] $\xrightarrow[C_2H_5OH]{\text{Pt(from } PtO_2)}$ (stereochemistry unknown) (*Ref. 53*)

(50) J. H. Brewster, *J. Am. Chem. Soc.*, **76**, 6361 (1954).

(51) (a) H. A. Weidlich, *Chemie*, **58**, 30 (1945); (b) A. L. Wilds, J. A. Johnson, Jr., and R. E. Sutton, *J. Am. Chem. Soc.*, **72**, 5524 (1950).

(52) (a) R. L. Augustine, *J. Org. Chem.*, **23**, 1853 (1958); (b) R. L. Augustine and A. D. Broom, *ibid.*, **25**, 802 (1960); (c) for a recent review, see L. Velluz, J. Valls, and G. Nominé, *Angew. Chem., Intern. Ed. Engl.*, **4**, 181 (1965).

(53) R. C. Fuson, J. Corse, and C. H. McKeever, *J. Am. Chem. Soc.*, **62**, 3250 (1940).

interpretation of the results from hydrogenation of conjugated systems is further complicated by the possible addition of hydrogen at the ends of the conjugated system, as in the reduction of the hindered ketone **[28]**, and by the possibility that the conjugated system may isomerize to a nonconjugated isomer prior to hydrogenation.

Consequently, in planning a synthesis there is good reason to anticipate that catalytic hydrogenation will proceed by the *cis* addition of hydrogen from the less hindered side of the molecule, particularly if the hydrogenation can be made to occur rapidly under mild conditions. However, one should be mindful of the fact that changes in the acidity of the reaction medium, changes in the quantity or type of catalyst employed, or changes in other, presumably inert, functional groups in the molecule being reduced[54] may well alter the stereochemical course of the reaction sufficiently to be preparatively useful. The latter possibility is particularly worthy of exploration if steric hindrance to approach of the catalyst from either side of the molecule being reduced is approximately equal.

(54) For example, see T. G. Halsall, W. J. Rodewald, and D. Willis, *Proc. Chem. Soc.*, **1958**, 231.

2

· METAL HYDRIDE REDUCTIONS

A SERIOUS SHORTCOMING OF CATALYTIC HYDROGENATION, the inability to reduce selectively the carbonyl function of ketones, acids, esters, and amides in the presence of carbon-carbon double bonds, has led to the widespread use of certain complex metal hydrides[1] for reductions of carbonyl groups. The common commercially available[2] salts include, in order of decreasing activity, lithium aluminum hydride,[3] lithium borohydride, and sodium

$$\mathrm{LiH} + \mathrm{AlH_3} \longrightarrow \mathrm{Li^{\oplus}} \quad \mathrm{H{-}\overset{\displaystyle H^{\ominus}}{\underset{\displaystyle H}{Al}}{-}H}$$

$$\mathrm{NaH} + \mathrm{BH_3} \longrightarrow \mathrm{Na^{\oplus}} \quad \mathrm{H{-}\overset{\displaystyle H^{\ominus}}{\underset{\displaystyle H}{B}}{-}H}$$

(1) N. G. Gaylord, *Reduction with Complex Metal Hydrides*, Wiley-Interscience, New York, 1956.

(2) Metal Hydrides, Inc., 12–24 Congress St., Beverly, Massachusetts.

(3) W. G. Brown, *Org. Reactions*, **6**, 469 (1951).

borohydride. The complex anions in these salts may be considered to have been derived from a simple metal hydride and either aluminum hydride or borine, as illustrated in the preceding equations. These anions are nucleophilic reagents that normally attack polarized multiple bonds (e.g., C═O, C═N, C≡N, N═O) at the more positive atom but usually do not attack isolated carbon-carbon multiple bonds. As will be described subsequently, it is possible to convert these salts back to the trivalent aluminum and boron compounds by reaction with appropriate acids. Such trivalent materials, with only six electrons in their valence shell, have the requisite structure for Lewis acids and may behave as electrophilic reagents.

Lithium borohydride and especially lithium aluminum hydride react rapidly with hydroxylic compounds. Consequently, these metal hydride reagents must be used under anhydrous conditions with purified, nonhydroxylic solvents. For lithium aluminum hydride reductions, ether, tetrahydrofuran, and 1,2-dimethoxyethane are the commonly employed solvents, whereas tetrahydrofuran and diglyme (the dimethyl ether of diethylene glycol) are useful solvents for lithium borohydride. Sodium borohydride reacts slowly enough with water, methanol, and ethanol—provided the reaction mixture is kept cool (25° or less) and alkaline—to permit the use of these solvents for reductions that occur readily. For reductions requiring higher temperatures or long reaction periods, isopropyl alcohol or diglyme are preferable as solvents.[4] Certain quaternary ammonium borohydrides have been found useful for reductions employing hydrocarbon solvents[5] in which the alkali metal borohydrides are not soluble.

Reduction of Aldehydes and Ketones

The reaction of an aldehyde or ketone with borohydride ion involves the transfer of a hydride ion to the carbonyl carbon atom, as illustrated in structure [**1**]. In a nonprotonic solvent, this step is followed by formation of an alkoxyborohydride anion [**2**], whereas in hydroxylic solvents, exchange with the solvent may occur as indicated by the reaction with methanol. A sequence comparable to the borohydride reaction in a nonprotonic solvent

(4) (a) H. C. Brown, E. J. Mead, and B. C. Subba Rao, *J. Am. Chem. Soc.*, **77**, 6209 (1955); (b) H. C. Brown and K. Ichikawa, *ibid.*, **83**, 4372 (1961).

(5) E. A. Sullivan and A. A. Hinckley, *J. Org. Chem.*, **27**, 3731 (1962).

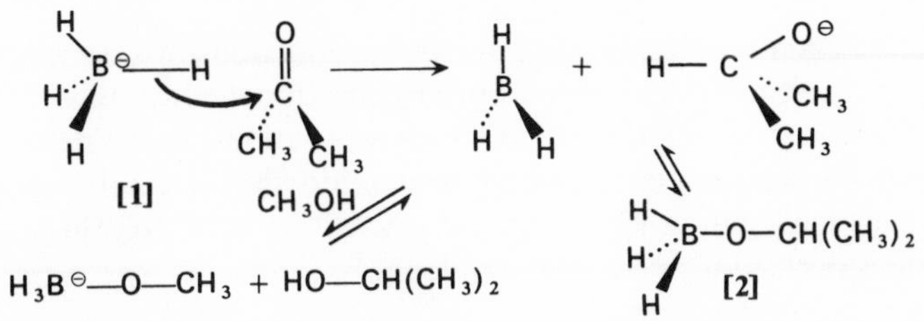

$$H_3B^{\ominus}\text{—}H + (CH_3)_2C{=}O \longrightarrow BH_3 + H\text{—}C(O^{\ominus})(CH_3)_2$$

[1]

$$\rightleftharpoons \quad H_3B\text{—}O\text{—}CH(CH_3)_2 \quad [2]$$

$$[1] \xrightleftharpoons{CH_3OH} H_3B^{\ominus}\text{—}O\text{—}CH_3 + HO\text{—}CH(CH_3)_2$$

is applicable to reductions with lithium aluminum hydride. Since all four hydrogen atoms may be used in reductions with either metal hydride anion, it is apparent that the series of consecutive reactions illustrated below are possible.[6] For reductions with the

$$AlH_4^{\ominus} + (CH_3)_2CO \xrightarrow[\text{A-1}]{} H_3Al^{\ominus}\text{—}O\text{—}CH(CH_3)_2 \xrightarrow[\text{A-2}]{(CH_3)_2CO}$$

$$H_2Al^{\ominus}[O\text{—}CH(CH_3)_2]_2 \xrightarrow[\text{A-3}]{(CH_3)_2CO} HAl^{\ominus}[O\text{—}CH(CH_3)_2]_3 \xrightarrow[\text{A-4}]{(CH_3)_2CO}$$

$$Al^{\ominus}[O\text{—}CH(CH_3)_2]_4$$

$$BH_4^{\ominus} + (CH_3)_2CO \xrightarrow[\text{B-1}]{} H_3B^{\ominus}\text{—}O\text{—}CH(CH_3)_2$$

$$\xrightarrow[\text{B-2}]{(CH_3)_2CO} H_2B^{\ominus}[O\text{—}CH(CH_3)_2]_2 \xrightarrow[\text{B-3}]{(CH_3)_2CO} HB^{\ominus}[O\text{—}CH(CH_3)_2]_3$$

$$\xrightarrow[\text{B-4}]{(CH_3)_2CO} B^{\ominus}[O\text{—}CH(CH_3)_2]_4$$

aluminum hydride anion, each successive step has been found to occur more slowly than the preceding step; in other words, the relative rates are A-1 > A-2 > A-3 > A-4. This reactivity order has allowed the preparation of reducing agents that are less reactive and more selective than lithium aluminum hydride by replacing two or three of the hydrogen atoms with certain primary or tertiary alkoxyl groups. However, the first step (B-1) in the reaction of the borohydride ion with ketones is rate determining, so that the relative rates are B-1 < B-2, B-3, or B-4. The nature of the

(6) (a) H. C. Brown, E. J. Mead, and C. J. Shoaf, *J. Am. Chem. Soc.*, **78**, 3616 (1956); (b) H. C. Brown and R. F. McFarlin, *ibid.*, **80**, 5372 (1958); (c) H. C. Brown, O. H. Wheeler, and K. Ichikawa, *Tetrahedron*, **1**, 214 (1957); (d) H. C. Brown and K. Ichikawa, *J. Am. Chem. Soc.*, **84**, 373 (1962); (e) H. Haubenstock and E. L. Eliel, *ibid.*, **84**, 2363, 2368 (1962); (f) W. M. Jones and H. E. Wise, Jr., *ibid.*, **84**, 997 (1962); (g) H. C. Brown and C. J. Shoaf, *ibid.*, **86**, 1079 (1964).

reducing agent at intermediate stages in reductions of ketones with either of these metal hydrides is open to question. There is reason[6e,6g] to believe that the indicated disproportionation (and other comparable disproportionations) to regenerate the original complex metal hydride anion occurs rapidly with some alkoxyaluminum hydrides derived from secondary alcohols.

$$2\,H_3Al^{\ominus}—O—CH(CH_3)_2 \rightleftharpoons Al^{\ominus}H_4 + H_2Al^{\ominus}[O—CH(CH_3)_2]_2$$

The differing effects of alkoxyl substitution on the reactivities of these two reducing agents have been attributed to a combination of two factors. The resonance interaction of the alkoxyl group, pictured in [**3**], would assist the transfer of a hydride ion and accelerate the reaction, while the electron-withdrawing inductive effect of the alkoxyl function would oppose loss of the hydride ion and retard the reaction. For the small boron atom,

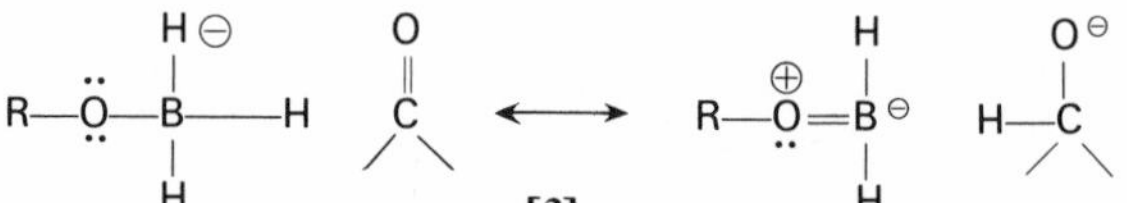

$$R—\ddot{O}—B^{\ominus}H_3 \;\; C{=}O \longleftrightarrow R—\overset{\oplus}{O}{=}B^{\ominus}H_2 \;\; H—C—O^{\ominus}$$

[**3**]

substantial *p*-orbital overlap of the type represented in [**3**] is possible and this factor predominates, resulting in an increase in reactivity as alkoxyl substituents are added. For the larger aluminum atom, however, this type of overlap is much less effective and the rate-retarding inductive effect of the alkoxyl group becomes the dominant factor.

The following equations illustrate typical laboratory reductions with sodium borohydride and lithium aluminum hydride:

$$CH_3(CH_2)_5—CHO + LiAlH_4 \xrightarrow[\text{reflux}]{(C_2H_5)_2O} \xrightarrow{H_3O^{\oplus}} CH_3(CH_2)_5CH_2OH \; (86\%)$$

(*Ref.* 7*a*)

$$\text{1-indanone-2-acetic acid} + NaBH_4 \xrightarrow[25^{\circ}]{0.2\,N\ NaOH \text{ in } H_2O} \xrightarrow{H_3O^{\oplus}} \text{hydroxy acid } (76\%) + \text{lactone } (20\%)$$

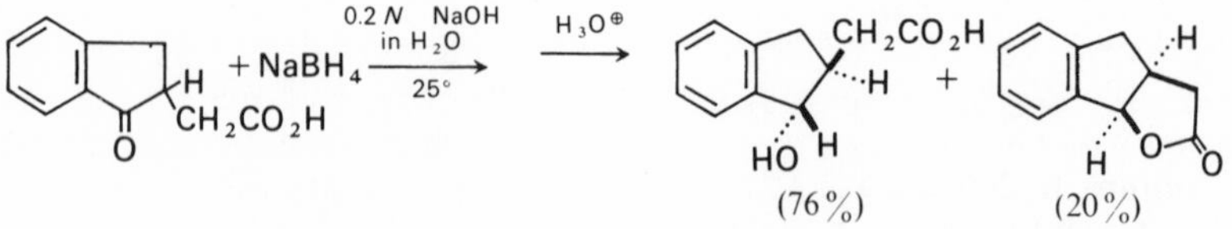

(*Ref.* 7*b*)

(7) (a) R. F. Nystrom and W. G. Brown, *J. Am. Chem. Soc.*, **69**, 1197 (1947); (b) H. O. House, H. Babad, R. B. Toothill, and A. W. Noltes, *J. Org. Chem.*, **27**, 4141 (1962); (c) N. J. Leonard, S. Swann, Jr., and J. Figueras, Jr., *J. Am. Chem. Soc.*, **74**, 4620 (1952).

$$\text{(indolizidin-1-one)} + LiAlH_4 \xrightarrow[25^\circ]{(C_2H_5)_2O} \xrightarrow{H_2O} \text{(indolizidin-1-ol)} \quad (58\%) \qquad (Ref.\ 7c)$$

It is customary in hydride reductions to employ a slight excess of the reducing reagent in the event that some of the metal hydride is unintentionally destroyed by reaction with hydroxyl-containing materials present in the reaction medium. Alternatively, a solution (filtered or decanted) of lithium aluminum hydride can be prepared and standardized prior to use, either by titration with iodine or by measuring the volume of hydrogen evolved when an aliquot of the solution is treated with water.[8] The isolation of organic products from sodium borohydride reductions is usually accomplished by diluting the reaction mixture with water, making it slightly acidic to destroy any excess hydride, and then extracting the organic product from the aqueous solution containing boric acid and its salt. The reaction of the alkoxyboron intermediates with water presumably occurs as follows:

$$B^{\ominus}(OR)_4 \rightleftharpoons RO^{\ominus} + B(OR)_3 \overset{H_2O}{\rightleftharpoons} ROH + HO{-}B^{\ominus}(OR)_3$$

$$HO{-}B^{\ominus}(OR)_3 \rightleftharpoons ROH + (RO)_2B{-}O^{\ominus} \overset{H_2O}{\rightleftharpoons} \overset{H_2O}{\rightleftharpoons} 2\,ROH + (HO)_2B{-}O^{\ominus}$$

Excess lithium aluminum hydride remaining in a reduction mixture is usually destroyed by the *dropwise* addition of ethanol or of ether saturated with water. Although the addition of ethyl acetate has also been employed, this procedure is not advisable when the product is an amine, since the amine itself may react with ethyl acetate.[9] If the reduction product is nonbasic, reasonably insoluble in water, and reasonably stable to acid, the reaction mixture may then be poured into cold, dilute, aqueous acid and the organic product extracted with ether. When this acid isolation procedure is not applicable, it is customary to add to the mixture, dropwise and with stirring, the calculated amount of water or dilute aqueous sodium hydroxide required to convert the lithium and aluminum salts to lithium aluminate ($LiAlO_2$), a granular precipitate that can be filtered from the organic solution and extracted with

(8) H. Felkin, *Bull. Soc. Chim. France*, **1951**, 347.

(9) W. B. Wright, *J. Org. Chem.*, **25**, 1033 (1960).

boiling tetrahydrofuran to remove any occluded organic product. Some workers recommend the addition of solid sodium sulfate or magnesium sulfate to aid coagulation prior to the filtration of the lithium aluminate. In this isolation procedure it is important not to add excess water since its presence will convert the reaction mixture to a gelatinous emulsion of the organic solvent, water, and aluminum hydroxide, which is very difficult either to filter or to extract. An alternative isolation procedure employs an aqueous solution of sodium potassium tartarate to hydrolyze and dissolve the aluminum salts present in the reaction mixture.

The stereochemical course of the reduction of a carbonyl group by a metal hydride, like other nucleophilic additions to carbonyl functions, may be influenced by asymmetry in the molecule. The best-studied examples are those having an asymmetric carbon atom adjacent to the carbonyl group, as in the ketone [**4**]. Since

$$C_2H_5(CH_3)CH{-}CO{-}C_6H_5 + LiAlH_4 \longrightarrow C_2H_5{-}C(CH_3){=}C(O^{\ominus}AlH_3)(Li^{\oplus}){-}C_6H_5 + \text{reduction products}$$

[**4**] [**5**]

the metal hydrides, particularly lithium aluminum hydride, may function as strong bases, one might expect an optically active ketone having an alpha hydrogen atom (e.g., [**4**]) to be converted to its enolate [**5**] and, consequently, racemized prior to reduction. However, little if any racemization is observed in the lithium aluminum hydride reduction of such compounds.[1]

Enolate anions react very slowly with lithium aluminum hydride, and the racemic ketone derived from [**5**] is usually produced by hydrolysis only during the isolation process when no excess hydride reducing agent remains. Since no protonic solvents are present during reductions with lithium aluminum hydride, the racemic ketone could be produced in the reaction mixture only by a proton transfer from the starting ketone [**4**] to the enolate [**5**]. The fact that little if any racemization is observed requires that the proton transfer must be slower than the reduction of the starting ketone [**4**] with lithium aluminum hydride. Since sodium borohydride reductions are typically carried out in hydroxylic solvents, a competing proton transfer to an enolate with racemization and subsequent reduction becomes very probable. However, the much lower base strength of the borohydride anion greatly diminishes the rate of formation of an enolate comparable to [5], and usually permits the reduction of a carbonyl function without racemization of an adjacent center of asymmetry.

The accompanying equation indicates the proportions of diastereoisomers [6] and [7] obtained by reduction of a ketone having three different alpha substituents (only one enantiomer of the racemic mixture employed is shown) with lithium aluminum hydride. The prediction of which diastereoisomer will predominate

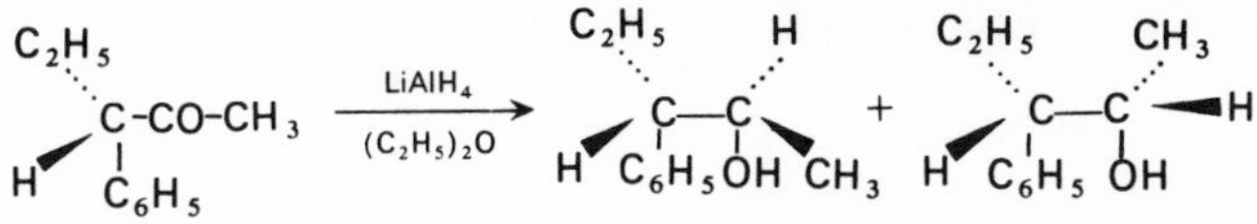

$\xrightarrow[(C_2H_5)_2O]{LiAlH_4}$ (*Ref. 10*)

[6] (75% of product) **[7]** (25% of product)

in such cases has been generalized as the Rule of steric control of asymmetric induction.[10,11] This rule is applied by considering that the starting ketone will react preferentially in the conformation illustrated in structure [8] (the conformation in which the carbonyl group is least hindered) and that the carbonyl group in this conformation will be attacked by the metal hydride anion from the less hindered side as pictured.

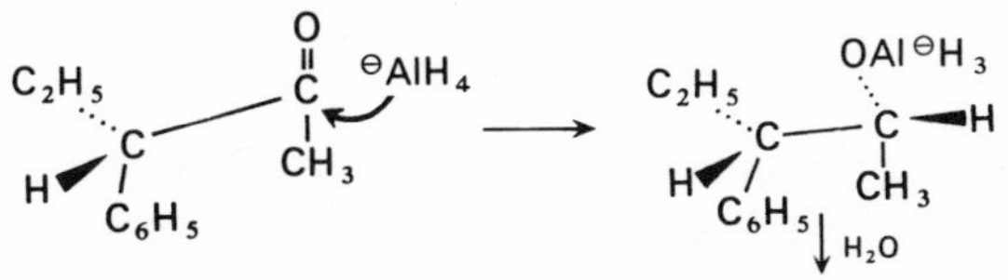

[8] **[6]**

This rule of asymmetric induction usually requires modification when the asymmetric center bears polar substituents, presumably because the assumption that steric factors determine the favored conformation for reaction is no longer valid.[11] Reductions of

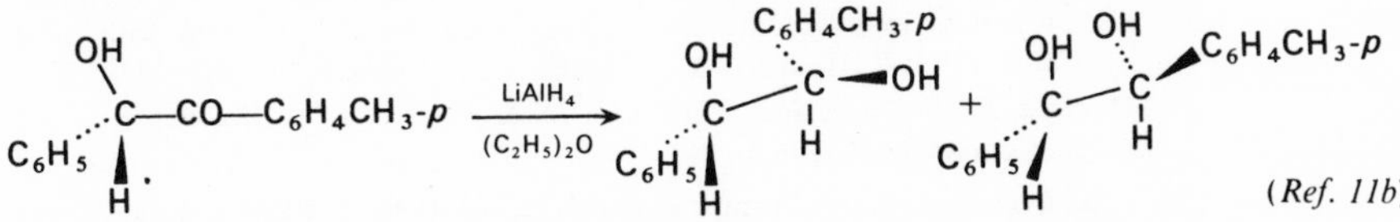

$\xrightarrow[(C_2H_5)_2O]{LiAlH_4}$ (*Ref. 11b*)

[9] (85% of product) **[10]** (15% of product)

(10) D. J. Cram and F. A. Abd Elhafez, *J. Am. Chem. Soc.*, **74**, 4828 (1952).

(11) (a) D. J. Cram and K. R. Kopecky, *ibid.*, **81**, 2748 (1959); (b) J. H. Stocker, P. Sidisunthorn, B. M. Benjamin, and C. J. Collins, *ibid.*, **82**, 3913 (1960); (c) D. J. Cram and D. R. Wilson, *ibid.*, **85**, 1245 (1963).

α-hydroxy and α-amino ketones often exhibit a relatively high degree of stereoselectivity, as illustrated in the accompanying example. These results have been attributed to the initial formation of a salt that reacts in conformation **[11]** with the metal hydride ion attacking from the less hindered side.[12]

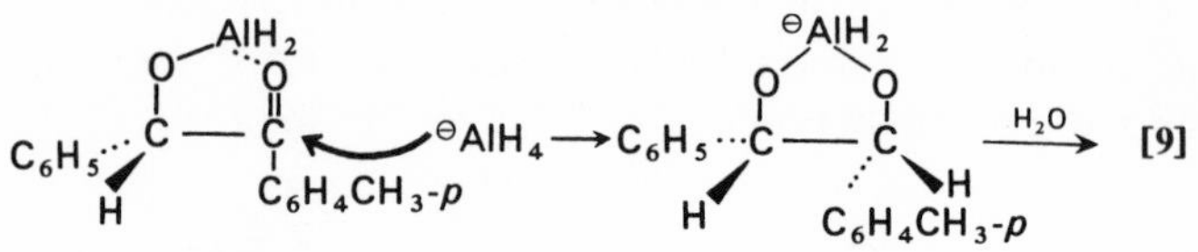

C_6H_5 ··· C(H)(O–AlH_2) — C(=O)($C_6H_4CH_3$-*p*) + $^{\ominus}AlH_4$ → C_6H_5 ··· C(H)(O) — C(O)(H)($C_6H_4CH_3$-*p*) ($^{\ominus}AlH_2$) $\xrightarrow{H_2O}$ **[9]**

[11]

When an asymmetric center bears a polar substituent that has no acidic hydrogen atom, a prediction of the stereochemical result becomes more difficult because the most reactive conformation of the molecule may be one in which the polar carbonyl function and the polar substituent are *trans* (e.g., **[12]**) to minimize dipole-dipole repulsion.[11c,13]

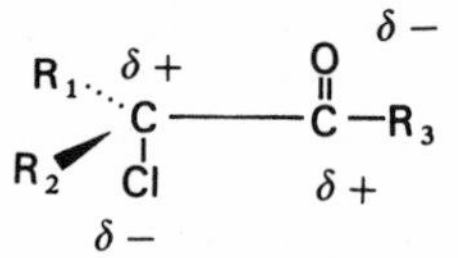

R_1, R_2 ··· C(δ+)(Cl, δ−) — C(=O, δ−)(δ+)—R_3

[12]

Although the reductions of a large number of cyclic ketones with metal hydrides have been studied, the stereochemical outcome of these reactions is often difficult to predict. Two usually opposing factors have been suggested to be important: steric hindrance to approach of the metal hydride ion to the carbonyl function, called steric approach control; and the stability of the final product, called product development control.[14] If structures **[13]** and **[14]**

(12) Polar groups at positions more remote from the carbonyl function have also been found to influence the rate and steric course of reductions with metal hydrides: (a) H. B. Henbest and J. McEntee, *J. Chem. Soc.*, **1961**, 4478; H. B. Henbest, *Proc. Chem. Soc.*, **1963**, 159; (b) H. Kwart and T. Takeshita, *J. Am. Chem. Soc.*, **84**, 2833 (1962).

(13) J. W. Cornforth, R. H. Cornforth, and K. K. Mathew, *J. Chem. Soc.*, **1959**, 112.

(14) (a) W. G. Dauben, G. J. Fonken, and D. S. Noyce, *J. Am. Chem. Soc.*, **78**, 2579 (1956); (b) E. L. Eliel and M. N. Rerick, *ibid.*, **82**, 1367 (1960); (c) O. R. Vail and D. M. S. Wheeler, *J. Org. Chem.*, **27**, 3803 (1962); (d) A. V. Kamernitzky and A. A. Akhrem, *Tetrahedron*, **18**, 705 (1962); (e) for an alternative interpretation, see D. M. S. Wheeler and J. W. Huffman, *Experientia*, **16**, 516 (1960); J. C. Richer, *J. Org. Chem.*, **30**, 324 (1965);

are used to represent the transition states for the two possible directions of reduction of a conformationally rigid cyclohexanone

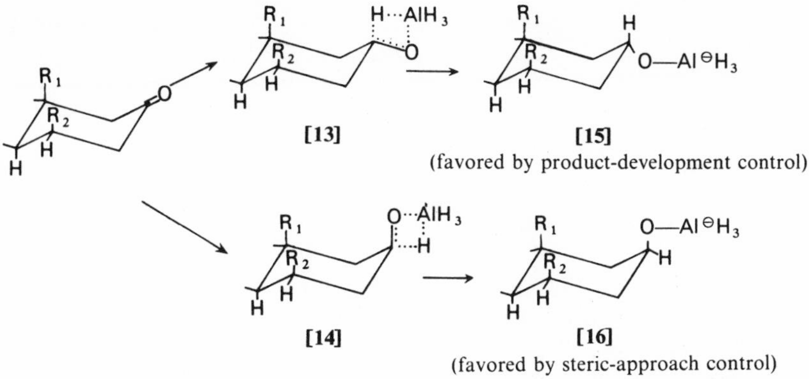

[13] [15]
(favored by product-development control)

[14] [16]
(favored by steric-approach control)

derivative, it can be seen that steric interference between the R_1 and R_2 groups in **[13]** and the metal hydride (steric-approach control) will oppose the formation of the equatorial alcohol **[15]**. Alternatively, steric interference between the developing alkoxy-aluminum function and the R_1 and R_2 groups in **[14]** (product-development control) will oppose the formation of the axial alcohol **[16]**. Unless approach to one side of the carbonyl function is clearly much more hindered than approach to the other side, as in the reduction of camphor **[17]**, the usual result of a metal hydride reduction is the formation of a mixture of alcohols in which the more stable alcohol predominates. This is illustrated by

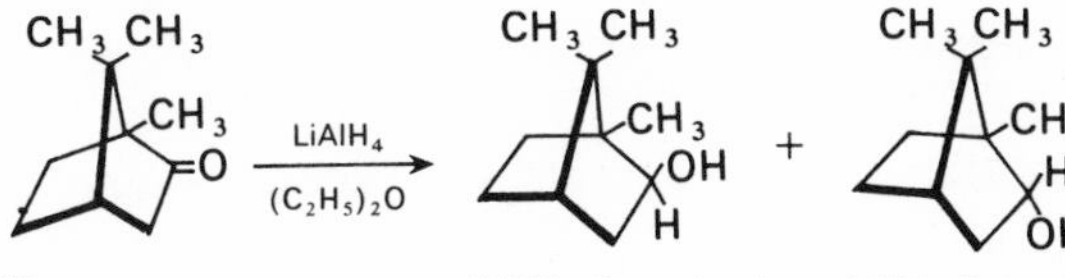

$\xrightarrow[(C_2H_5)_2O]{LiAlH_4}$ (*Ref. 15*)

[17] (90% of product) (10% of product)

(f) use of lithium tri-*t*-butoxyaluminum hydride has been reported to favor the formation of equatorial alcohols: see O. H. Wheeler and J. L. Mateos, *Can. J. Chem.*, **36**, 1431 (1958); a similar result has been obtained by reduction of ketones with lithium aluminum hydride in pyridine solution: see C. D. Ritchie, *Tetrahedron Letters*, **No. 30**, 2145 (1963).

(15) (a) D. S. Noyce and D. B. Denney, *J. Am. Chem. Soc.*, **72**, 5743 (1950); (b) for reductions of norcamphor and its derivatives where the opposite stereochemical result was obtained, see C. H. DePuy and P. R. Story, *ibid.*, **82**, 627 (1960).

the formation primarily of the equatorial alcohol **[18]** on reduction of the ketone **[19]**.

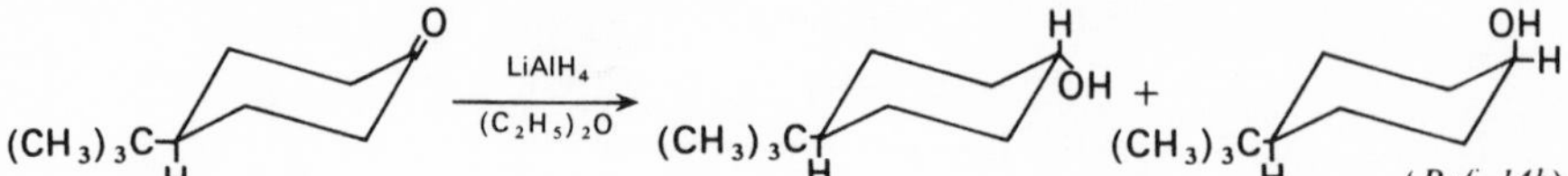

$(CH_3)_3C$ ... $\xrightarrow[(C_2H_5)_2O]{LiAlH_4}$ (88–90%) + (10–12%) (*Ref. 14b*)

[19] **[18]**

If both aluminum chloride and an excess of the ketone being reduced are present in a reduction mixture, equilibration of the initially formed products has been found to occur.[14b] This equilibration presumably proceeds by the path illustrated in the accompanying equation, which is analogous to the Meerwein-Ponndorf-Verley reduction of ketones with aluminum isopropoxide.[16] For such equilibration to occur, it is necessary that both some ketone and a trivalent aluminum alkoxide be present in the reaction mixture. Since this procedure is more rapid than the Meerwein-Ponndorf-Verley method and also frequently leads to a higher proportion of the more stable alcohol (present in the reaction mixture as the aluminum alkoxide), its use is advantageous in preparative work.

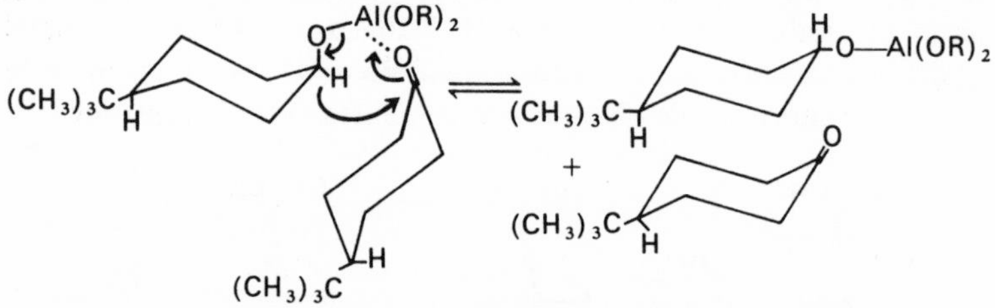

$(CH_3)_3C$ ... O–$Al(OR)_2$ ⇌ $(CH_3)_3C$ ... O—$Al(OR)_2$ + $(CH_3)_3C$ ... O

Reductions of Other Functional Groups

Although sodium borohydride will reduce esters slowly[17] and lactones and acid chlorides rapidly, it is normally possible to reduce ketones and aldehydes selectively with this reagent in the presence of a variety of such functional groups as esters, amides,

(16) A. L. Wilds, *Org. Reactions*, **2**, 178 (1944).

(17) (a) M. S. Brown and H. Rapoport, *J. Org. Chem.*, **28**, 3261 (1963); (b) the ester function of α-cyano esters is reduced readily by sodium borohydride: see J. A. Meschino and C. H. Bond, *ibid.*, **28**, 3129 (1963).

cyano groups, nitro groups, and alkyl halides. The following examples are illustrative. Lithium borohydride will reduce esters more rapidly and has been used for this purpose.

$$CH_3\text{—}CO(CH_2)_2CH_2\text{—}NO_2 \xrightarrow[\substack{CH_3OH\text{–}H_2O \\ 25^\circ}]{NaBH_4} CH_3\text{—}\underset{\displaystyle OH}{\underset{|}{CH}}\text{—}(CH_2)_2CH_2\text{—}NO_2 \quad (87\%)$$

(*Ref. 18a*)

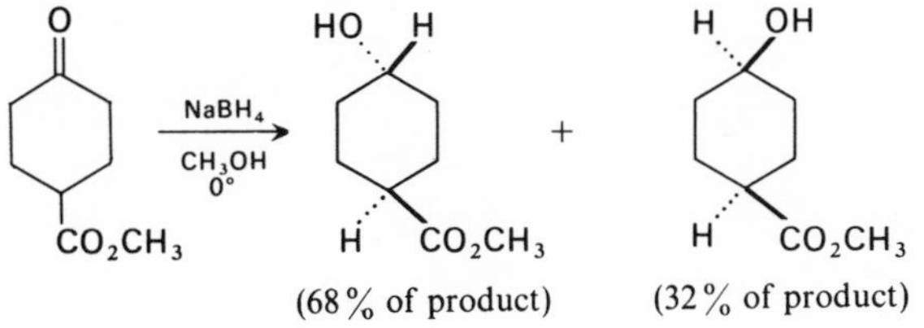

4-Oxocyclohexanecarboxylic acid methyl ester $\xrightarrow[\substack{CH_3OH \\ 0^\circ}]{NaBH_4}$ cis-4-hydroxycyclohexane-CO_2CH_3 (68% of product) + trans-4-hydroxycyclohexane-CO_2CH_3 (32% of product) (*Ref. 7b*)

$$C_6H_5\text{—}CO\text{—}CH_2Br \xrightarrow[\substack{CH_3OH \\ 25^\circ}]{NaBH_4} C_6H_5\text{—}\underset{\displaystyle OH}{\underset{|}{CH}}\text{—}CH_2Br \quad (71\%)$$

(*Ref. 18b*)

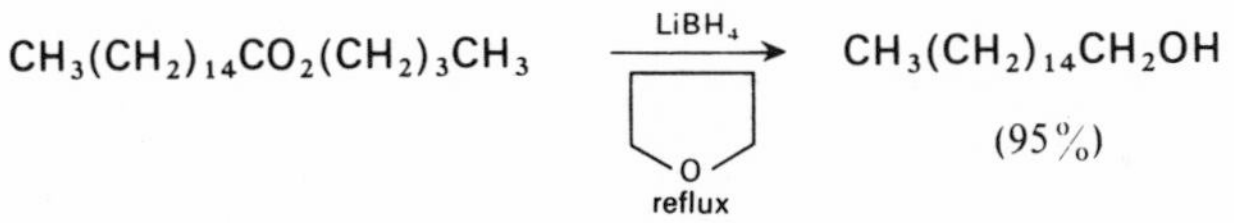

$$CH_3(CH_2)_{14}CO_2(CH_2)_3CH_3 \xrightarrow[\substack{\text{THF} \\ \text{reflux}}]{LiBH_4} CH_3(CH_2)_{14}CH_2OH \quad (95\%)$$

(*Ref. 19*)

Lithium aluminum hydride is useful for the reduction of a variety of functional groups; a list of typical reductions is presented

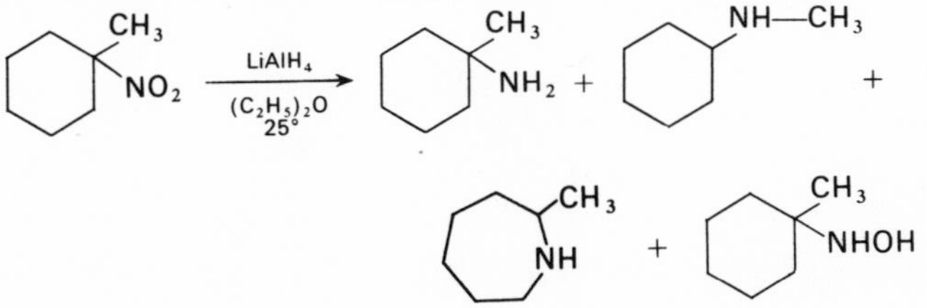

1-Methyl-1-nitrocyclohexane $\xrightarrow[\substack{(C_2H_5)_2O \\ 25^\circ}]{LiAlH_4}$ 1-methylcyclohexyl-NH_2 + cyclohexyl-NH—CH_3 + 2-methylazepane (NH) + 1-methylcyclohexyl-NHOH (*Ref. 20*)

(18) (a) H. Shechter, D. E. Ley, and L. Zeldin, *J. Am. Chem. Soc.*, **74**, 3664 (1952); (b) S. W. Chaikin and W. G. Brown, *ibid.*, **71**, 122 (1949).

(19) R. F. Nystrom, S. W. Chaikin, and W. G. Brown, *ibid.*, **71**, 3245 (1949).

(20) H. J. Barber and E. Lunt, *J. Chem. Soc.*, **1960**, 1187.

in Table 2-1. Although the reduction of *aliphatic* nitro compounds has been used for the preparation of primary amines, the reduction of tertiary alkyl nitro compounds is complicated by partial rearrangement of the intermediate hydroxylamine derivative to form both primary and secondary amines.

TABLE 2-1 ▪

Common Functional Groups Reduced with Lithium Aluminum Hydride

Functional group	Product
$\rangle C{=}O$	$\rangle CH{-}OH$
$-CO_2R$	$-CH_2OH + ROH$
$-CO_2H$ or $-CO_2^{\ominus}Li^{\oplus}$	$-CH_2OH$
$-CO{-}NH{-}R$	$-CH_2{-}NH{-}R$
$-CO{-}NR_2$	$-CH_2{-}NR_2$ or $[-CH(OH){-}NR_2] \rightarrow -CHO + R_2NH$
$-C{\equiv}N$	$-CH_2{-}NH_2$ or $[-CH{=}NH] \xrightarrow{H_2O} -CHO$
$\rangle C{=}NOH$	$\rangle CH{-}NH_2$
$-\overset{\mid}{\underset{\mid}{C}}-NO_2$ (aliphatic)	$-\overset{\mid}{\underset{\mid}{C}}-NH_2$
$-CH_2{-}O{-}SO_2{-}C_6H_5$ or $-CH_2Br$	$-CH_3$
$\rangle CH{-}O{-}SO_2{-}C_6H_5$ or $\rangle CH{-}Br$	$\rangle CH_2$
$-CH{-}\overset{\mid}{C}{-}$ (epoxide, bridged by O)	$-CH_2{-}\overset{\mid}{\underset{OH}{C}}{-}$

The reduction of substituted amides to amines, as exemplified in the next equation, is believed to proceed by an initial reduction to a geminal amino alcohol derivative (e.g., [**20**]), followed by elimination and subsequent reduction of the resulting iminium salt (or imine from a monosubstituted amide). It is evident that if the reaction sequence could be stopped at the amino alcohol stage (i.e., [**20**]), this intermediate would be hydrolyzed to form an

$$C_6H_{11}\text{—CO—N}(CH_3)_2 \xrightarrow[\text{refluxing }(C_2H_5)_2O]{LiAlH_4} C_6H_{11}\text{—}CH_2\text{—N}(CH_3)_2 \quad 88\%$$

(*Ref. 21*)

$$C_6H_{11}\text{—CH(OAlH}_3\text{)—}\ddot{N}(CH_3)_2 \;[\mathbf{20}] \longrightarrow C_6H_{11}\text{—CH=N}^{\oplus}(CH_3)_2$$

aldehyde. Although such a synthesis of aldehydes has been effected using a limited amount of lithium aluminum hydride and low reaction temperatures,[22] better results have been obtained by use of the less reactive reducing agent $LiAlH_2(OC_2H_5)_2$ or $LiAlH(OC_2H_5)_3$ at 0°[23] or by reduction of the amides derived from ethylenimine, carbazole, N-methylaniline, or imidazole.[24] With amides of these types the participation of the electron pair on nitrogen in the elimination process depicted in structure [**20**] is not favored.

$$LiAlH_4 + 1\text{ equiv. } CH_3CO_2C_2H_5 \;(\text{or 2 equiv. } C_2H_5OH) \xrightarrow{(C_2H_5)_2O} LiAlH_2(OC_2H_5)_2$$

(*Ref. 23*)

$$C_6H_{11}\text{—CO—N}(CH_3)_2 + LiAlH_2(OC_2H_5)_2 \xrightarrow[0°]{(C_2H_5)_2O} \xrightarrow{H_3O^{\oplus}} C_6H_{11}\text{—CHO} \quad (71\%)$$

$$C_3H_5\text{—CO—N}(CH_2)_2 \xrightarrow[(C_2H_5)_2O,\ 0°]{LiAlH_4} \xrightarrow{H_3O^{\oplus}} C_3H_5\text{—CHO} \quad (60\%)$$

(*Ref. 24a*)

(21) (a) A. C. Cope and E. Ciganek, *Org. Syn.*, **39**, 19 (1959); (b) M. S. Newman and T. Fukunaga [*J. Am. Chem. Soc.*, **82**, 693 (1960)] have presented evidence indicating that the reduction of *unsubstituted* amides with lithium aluminum hydride proceeds by the initial dehydration of the amide to form a nitrile; (c) both substituted and unsubstituted amides can be reduced readily to amines with diborane in tetrahydrofuran solution; see H. C. Brown and P. Heim, *J. Am. Chem. Soc.*, **86**, 3566 (1964).

(22) E. Mosettig, *Org. Reactions*, **8**, 218 (1954).

(23) H. C. Brown and A. Tsukamoto, *J. Am. Chem. Soc.*, **81**, 502 (1959); *ibid.*, **86**, 1089 (1964).

(24) (a) H. C. Brown and A. Tsukamoto, *J. Am. Chem. Soc.*, **83**, 4549 (1961); (b) G. Wittig and P. Hornberger, *Ann. Chem.*, **577**, 11 (1952); (c) F. Weygand and

A similar possibility exists in the reduction of nitriles (e.g., **[21]**) to amines since hydrolysis of the intermediate imine salt **[22]** would produce an aldehyde.[22] This possibility has been realized

$$o\text{-}CH_3C_6H_4C{\equiv}N \; [21] \xrightarrow[\text{refluxing } (C_2H_5)_2O]{LiAlH_4} \left[o\text{-}CH_3C_6H_4CH{=}N{-}Al^{\ominus}H_3 \right] [22] \xrightarrow[2.\ H_3O^{\oplus}]{1.\ LiAlH_4} o\text{-}CH_3C_6H_4CH_2{-}NH_2 \; (88\%)$$

(*Ref. 25*)

by the use of the reducing agent $LiAlH(OC_2H_5)_3$, as illustrated below for the nitrile **[23]**.

$$CH_3(CH_2)_2C{\equiv}N \; [23] \xrightarrow[(C_2H_5)_2O]{LiAlH(OC_2H_5)_3} \xrightarrow{H_3O^{\oplus}} CH_3(CH_2)_2CHO \; (68\%)$$

(*Ref. 26*)

Application of the same principle of partial reduction to acid chlorides also provides a synthesis of aldehydes. In this case the reagent, $LiAlH[OC(CH_3)_3]_3$, is prepared by reaction of lithium aluminum hydride in ether with three equivalents of *t*-butyl alcohol.[6b] The ether-insoluble reagent is collected and used as illustrated below.

$$O_2N{-}C_6H_4{-}CO{-}Cl + 1 \text{ equiv. } LiAlH[OC(CH_3)_3]_3 \xrightarrow[-78°]{\text{diglyme}} O_2N{-}C_6H_4{-}CHO \; (81\%)$$

(*Ref. 27*)

The reduction of enolizable 1,3-dicarbonyl compounds (e.g., **[24]**) is complicated by an elimination reaction (cf. amide reductions) of the intermediate products **[25]** and **[26]** to produce allylic

---

co-workers, *Angew. Chem.*, **64**, 458 (1952); **65**, 525 (1953); **66**, 174 (1954); (d) H. A. Staab and H. Braunling, *Ann. Chem.*, **654**, 119 (1962); (e) a reaction analogous to the partial reduction of amides is the partial reduction of lactones with lithium almuminum hydride to form hydroxyaldehydes: see G. E. Arth, *J. Am. Chem. Soc.*, **75**, 2413 (1953).

(25) R. F. Nystrom and W. G. Brown, *J. Am. Chem. Soc.*, **70**, 3738 (1948).

(26) (a) H. C. Brown, C. J. Shoaf, and C. P. Garg, *Tetrahedron Letters*, **No. 3,** 9 (1959); H. C. Brown and C. P. Garg, *J. Am. Chem. Soc.*, **86**, 1085 (1964); (b) for the use of triethoxyaluminum hydride to reduce aromatic nitriles to aldehydes, see G. Hesse and R. Schrödel, *Ann. Chem.*, **607**, 24 (1957).

(27) H. C. Brown and B. C. Subba Rao, *J. Am. Chem. Soc.*, **80**, 5377 (1958).

alcohols rather than 1,3-diols as the major reduction products. This difficulty may be overcome with acyclic dicarbonyl compounds if sodium borohydride is used as the reducing agent in

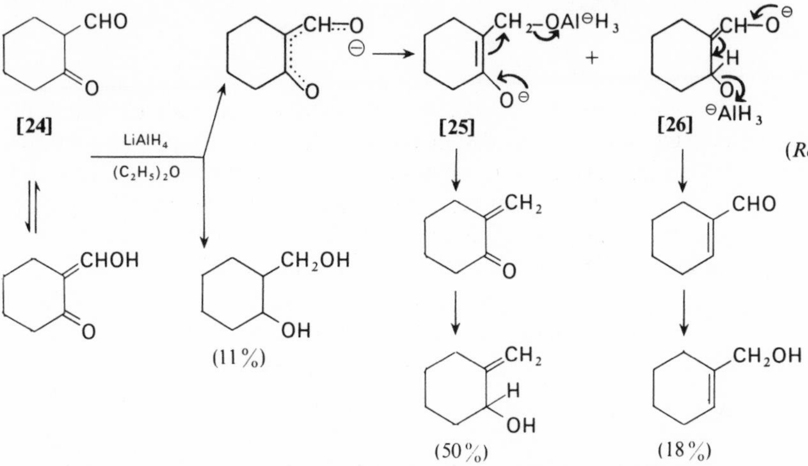

[24] [25] [26] LiAlH$_4$ $(C_2H_5)_2O$ (11%) (50%) (18%) (*Ref.* 28)

hydroxylic media. Under these reaction conditions protonation of intermediate enolates is possible and the tendency for enolate formation is reduced because of the low basicity of the borohydride anion. However, isolation of the diols is sometimes difficult because of the formation of relatively stable cyclic borate esters in the reaction mixture.

$$CH_3CO—CH_2—CO—CH_3 \xrightarrow[H_2O\text{–}CH_3OH,\ 15^\circ]{NaBH_4} CH_3—CH(OH)—CH_2—CH(OH)—CH_3$$

(90% *meso* and 2% racemic) (*Ref.* 29)

Reduction of the enol ethers of 1,3-dicarbonyl compounds provides a synthesis of α,β-unsaturated ketones since the reduction product **[27]** undergoes an allylic rearrangement when treated with aqueous acid.

Primary and secondary halides and sulfonate esters as well as epoxides react with lithium aluminum hydride in a nucleophilic displacement (S_N2) reaction to produce a new C—H bond. The use of trialkyltin hydrides for the reduction of carbon-halogen bonds to C—H bonds is a more general method, since this reaction, a

(28) (a) A. S. Dreiding and J. A. Hartman, *J. Am. Chem. Soc.*, **75**, 939, 3723 (1953); (b) J. C. Richer and R. Clarke, *Tetrahedron Letters*, **No. 16**, 935 (1964).

(29) J. Dale, *J. Chem. Soc.*, **1961,** 910.

O; OC_2H_5 $\xrightarrow[(C_2H_5)_2O]{LiAlH_4}$ H, $OAl^{\ominus}H_3$; OC_2H_5 **[27]** $\xrightarrow{H_3O^{\oplus}}$ [OH; OC_2H_5] → O (62–75%) (*Ref.* 30)

free-radical chain process, is not restricted to halides that will undergo nucleophilic displacement and can be applied to both alkyl (e.g., [**28**]) and aryl halides.[31] An alternative procedure for the formation of a saturated methylene group or a methyl group consists of the reduction of the *p*-toluenesulfonylhydrazone of a ketone or aldehyde with lithium aluminum hydride.[31h]

[28] Cl, Br + $(n\text{-}C_4H_9)_3SnH$ $\xrightarrow{0°}$ H, Cl (97%, both stereoisomers) + $(n\text{-}C_4H_9)_3SnBr$ (96%) (*Ref.* 31b)

As would be anticipated for an S_N2 process, reaction of lithium aluminum hydride with epoxides occurs at the less highly substituted position to produce the more highly substituted alcohol. The addition of aluminum chloride to lithium aluminum hydride in the ratio 1 : 3 has been found to alter the course of this reaction,

$(CH_3)_3C—CH—C(CH_3)_2$ (epoxide, O) $\xrightarrow[(C_2H_5)_2O]{LiAlH_4}$ $(CH_3)_3C—CH_2—C(CH_3)_2$ with OH on $C(CH_3)_2$ (21%; only alcohol formed) (*Ref.* 32)

presumably because the reducing species is the electrophilic reagent, aluminum hydride (AlH_3), which is stable in ether solution for short periods of time. More profound changes in the course of the

(30) (a) W. F. Gannon and H. O. House, *Org. Syn.*, **40**, 14 (1960); (b) M. Stiles and A. Longroy, *Tetrahedron Letters*, **No. 10**, 337 (1961).

(31) (a) W. P. Neumann, *Angew. Chem., Intern. Ed. Engl.*, **2**, 165 (1963); (b) D. Seyferth, H. Yamazaki, and D. L. Alleston, *J. Org. Chem.*, **28**, 703 (1963); (c) H. G. Kuivila and L. W. Menapace, *ibid.*, **28**, 2165 (1963); (d) D. H. Lorenz, P. Shapiro, A. Stern, and E. I. Becker, *ibid.*, **28**, 2332 (1963); (e) E. J. Kupchik and R. J. Kiesel, *ibid.*, **29**, 764 (1964); (f) L. W. Menapace and H. G. Kuivila, *J. Am. Chem. Soc.*, **86**, 3047 (1964); (g) H. G. Kuivila in F. G. A. Stone and R. West (ed.), *Advances in Organometallic Chemistry*, Vol. 1, Academic Press, New York, 1964; (h) L. Caglioti and M. Magi, *Tetrahedron*, **19**, 1127 (1963).

(32) E. L. Eliel and M. N. Rerick, *J. Am. Chem. Soc.*, **82**, 1362 (1960).

reaction have been observed if an excess of aluminum chloride is employed.[33]

$$(C_6H_5)_2C\overset{O}{\diagdown\!\diagup}CH—C_6H_5 \xrightarrow[(C_2H_5)_2O,\ 25^\circ]{1\ AlCl_3 + 3\ LiAlH_4} (C_6H_5)_2CH—\underset{OH}{CH}—C_6H_5 \quad (90\%) \qquad (Ref.\ 33)$$

The mixed aluminum chloride–lithium aluminum hydride reagent has also found use for the reduction of ketals and acetals,[34] as illustrated in the accompanying equation. For these reductions,

$$C_6H_5—\overset{CH_3}{C}(OC_2H_5)_2 \xrightarrow[(C_2H_5)_2O,\ 25^\circ]{4\ AlCl_3 + 1\ LiAlH_4} C_6H_5—\overset{CH_3}{CH}—OC_2H_5 \quad (82\%) \qquad (Ref.\ 34b)$$

the best yields were obtained when an $AlCl_3 : LiAlH_4$ ratio of 4 : 1 was employed. It is not certain whether the actual reducing agent is a chloroaluminum hydride (e.g., $AlHCl_2$ or AlH_2Cl) or whether the excess aluminum chloride is merely serving as an acid catalyst for reduction by AlH_3. It seems probable that the excess Lewis acid serves to cleave the ketal to an oxonium ion (e.g., **[29]**), which is then reduced by the aluminum hydride species present.

$$C_6H_5—\overset{CH_3}{\underset{:\ddot{O}—C_2H_5}{C}}—O(\rightarrow AlCl_3)—C_2H_5 \longrightarrow C_6H_5—\overset{CH_3}{C}{=}\overset{\oplus}{\ddot{O}}—C_2H_5\ \textbf{[29]} \xrightarrow{AlH_3} C_6H_5—\overset{CH_3}{CH}—O—C_2H_5$$

Carbon-carbon double bonds are generally not reduced with either sodium borohydride or lithium aluminum hydride. The most frequent exceptions to this rule have been reported in the reduction of β-aryl-α,β-unsaturated carbonyl compounds (e.g., **[30]**) with lithium aluminum hydride. Even in these cases reduction of only the carbonyl function is possible if short reaction times (5 min or

(33) M. N. Rerick and E. L. Eliel, *ibid.*, **84**, 2356 (1962).

(34) (a) E. L. Eliel, *Record Chem. Progr.*, **22**, 129 (1961); (b) E. L. Eliel, V. G. Badding, and M. N. Rerick, *J. Am. Chem. Soc.*, **84**, 2371 (1962); (c) E. L. Eliel, L. A. Pilato, and V. G. Badding, *ibid.*, **84**, 2377 (1962); (d) reduction of alcohols that can form reasonably stable carbonium ions (e.g., allylic and benzylic alcohols) with the aluminum chloride–lithium aluminum hydride reagent to produce hydrocarbons has also been realized: see J. H. Brewster and H. O. Bayer, *J. Org. Chem.*, **29**, 105, 116 (1964); J. H. Brewster, H. O. Bayer, and S. F. Osman, *ibid.*, **29**, 110 (1964); J. H. Brewster, S. F. Osman, H. O. Bayer, and H. B. Hopps, *ibid.*, **29**, 121 (1964); (e) B. E. Leggetter and R. K. Brown, *Can. J. Chem.*, **41**, 2671 (1963).

$$C_6H_5—CH{=}CH—CHO \xrightarrow[(C_2H_5)_2O,\ 25°]{\text{excess } LiAlH_4} C_6H_5—CH_2CH_2CH_2OH \ (87\%)$$

[30] (*Refs. 25, 35*)

$$C_6H_5—CH{=}CH—CHO \xrightarrow[(C_2H_5)_2O,\ -10°]{LiAlH_4 \text{ added to aldehyde}} C_6H_5—CH{=}CH—CH_2OH \ (90\%)$$

less) and low reaction temperatures (25° or less) are employed. Sometimes addition of the hydride reagent to the carbonyl compound (inverse addition) has also proved beneficial. The further reduction of allylic alcohols to saturated alcohols with lithium aluminum hydride is believed to involve an intermediate organoaluminum compound such as **[31]**, since only one of the two hydrogen atoms added to the carbon-carbon double bond is derived from the metal hydride and reaction of the complex (presumably **[31]**) with a deuterated solvent forms the indicated deuterated alcohol.

$$(C_6H_5—CH{=}CH—CH_2—O—)_2Al^{\ominus}H_2 \longrightarrow$$

$$[31] \xrightarrow{ROD} C_6H_5—CH(D)—CH_2CH_2OH$$

[31] ($\ominus$ Al bearing two six-membered rings: C_6H_5—CH—CH_2—CH_2—O—Al and Al—CH(C_6H_5)—CH_2—CH_2—O—Al)

Aluminum hydride, prepared in the reaction vessel from lithium aluminum hydride and aluminum chloride, has been found to reduce unsaturated carbonyl compounds to unsaturated alcohols without the complication of further reduction.[35b] Also, sodium borohydride reductions of α,β-unsaturated carbonyl compounds are only rarely complicated by reduction of the carbon-carbon double bond.

N-alkylpyridinium salts are reduced by lithium aluminum hydride to 1,2-dihydropyridines, whereas reduction of these salts with sodium borohydride in protonic solvents leads to 1,2,5,6-

(35) (a) F. A. Hochstein and W. G. Brown, *J. Am. Chem. Soc.*, **70**, 3484 (1948); (b) M. J. Jorgenson, *Tetrahedron Letters*, **No. 13**, 559 (1962); (c) an analogous reaction was observed in the reduction of enol acetates to alcohols with lithium aluminium hydride: see W. G. Dauben and J. F. Eastham, *J. Am. Chem. Soc.*, **75**, 1718 (1953).

tetrahydropyridines.[36] The probable course of this borohydride reduction is indicated below:

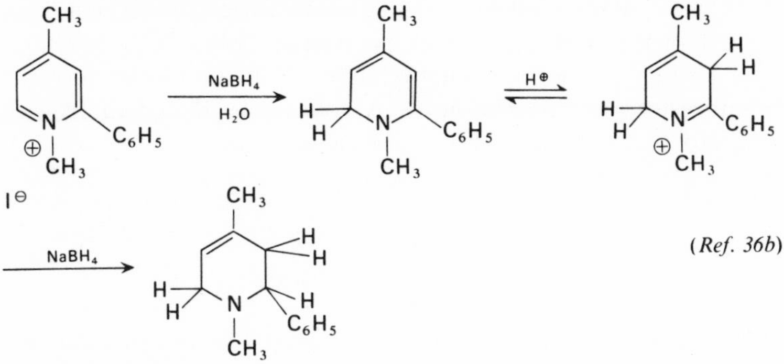

CH3 CH3 CH3 H H N C6H5 ⊕ CH3 I⊖ NaBH4 H2O H H N C6H5 CH3 H⊕ H H N C6H5 ⊕ CH3

NaBH4 CH3 H H H H N H C6H5 CH3

(*Ref. 36b*)

Hydroboration

The interesting modifications in the reducing properties of lithium aluminum hydride that were achieved by the addition of aluminum chloride prompted analogous studies of the "mixed reagents" obtained from sodium borohydride and a number of Lewis acids. Although early papers dealing with this subject refer to various mixed reagents, it soon became apparent that the actual reducing agent was borine (BH_3), which exists as a gaseous dimer, diborane. The most unique reducing property of this metal hydride is the ease with which it will add to isolated carbon-carbon multiple bonds in the presence of an ethereal solvent.[37]

Although a variety of methods are available for the preparation of diborane,[38] perhaps the most convenient consists of the addition of a solution of sodium borohydride in diglyme to boron trifluoride etherate. This diborane solution can be used directly or, preferably, can be heated under an inert atmosphere to distil the diborane into a receiver containing tetrahydrofuran. The resulting tetra-

$$3NaBH_4 + 4BF_3 \xrightarrow{\text{diglyme}} 3NaBF_4 + 2B_2H_6$$

(36) (a) R. E. Lyle, D. A. Nelson, and P. S. Anderson, *Tetrahedron Letters*, **No. 13,** 553 (1962); (b) P. S. Anderson and R. E. Lyle, *Tetrahedron Letters*, **No. 3,** 153 (1964).

(37) (a) H. C. Brown, *Tetrahedron*, **12**, 117 (1961); (b) G. Zweifel and H. C. Brown, *Org. Reactions*, **13**, 1 (1963); (c) H. C. Brown, *Hydroboration*, Benjamin, New York, 1962.

(38) H. C. Brown, K. J. Murray, L. J. Murray, J. A. Snover, and G. Zweifel, *J. Am. Chem. Soc.*, **82**, 4233 (1960). Solutions of diborane in tetrahydrofuran are commercially available (Ref. 3).

hydrofuran solution of diborane, probably present in equilibrium with the illustrated tetrahydrofuran-borine complex, is free from inorganic contaminants and may be standardized by reaction of an aliquot of the solution with excess acetone followed by addition of a known excess of standard aqueous alkali to saponify the borate ester present. The aqueous solution is then treated with mannitol and titrated with standard acid.

$$H_2B(\mu\text{-}H)_2BH_2 + 2\ \text{(tetrahydrofuran)} \rightleftharpoons \text{(tetrahydrofuran)}\overset{\oplus}{O}-\overset{\ominus}{B}H_3$$

Although diborane is capable of reducing a variety of functional groups (Table 2-2),[39] the most useful synthetic applications of the reagent have involved addition to carbon-carbon multiple bonds, called hydroboration. The rate of addition of diborane to carbon-carbon double bonds decreases as the number of alkyl substituents about the double bond increases.[40] With mono- and disubstituted

$$n\text{-}C_4H_9{-}CH{=}CH_2 + B_2H_6 \xrightarrow[\text{C-1}]{} n\text{-}C_4H_9{-}CH_2{-}CH_2{-}BH_2 \xrightarrow[\text{C-2}]{n\text{-}C_4H_9-CH=CH_2}$$

$$(n\text{-}C_4H_9{-}CH_2{-}CH_2)_2BH \xrightarrow[\text{C-3}]{n\text{-}C_4H_9-CH=CH_2} (n\text{-}C_4H_9{-}CH_2{-}CH_2)_3B$$

olefins, all three hydrogen atoms of the borine are used in the reduction.[41] Each successive addition step is slower than the preceding step (i.e., C-1 > C-2 > C-3), a result that has been attributed to the increasing steric bulk of the partially alkylated boron reagent. In agreement with this idea, trisubstituted olefins normally

(39) (a) H. C. Brown and B. C. Subba Rao, *J. Am. Soc.*, **82**, 681 (1960); (b) H. C. Brown and W. Korytnyk, *ibid.*, **82**, 3866 (1960); (c) H. C. Brown and D. B. Bigley, *ibid.*, **83**, 486 (1961); (d) carboxyl and cyano functions have been selectively reduced in the presence of ketone functions with diborane: see B. C. Subba Rao and G. P. Thakar, *Current Sci.* (*India*), **32**, 404 (1963); *CA*, **60**, 438 (1964); (e) for the reduction of enamines with sodium borohydride and acetic acid (a procedure that involves reaction of the imminium salt with diborane), see J. A. Marshall and W. S. Johnson, *J. Org. Chem.*, **28**, 421 (1963); (f) the pyridine-borine complex in acetic acid solution is also a useful reducing agent for ketones: see K. V. Yorka, W. L. Truett, and W. S. Johnson, *ibid.*, **27**, 4580 (1962).

(40) H. C. Brown and G. Zweifel, *J. Am. Chem. Soc.*, **82**, 3222, 3223, 4708 (1960).

(41) (a) H. C. Brown and B. C. Subba Rao, *ibid.*, **81**, 6423, 6428 (1959); (b) H. C. Brown and A. W. Moerikofer, *ibid.*, **84**, 1478 (1962); **85**, 2063 (1963).

react with diborane to give dialkylboranes (e.g., **[32]**), and tetra-substituted olefins form monoalkylboranes with solutions of diborane at room temperature.[41] As was the case with lithium aluminum hydride, this order of reactivity permits the preparation of mono- and dialkylboranes that are less reactive and more selective than diborane itself.

TABLE 2-2

Reductions of Functional Groups with Diborane[39]

Reactant[a]	Product (after hydrolysis unless otherwise noted)
$—CO_2H$	$—CH_2OH$
$—CH{=}CH—$	$—CH_2—CH(BH_2)—$ (product before hydrolysis)
$>C{=}O$	$>CH—OH$
$—C{\equiv}N$	$—CH_2—NH_2$
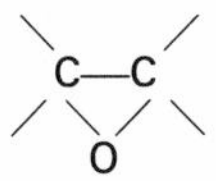 $>C—C<$ (epoxide, bridged by O)	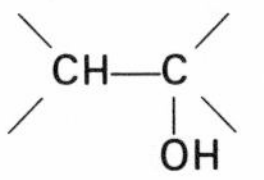 $>CH—C(OH)<$
$—CO_2R$	$—CH_2OH + ROH$
$—CO—Cl$	Inert
$—NO_2$	Inert

[a]Functional groups are listed in approximate order of decreasing ease of reduction.

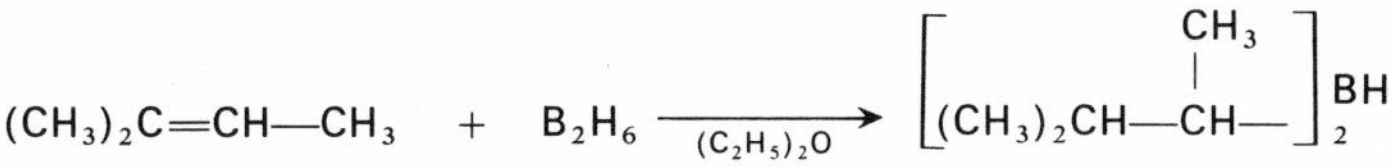

$$(CH_3)_2C{=}CH{—}CH_3 + B_2H_6 \xrightarrow{(C_2H_5)_2O} [(CH_3)_2CH{—}CH(CH_3){—}]_2BH$$

[32]

(*Ref. 41*)

$$(CH_3)_2C{=}C(CH_3)_2 + B_2H_6 \xrightarrow{(C_2H_5)_2O} (CH_3)_2CH{—}C(CH_3)_2{—}BH_2$$

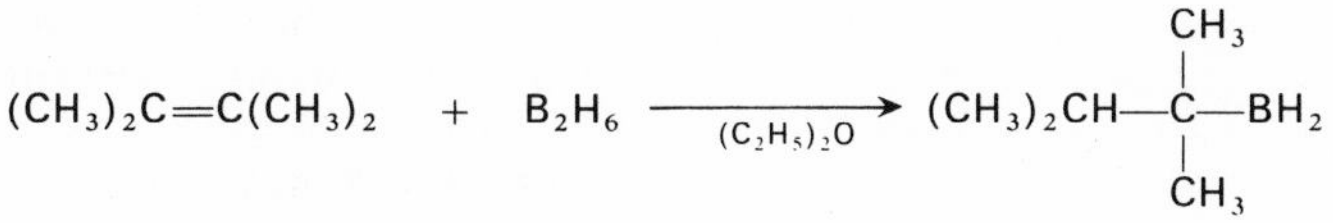

The direction of addition of borine to unsymmetrical olefins is such that the predominant product has the boron atom bonded to the less highly substituted carbon atom. The following examples of product distributions[40] illustrate not only this generalization but also the fact that the direction of addition is affected (though to a lesser extent) by electrical effects (e.g., **[33]**) and by the steric bulk of groups near the double bond (e.g., **[34]**). The use of the sterically more hindered reagent bis(3-methyl-2-butyl)borane

$$n\text{-}C_4H_9\text{—}CH{=}CH_2 \xrightarrow[\text{diglyme}]{B_2H_6} n\text{-}C_4H_9\text{—}CH_2\text{—}CH_2\text{—}B\lt \;(94\%) + n\text{-}C_4H_9\text{—}CH(B\lt)\text{—}CH_3 \;(6\%)$$

$$X\text{—}C_6H_4\text{—}CH{=}CH_2 \;[33] \xrightarrow[\text{diglyme}]{B_2H_6} X\text{—}C_6H_4\text{—}CH_2\text{—}CH_2\text{—}B\lt \;[33A] + X\text{—}C_6H_4\text{—}CH(B\lt)\text{—}CH_3 \;[33B]$$

X	product composition	
	[33A]	**[33B]**
$\text{—}OCH_3$	91%	9%
$\text{—}CH_3$	82%	18%
—H	80%	20%
—Cl	65%	35%

$$(CH_3)_2CH\text{—}CH{=}CH\text{—}CH_3 \;[34]\;(\textit{trans}\text{ isomer}) \xrightarrow[\text{diglyme}]{B_2H_6} (CH_3)_2CH\text{—}CH_2\text{—}CH(B\lt)\text{—}CH_3 \;(57\%) + (CH_3)_2CH\text{—}CH(B\lt)\text{—}CH_2CH_3 \;(43\%)$$

[32] with these same olefins gives a substantial increase in the selectivity, as shown in the formulas below. Figures in parentheses refer to the fractions of product in which the boron atom is bonded to the carbon atom indicated.[42]

(42) (a) H. C. Brown and G. Zweifel, *J. Am. Chem. Soc.*, **83**, 1241 (1961); (b) H. C. Brown and K. A. Keblys, *ibid.*, **86**, 1791, 1795 (1964); (c) H. C. Brown and O. J. Cope, *ibid.*, **86**, 1801 (1964); (d) M. Nussim, Y. Mazur, and F. Sondheimer, *J. Org. Chem.*, **29**, 1120, 1131 (1964).

product composition from hydroboration with $\left[(CH_3)_2CH{-}CH(CH_3)\right]_2BH$ in diglyme

[32]

$n\text{-}C_4H_9{-}CH{=}CH_2$ (1%) (99%)

$C_6H_5{-}CH{=}CH_2$ (2%) (98%)

$(CH_3)_2CH{-}CH{=}CH{-}CH_3$ (5%) (95%)

The utility of the hydroboration reaction arises from the fact that the intermediate alkylboranes can be either oxidized to alcohols or carbonyl compounds or hydrolyzed to hydrocarbons. The following examples illustrate these possibilities. It will be noted that

$$n\text{-}C_8H_{17}{-}CH{=}CH_2 \xrightarrow[\text{diglyme, }25°]{B_2H_6} (n\text{-}C_8H_{17}CH_2{-}CH_2{-})_3B \xrightarrow[H_2O\text{-diglyme}]{H_2O_2,\ NaOH} n\text{-}C_8H_{17}{-}CH_2{-}CH_2OH$$

(not isolated) (93%)

(*Ref. 41a*)

$$n\text{-}C_4H_9{-}CH{=}CH_2 \xrightarrow[\text{diglyme, }25°]{B_2H_6} (n\text{-}C_4H_9{-}CH_2{-}CH_2)_3B \xrightarrow[\text{reflux}]{CH_3CH_2CO_2H} n\text{-}C_4H_9{-}CH_2{-}CH_3$$

(not isolated) (91%)

(*Ref. 43*)

1-methylcyclohexene $\xrightarrow[(C_2H_5)_2O,\ 25°]{B_2H_6}$ (2-methylcyclohexyl)$_2$BH (not isolated) $\xrightarrow[H_3O^{\oplus},\ (C_2H_5)_2O]{CrO_3}$ 2-methylcyclohexanone (78%)

(*Ref. 44*)

hydroboration followed by oxidation of the alkylborane to an alcohol results in the over-all addition of water to a double bond in a direction opposite to that obtained by the direct hydration of a double bond with aqueous acid, an addition which follows the Markownikoff rule. The formation of a hydrocarbon by hydroboration of an olefin and subsequent acidic hydrolysis would normally offer no advantage over the simpler catalytic hydrogenation unless the selective reduction of a double bond in the presence of some easily hydrogenated function (e.g., a nitro group) were desired. However, this sequence for multiple-bond reduction has been found useful for the preparation of a hydrocarbon

(43) (a) H. C. Brown and K. Murray, *J. Am. Chem. Soc.*, **81**, 4108 (1959); (b) H. C. Brown and K. Murray, *J. Org. Chem.*, **26**, 631 (1961).

(44) H. C. Brown and C. P. Garg, *J. Am. Chem. Soc.*, **83**, 2951 (1961).

containing deuterium atoms in specific locations, since the deuterium-hydrogen scrambling observed on catalytic hydrogenation appears not to be a problem in hydroboration reactions at room temperature.

$$LiAlD_4 + BF_3 \xrightarrow{(C_2H_5)_2O} B_2D_6$$

$+ B_2D_6 \xrightarrow[0°]{(C_2H_5)_2O}$ B $\xrightarrow[25°]{CH_3CO_2D}$ (43%)

(*Ref.* 45)

The addition of borine to a double bond has been found to occur in a *cis* manner from the less hindered side of the double bond, as indicated in the following example.[46] Both the oxidation of the

CH_3 CH_3 H CH_3 $\xrightarrow[25°]{B_2H_6}$ BH $\xrightarrow[NaOH, H_2O]{H_2O_2}$ OH (89%) (*Ref.* 46)

carbon-boron bond to form an alcohol[46] and the hydrolysis of this bond to form a hydrocarbon[43b] have been found to occur with retention of configuration. These results are consistent with an addition mechanism involving the initial formation of a pi complex [**35**] followed by an intramolecular transfer of a hydride ion from boron to carbon. The accompanying equations also illustrate a

C=C + BH_3 ⇌ [**35**] ⇌ H, BH_2

$$R_3B \xrightarrow{HOO^\ominus} R_2\overset{\ominus}{B}(R)\text{—O—OH} \longrightarrow R_2B\text{—O—R} \xrightarrow{^\ominus OH} R_2B\text{—O—R}$$

$$\longrightarrow R_2B\text{—O}^\ominus + R\text{—O—H}$$

(45) A. C. Cope, G. A. Berchtold, P. E. Peterson, and S. H. Sharman, *J. Am. Chem. Soc.*, **82**, 6370 (1960).

(46) (a) H. C. Brown and G. Zweifel, *J. Am. Chem. Soc.*, **83**, 2544 (1961); **86**, 393 (1964); (b) for the use of the dialkylborane derived from α-pinene for the preparation of optically active alcohols by asymmetric induction, see also H. C. Brown, N. R. Ayyangar and G. Zweifel, *ibid.*, **86**, 397 (1964); G. Zweifel, N. R. Ayyangar, T. Munekata and H. C. Brown, *ibid.*, **86**, 1076 (1964).

possible mechanism for the subsequent oxidation of the alkylborane to form an alcohol.

The reversibility of the addition of borine has been demonstrated by heating initially formed alkylboranes to temperatures above 80° (usually in refluxing diglyme).[47] Since reversal of the hydroboration reaction can usually occur in two directions with the alkylboranes derived from nonterminal olefins, the net result of heating such an alkylborane is to isomerize it to the more stable terminal alkylborane, as illustrated below. A variety of applications of this isomerization process have been described.[37,47] It is apparent from the foregoing discussion that the isomerization of

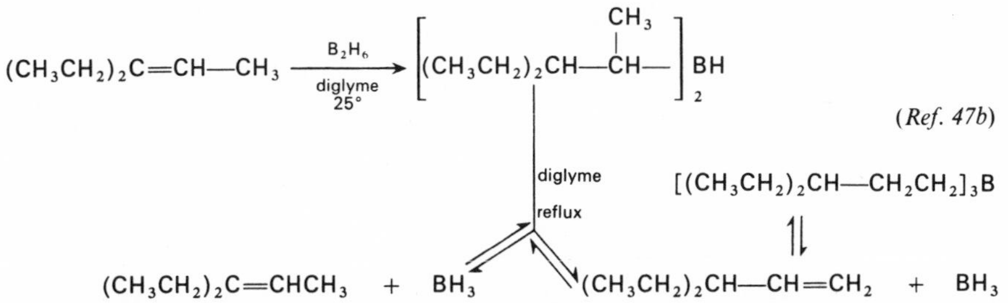

$$(CH_3CH_2)_2C{=}CH{-}CH_3 \xrightarrow[\text{diglyme, } 25^\circ]{B_2H_6} [(CH_3CH_2)_2CH{-}CH(CH_3){-}]_2BH$$

(*Ref. 47b*)

$$[(CH_3CH_2)_2CH{-}CH(CH_3){-}]_2BH \xrightarrow{\text{diglyme, reflux}} (CH_3CH_2)_2C{=}CHCH_3 + BH_3 \rightleftharpoons (CH_3CH_2)_2CH{-}CH{=}CH_2 + BH_3 \rightleftharpoons [(CH_3CH_2)_2CH{-}CH_2CH_2]_3B$$

an alkylborane cannot occur past a carbon atom that is not bonded to at least one hydrogen atom. When the alkylborane **[36]**, which cannot undergo the usual isomerization to a terminal alkylborane, was heated, the compound underwent an interesting insertion reaction to form the cyclic borane **[37]**.

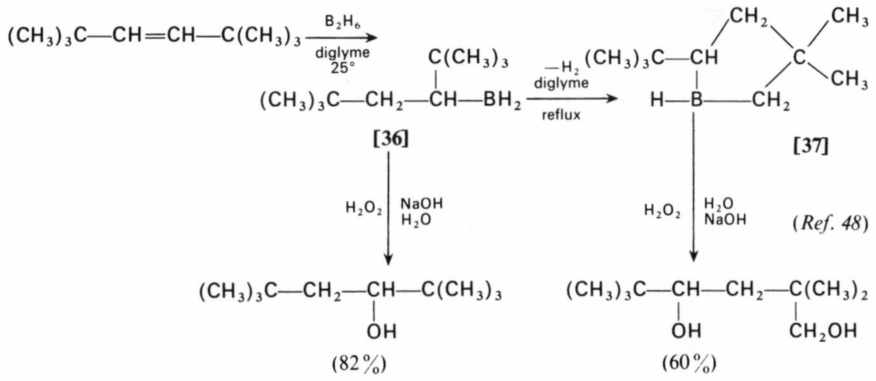

$$(CH_3)_3C{-}CH{=}CH{-}C(CH_3)_3 \xrightarrow[\text{diglyme, } 25^\circ]{B_2H_6} (CH_3)_3C{-}CH_2{-}CH(C(CH_3)_3){-}BH_2 \; \textbf{[36]}$$

$$\textbf{[36]} \xrightarrow[\text{diglyme, reflux}]{-H_2} \text{cyclic borane } \textbf{[37]}: (CH_3)_3C{-}CH{<}(CH_2{-}C(CH_3)_2{-}CH_2{-}BH{-})$$

(*Ref. 48*)

$$\textbf{[36]} \xrightarrow{H_2O_2,\ NaOH,\ H_2O} (CH_3)_3C{-}CH_2{-}CH(OH){-}C(CH_3)_3 \quad (82\%)$$

$$\textbf{[37]} \xrightarrow{H_2O_2,\ H_2O,\ NaOH} (CH_3)_3C{-}CH(OH){-}CH_2{-}C(CH_3)_2{-}CH_2OH \quad (60\%)$$

(47) (a) H. C. Brown and G. Zweifel, *J. Am. Chem. Soc.*, **82**, 1504 (1960); (b) H. C. Brown and M. V. Bhatt, *ibid.*, **82**, 2074 (1960); (c) H. C. Brown and B. S. Subba Rao, *ibid.*, **81**, 6434 (1959).

(48) T. J. Logan and T. J. Flautt, *J. Am. Chem. Soc.*, **82**, 3446 (1960).

The hydroboration of nonterminal acetylenes may be stopped at the monoaddition stage to form vinylborane derivatives (e.g., [**38**]).[49] Subsequent hydrolysis produces *cis*-olefins of purity at least as high as that obtained by the previously discussed catalytic hydrogenation of acetylenes. As would be expected, oxidation of the vinylborane derivatives produces carbonyl compounds. The hydroboration of terminal acetylenes with diborane has proved

$$C_2H_5—C{\equiv}C—C_2H_5 \xrightarrow[\text{diglyme, } 0^\circ]{B_2H_6} \left(\begin{matrix} C_2H_5—C—H \\ \| \\ C_2H_5—C— \end{matrix}\right)_3 B \xrightarrow[25^\circ]{CH_3CO_2H} \begin{matrix} C_2H_5—C—H \\ \| \\ C_2H_5—C—H \end{matrix}$$

[**38**] (68%)

(*Ref. 49a*)

$$[\mathbf{38}] \xrightarrow[(pH\ 8)]{H_2O_2,\ H_2O} C_2H_5—CH_2—CO—C_2H_5 \quad (62\%)$$

difficult to stop at the monoaddition stage. However, use of the more selective reagent, bis(3-methyl-2-butyl)borane [**32**], permits the reaction to be stopped after monoaddition. Subsequent hydrolysis yields a terminal olefin and subsequent peroxide oxidation produces an aldehyde.

$$n\text{-}C_6H_{13}—C{\equiv}CH + [(CH_3)_2CH—\overset{\displaystyle CH_3}{\overset{|}{C}H}—]_2BH \xrightarrow[0\text{–}10^\circ]{\text{diglyme}} [(CH_3)_2CH—\overset{\displaystyle CH_3}{\overset{|}{C}H}—]_2B—CH{=}CH—C_6H_{13}\text{-}n$$

$$\xrightarrow{H_2O_2,\ NaOH,\ H_2O} n\text{-}C_6H_{13}—CH_2—CHO \quad (70\%)$$

(*Ref. 49*)

An interesting reduction of certain types of esters to ethers and the reductive cleavage of benzyl-oxygen bonds have been described with sodium borohydride and a large excess of the Lewis acid,

(49) (a) H. C. Brown and G. Zweifel, *J. Am. Chem. Soc.*, **81**, 1512 (1959); **83**, 3834 (1961); **85**, 2066 (1963); (b) D. J. Pasto, *ibid.*, **86**, 3039 (1964).

boron trifluoride.[50] This ester reduction, illustrated by the following examples, is presumably related mechanistically to the reduction of amides to amines with lithium aluminum hydride and the reduction of ketals to ethers with aluminum hydride–aluminum

1 $NaBH_4$ + 15 BF_3, diglyme → (80%) (*Ref.* 50*c*)

1 $NaBH_4$ + 15 BF_3, diglyme → (76%) (*Ref.* 50*c*)

chloride mixtures. It seems probable that the reducing agent in these cases is diborane and that the excess Lewis acid serves to form an oxonium ion from the intermediate reduction product (cf. **[20]** from an amide).

(50) (a) G. R. Pettit, U. R. Ghatak, B. Green, T. R. Kasturi, and D. M. Piatak, *J. Org. Chem.*, **26**, 1686 (1961); (b) G. R. Pettit and T. R. Kasturi, *ibid.*, **26**, 4557 (1961); (c) G. R. Pettit and D. M. Piatak, *ibid.*, **27**, 2127 (1962); (d) G. R. Pettit, B. Green, P. Hofer, D. C. Ayres, and P. J. S. Pauwels, *Proc. Chem. Soc.*, **1962**, 357.

3

DISSOLVING METAL REDUCTIONS ·

A VARIETY OF ORGANIC MOLECULES ARE REDUCED by reaction with a metal, either in the presence of a proton donor or followed by treatment with a proton donor. Although this method of reduction, which was one of the first used for organic compounds, has been replaced by catalytic hydrogenation and metal hydride reduction for some classes of compounds, there remains a substantial group of dissolving metal reductions that are currently used synthetically because of advantages offered in selectivity of reduction or in stereoselectivity. The metals commonly involved include the alkali metals—lithium, sodium, and potassium—as well as calcium, zinc, magnesium, tin, and iron. The alkali metals and calcium have been used as *solutions* in liquid ammonia, b.p. $-33°$ (the Birch reduction[1]); in low-molecular-weight aliphatic amines; or in certain ethers such

(1) (a) A. J. Birch, *Quart. Rev.* (*London*), **4**, 69 (1950); (b) A. J. Birch and H. Smith, *ibid.*, **12**, 17 (1958); (c) G. W. Watt, *Chem. Rev.*, **46**, 317 (1950); (d) C. Djerassi (ed.), *Steroid Reactions*, Holden-Day, Inc., San Francisco, 1963, pp. 267–288, 299–325; (e) H. Smith, "Organic Reactions in Liquid Ammonia. Chemistry in Non-aqueous Ionizing Solvents," Vol. 1, part 2, Wiley, New York, 1963.

as 1,2-dimethoxyethane.[2] These same metals as well as zinc and magnesium have been used as *suspensions* in inert solvents such as ether, toluene, or xylene. For both procedures a proton source (frequently ethanol, isopropyl alcohol, *t*-butyl alcohol, or water) is present in the reaction medium, is added concurrently with the compound to be reduced, or is added during the isolation. Finally, sodium and especially zinc, tin, and iron have been added directly to solutions of the compound being reduced in hydroxylic solvents such as ethanol, isopropyl alcohol, *n*-butyl alcohol, isoamyl alcohol, acetic acid, water, or an aqueous mineral acid.

The early hypothesis that dissolving metal reductions were effected by reaction of the "nascent" hydrogen (liberated from the metal and the hydroxylic solvent) with the molecule being reduced appears to be untenable.[1a,3] In fact, the formation of hydrogen gas during these reductions is normally an undesirable side reaction. The dissolving metal reductions are better considered as "internal" electrolytic reductions (cf. Ref. 3b), in which an electron is transferred from the metal surface (or from the metal in solution) to the organic molecule being reduced. The anion radicals produced

$C_6H_5—C(=O)—C_6H_5$ [1] $\xrightleftharpoons[(C_2H_5)_2O \text{ or liquid } NH_3]{Na}$ $C_6H_5—\dot{C}(—\ddot{O}:^{\ominus})—C_6H_5 \; Na^{\oplus}$ $\leftrightarrow$ $C_6H_5—\ddot{C}^{\ominus}(—\dot{O}:)—C_6H_5$ $\rightleftharpoons$ $(C_6H_5)_2C(O^{\ominus})—C(O^{\ominus})(C_6H_5)_2 \; 2\,Na^{\oplus}$ (*Ref. 4*)

[2] (blue)

[3] $\xrightleftharpoons[CH_3OCH_2CH_2OCH_3]{Na}$ [4] (dark green) $Na^{\oplus}$ (*Ref. 5*)

(2) M. C. R. Symons, *Quart. Rev. (London)*, **13**, 99 (1959); M. Gold, W. L. Jolly, and K. S. Pitzer, *J. Am. Chem. Soc.*, **84**, 2264 (1962).

(3) (a) J. H. Brewster, *J. Am. Chem. Soc.*, **76**, 6361 (1954); (b) F. D. Popp and H. P. Schultz, *Chem. Rev.*, **62**, 19 (1962).

(4) W. E. Bachmann, *J. Am. Chem. Soc.*, **55**, 1179 (1933); C. B. Wooster, *ibid.*, **59**, 377 (1937).

(5) (a) N. D. Scott, J. F. Walker, and V. L. Hansley, *ibid.*, **58**, 2442 (1936); (b) J. F. Walker and N. D. Scott, *ibid.*, **60**, 951 (1938); (c) for a study of the naphthalene dianion, see G. Henrici-Olive and S. Olive, *Z. Physik. Chem.*, **43**, 327, 334, 340 (1964).

by this electron transfer are illustrated by the reaction of benzophenone [**1**] to form the ketyl [**2**] and by the reaction of naphthalene [**3**] to form the naphthalide ion radical [**4**]. These two examples represent cases where relatively high concentrations of stable anion radicals are obtained as solutions in nonprotonic solvents. Even relatively stable ion radicals such as these are bases of sufficient strength to readily abstract a proton from materials with acidic hydrogen atoms (e.g., triphenylmethane).[6] The presence in these anion radicals of an unpaired electron, which interacts with the atoms in the conjugated system, has been established by measurement of the e.s.r. spectra of various anion radical solutions.[7] The more reactive anion radicals formed from systems that offer less possibility for resonance stabilization normally either react with the solvent to abstract a proton or dimerize (or polymerize) in the absence of a protonic solvent. However, it has been possible to intercept even the more reactive anion radicals prior to reaction with other molecules in the reaction medium if the initially formed ion radicals are capable of undergoing an intramolecular reaction. The following examples are illustrative. The intermolecular transfer of an electron from one anion radical to another conjugated system in the same solution,

$CH_2—OSO_2C_6H_4CH_3$-*p* —(Li, THF, liquid NH_3)→ $CH_2—OSO_2C_6H_4CH_3$-*p* $Li^{\oplus}$ → (*Ref. 8*)

—(Li)→ $Li^{\oplus}$ —($H_3O^{\oplus}$)→ (45%)

(6) (a) H. Normant and B. Angelo, *Bull. Soc. Chim. France*, **1960**, 354; **1962**, 810; (b) J. J. Eisch and W. C. Kaska, *J. Org. Chem.*, **27**, 3745 (1962).

(7) (a) A. Carrington, *Quart. Rev.* (*London*), **17**, 67 (1963); (b) B. J. McClelland, *Chem. Rev.*, **64**, 301 (1964).

(8) (a) G. Stork and J. Tsuji, *J. Am. Chem. Soc.*, **83**, 2783 (1961); (b) see also D. J. Cram and C. K. Dalton, *ibid.*, **85**, 1268 (1963); S. Rakhit and M. Gut, *ibid.*, **86**, 1432 (1964).

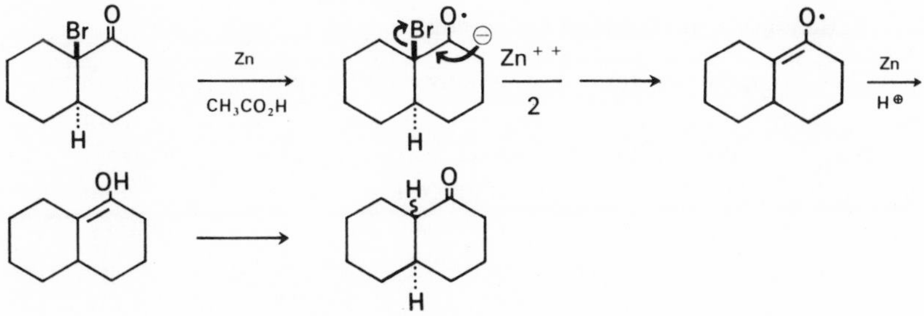

(*Ref.* 9)

(*cis* and *trans* isomers)

as illustrated in the equation below, has also been demonstrated.

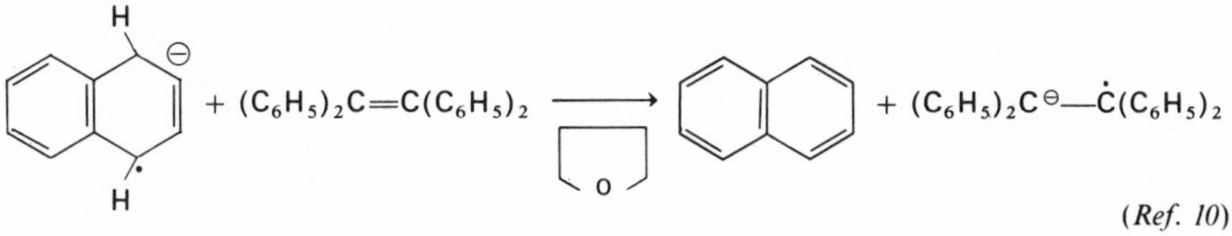

$$+ (C_6H_5)_2C{=}C(C_6H_5)_2 \longrightarrow + (C_6H_5)_2C^{\ominus}{-}\dot{C}(C_6H_5)_2$$

(*Ref.* 10)

If an anion radical has a structure that permits extensive delocalization of the extra electron present, it is possible under certain conditions to add a second electron to the system to form a dianion such as [**5**]. This dianion formation is expected to be favored by

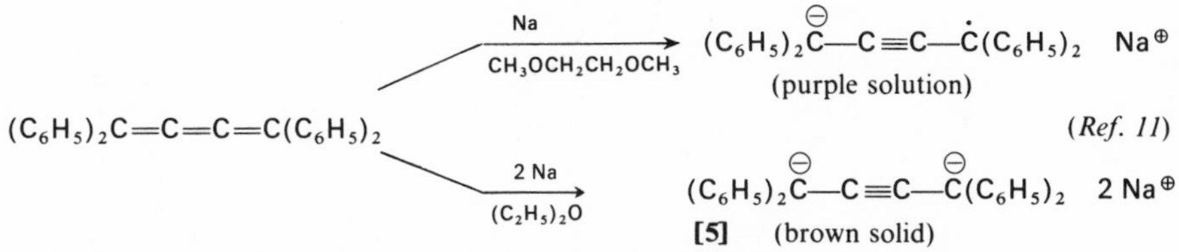

$$(C_6H_5)_2C{=}C{=}C{=}C(C_6H_5)_2 \xrightarrow[CH_3OCH_2CH_2OCH_3]{Na} (C_6H_5)_2\overset{\ominus}{C}{-}C{\equiv}C{-}\dot{C}(C_6H_5)_2\ Na^{\oplus}$$

(purple solution)

(*Ref.* 11)

$$(C_6H_5)_2C{=}C{=}C{=}C(C_6H_5)_2 \xrightarrow[(C_2H_5)_2O]{2\ Na} (C_6H_5)_2\overset{\ominus}{C}{-}C{\equiv}C{-}\overset{\ominus}{C}(C_6H_5)_2\ 2\ Na^{\oplus}$$

[**5**] (brown solid)

the use of solvents of low dielectric constant and poor solvating ability (e.g., diethyl ether), which do not favor the dissociation of the initially formed anion radical from its cation.

(9) (a) H. E. Zimmerman and A. Mais, *ibid.*, **81**, 3644 (1959); (b) for an example of the loss of methyllithium from an ion radical, see H. L. Dryden, Jr., G. M. Webber and J. J. Wieczorek, *ibid.*, **86**, 742 (1964).

(10) (a) A. G. Evans, J. C. Evans, E. D. Owen, and B. J. Tabner, *Proc. Chem. Soc.*, **1962**, 226; (b) A. G. Evans, J. C. Evans, and B. J. Tabner, *ibid.*, **1962**, 338; (c) J. E. Bennett, A. G. Evans, J. C. Evans, E. D. Owen, and B. J. Tabner, *J. Chem. Soc.*, **1963**, 3954; (d) A. G. Evans and J. C. Evans, *ibid.*, **1963**, 6036.

(11) (a) A. Zweig and A. K. Hoffmann, *J. Am. Chem. Soc.*, **84**, 3278 (1962); (b) see also E. R. Zabolotny and J. F. Garst, *ibid.*, **86**, 1645 (1964); J. F. Garst, E. R. Zabolotny and R. S. Cole, *ibid.*, **86**, 2257 (1964).

Reduction of Carbonyl Functions

Ketones and esters may be successfully reduced with lithium or sodium (either the free metal or its solution in liquid ammonia) and an alcohol. Unconjugated carbon-carbon double bonds are normally inert to these reducing conditions. Although this method (the Bouveault-Blanc reduction) for the reduction of esters offers occasional advantages, as in the selective reduction of the acid ester [6], it has largely been replaced in the laboratory by the more

H, CO_2CH_3, $CH_2CH_2CO_2H$, H $\xrightarrow[\text{liquid } NH_3]{Na,\ C_2H_5OH}$ H, CH_2OH, $CH_2CH_2CO_2Na$, H $\xrightarrow{H_3O^{\oplus}}$ H, O, O, H

[6] (72%)

(*Ref. 12*)

convenient reductions of esters with lithium aluminum hydride or by catalytic hydrogenation. The reduction of ketones (e.g., **[7]**) with sodium and isopropyl alcohol in refluxing toluene is relatively

O $\xrightarrow[(CH_3)_2CHOH,\ C_6H_5CH_3,\ \text{reflux}]{Na}$ H, OH (*Ref. 13*)

[7] (85–90%)

convenient and offers the stereochemical advantage that the more stable alcohol is frequently (but not always) the predominant product. This reaction is believed to follow the course indicated below, where the initially formed anion radical **[8]** is protonated from the less hindered side and then reacts further with the metal to form the alkoxide **[9]**. The alkoxide **[9]**, once formed, can react with the starting ketone by the process indicated in structure **[10]**,

(12) (a) L. A. Paquette and N. A. Nelson, *J. Org. Chem.*, **27**, 2272 (1962); use of the more powerful reducing system, lithium in ethylamine, in the absence of an added proton source has been found to slowly reduce carboxylic acids to aldehydes: see (b) A. W. Burgstahler, L. R. Worden, and T. B. Lewis, *ibid.*, **28**, 2918 (1963); (c) A. W. Burgstahler and L. R. Worden, *J. Am. Chem. Soc.*, **86**, 96 (1964).

(13) S. Dev, *J. Indian Chem. Soc.*, **33**, 769 (1956).

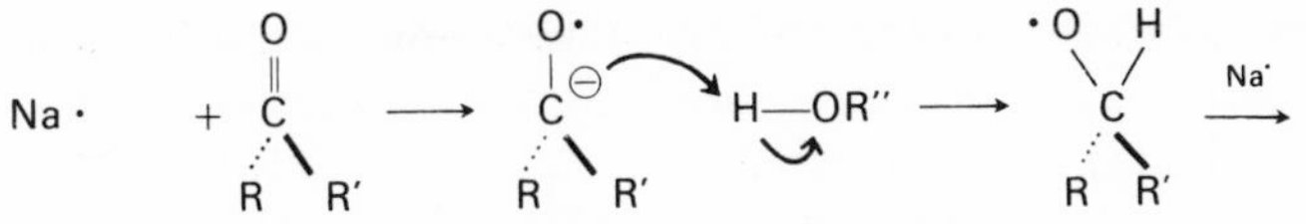

Na· + C(=O)RR' ⟶ [8] ⟶ H—OR'' ⟶ ·C(O)(H)RR' $\xrightarrow{Na^{\cdot}}$

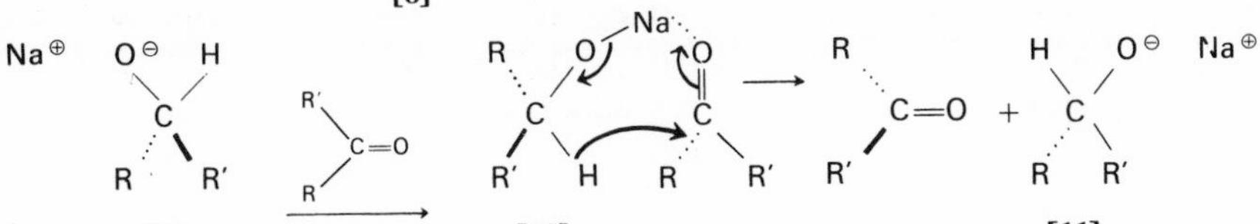

[9] ⟶ [10] ⟶ [11]

analogous to the Meerwein-Ponndorf-Verley reduction,[14] to produce the isomeric (and usually more stable) alkoxide **[11]**. For this final equilibrium to occur, it is necessary that the rate of the equilibrium reaction **[10]** → **[11]** be either comparable to, or faster than, the rate of reduction of the starting ketone, since both the ketone and the alkoxide must be present for equilibration. In cases where the starting ketone is either strained or sterically hindered (opposing conversion of the tetrahedral alkoxide **[9]** back to the starting ketone, as in **[10]**), the less stable alcohol

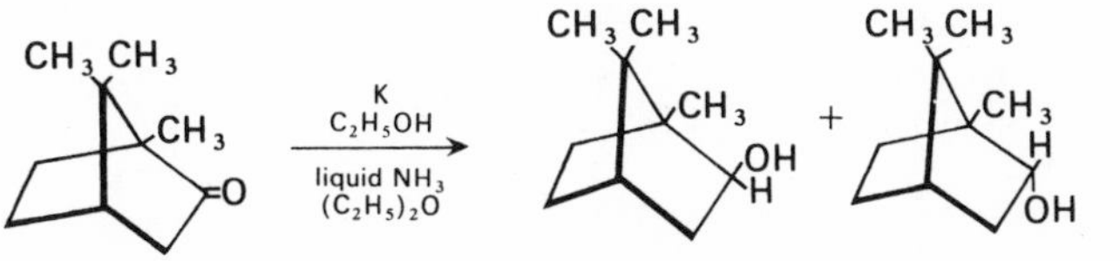

[12] $\xrightarrow[\text{liquid } NH_3,\ (C_2H_5)_2O]{K,\ C_2H_5OH}$ (70% of product) + (30% of product) (*Ref. 15*)

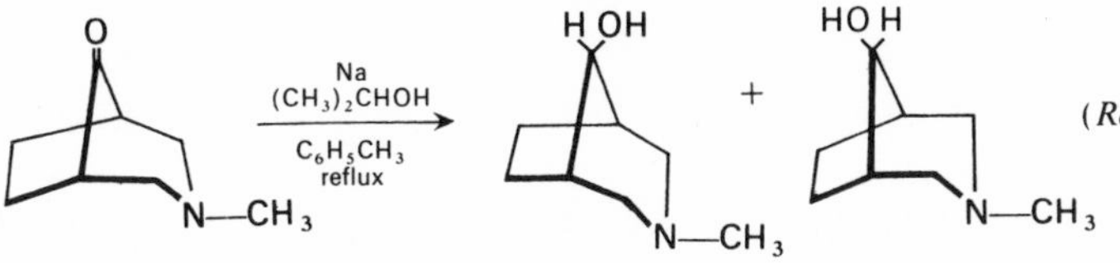

[13] $\xrightarrow[C_6H_5CH_3,\ \text{reflux}]{Na,\ (CH_3)_2CHOH}$ (93% of product) + (7% of product) (*Ref. 16a*)

(14) A. L. Wilds, *Org. Reactions*, **2**, 178 (1944).

(15) G. Ourisson and A. Rassat, *Tetrahedron Letters*, **No. 21**, 16 (1960); these authors noted that the stereochemical course of this reduction could be modified by changing the metal used as the reducing agent.

(16) (a) H. O. House, H. C. Müller, C. G. Pitt, and P. P. Wickham, *J. Org. Chem.*, **28**, 2407 (1963); (b) see also J. W. Huffman, D. M. Alabran, and T. W. Bethea, *ibid.*, **27**, 3381 (1962).

(17) (a) W. E. Doering, G. Cortes, and L. H. Knox, *J. Am. Chem. Soc.*, **69**, 1700 (1947); (b) W. E. Doering and T. C. Aschner, *ibid.*, **71**, 838 (1949); **75**, 393 (1953).

formed by protonation of the intermediate anion radical from the less hindered side is often the product observed. In such cases (e.g., **[12]** and **[13]**) it is sometimes possible to achieve equilibration to the more stable isomer by adding certain ketones such as benzophenone or fluorenone[17] to the alkoxide solution *after the sodium has been consumed* and then refluxing the solution as illustrated in the following equation.

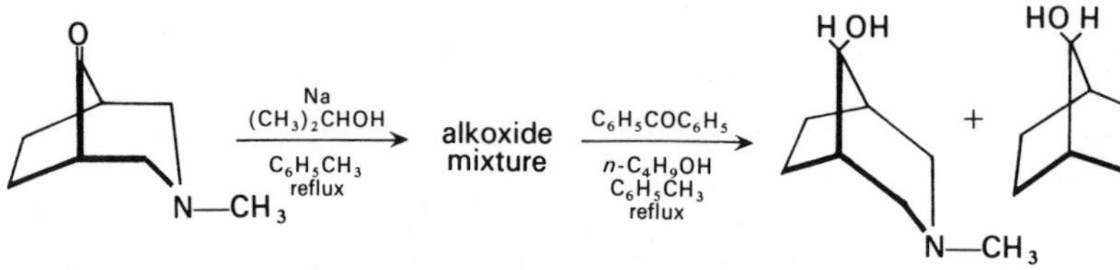

Na, $(CH_3)_2CHOH$, $C_6H_5CH_3$, reflux → alkoxide mixture → $C_6H_5COC_6H_5$, n-C_4H_9OH, $C_6H_5CH_3$, reflux (*Ref. 16a*)

[13] (34% of product) (66% of product)

As noted earlier, the conversion of an α-substituted ketone (e.g., **[14]**) to its anion radical may be followed by the loss of the alpha-substituent if the latter is a reasonably good leaving group. This

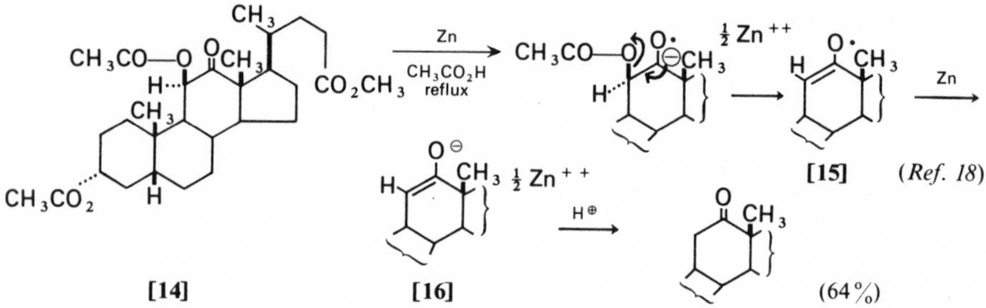

Zn, CH_3CO_2H, reflux; Zn; $H^{\oplus}$ (*Ref. 18*)

[14] **[15]** **[16]** (64%)

elimination is followed by the further reaction of the radical **[15]** with the metal to form an enolate anion **[16]**, which may be protonated in the reaction mixture or during isolation or may be acetylated (if the reaction solvent is acetic anhydride) to form an enol acetate. Typical reactions of this type include the reductions of α-halo, α-amino, α-acyloxy, and α-hydroxy ketones as illustrated below. These reductions are most often effected with zinc

(18) (a) R. S. Rosenfeld and T. F. Gallagher, *J. Am. Chem. Soc.*, **77**, 4367 (1955); (b) J. H. Chapman, J. Elks, G. H. Phillipps, and L. J. Wyman [*J. Chem. Soc.*, **1956**, 4344] describe the use of calcium in liquid ammonia to achieve the same type of reduction.

in acetic anhydride, acetic acid, or aqueous mineral acid or with calcium in liquid ammonia.[18b]

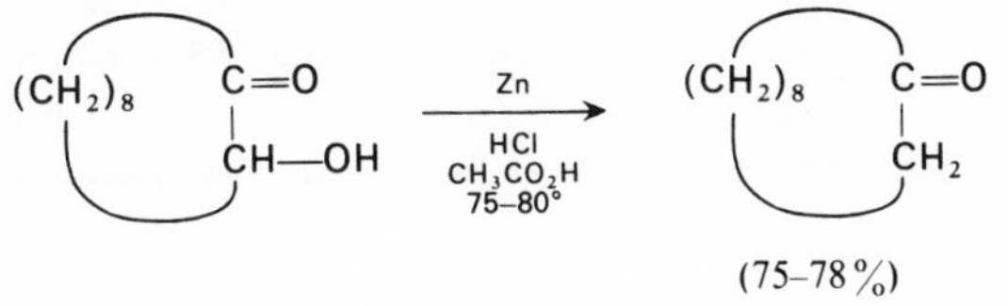

$(CH_2)_8$ C=O / CH—OH $\xrightarrow[\text{HCl, } CH_3CO_2H,\ 75\text{–}80°]{\text{Zn}}$ $(CH_2)_8$ C=O / CH_2 (75–78%) (*Ref. 19*)

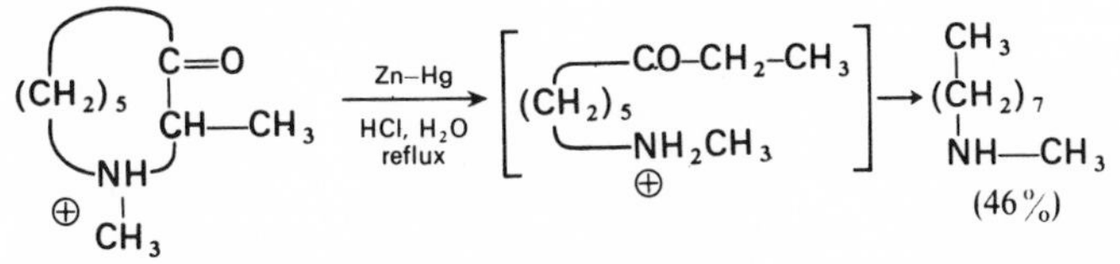

$(CH_2)_5$ C=O / CH—CH_3 / $\overset{\oplus}{N}H$—CH_3 $\xrightarrow[\text{HCl, } H_2O,\ \text{reflux}]{\text{Zn–Hg}}$ [$(CH_2)_5$ CO–CH_2–CH_3 / $\overset{\oplus}{N}H_2CH_3$] → CH_3–$(CH_2)_7$–NH—CH_3 (46%) (*Ref. 20*)

In order for this type of reduction to proceed, it is necessary that the alpha substituent be able to occupy a conformation in which it is perpendicular to the plane of the carbonyl group, as illustrated in formula **[17]**. This conformation allows a minimum expenditure of energy for the elimination, since breaking the carbon-substituent bond may be accompanied by a continuous overlap of the developing *p* orbital at the alpha carbon atom with the pi-orbital system of the ion radical. A consequence of this stereoelectronic requirement is that cyclohexanones with axial alpha substituents (e.g., **[14a]**) are reductively cleaved more readily than analogous compounds (e.g., **[14e]**) with equatorial alpha substituents.[18]

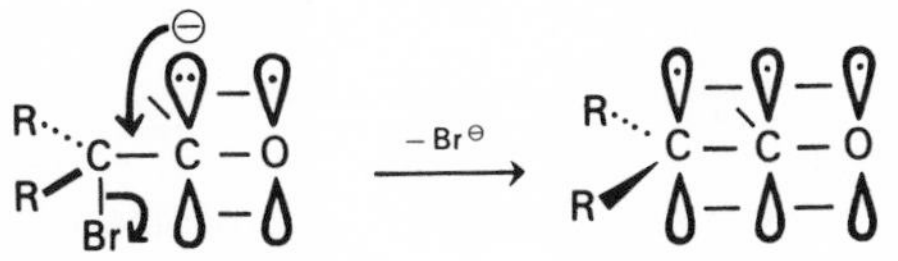

$\xrightarrow{-Br^{\ominus}}$

[17]

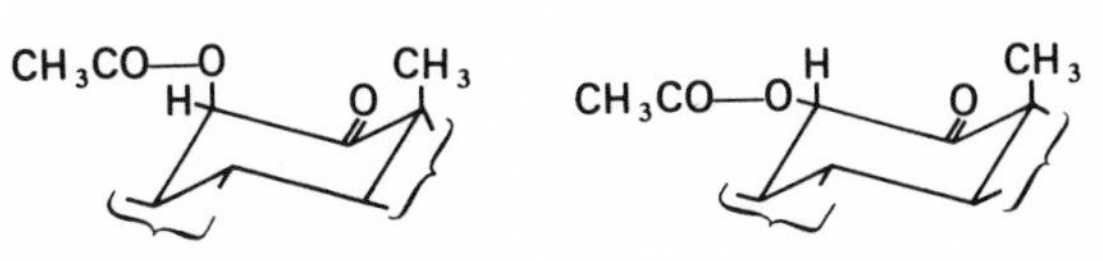

[14a] **[14e]**

(19) A. C. Cope, J. W. Barthel, and R. D. Smith, *Org. Syn.*, **Coll. Vol. 4**, 218 (1963).
(20) N. J. Leonard and R. C. Sentz, *J. Am. Chem. Soc.*, **74**, 1704 (1952).

Although similar reductive cleavages of α-substituted ketones have been achieved with chromium (II) salts in acetone or acetic acid,[21] it is not certain that the mechanism of this reductive cleavage is analagous to that of the dissolving metal reductions.

The reduction of ketones with zinc amalgam in strong aqueous acids, the Clemmensen reduction,[22] has been used to convert ketones to methylene groups. As illustrated in the following equation, the reaction is conveniently run as a three-phase mixture

$$C_6H_5\text{—CO—}CH_2CH_2\text{—}CO_2H \xrightarrow[\text{HCl, } H_2O \text{, toluene, reflux}]{\text{Zn–Hg}} C_6H_5(CH_2)_3CO_2H \quad (82\text{–}89\%) \qquad (Ref.\ 23)$$

$$n\text{-}C_6H_{13}\text{—CO—}CH_3 \xrightarrow[\text{HOAc, } H_2O\text{, HCl, reflux}]{\text{Zn–Hg}} n\text{-}C_6H_{13}\text{—}CH_2\text{—}CH_3 \quad (62\%) \qquad (Ref.\ 22d)$$

of toluene, aqueous hydrochloric acid, and zinc amalgam. Under these conditions a low concentration of the ketone and its conjugate acid are present in the aqueous phase, which is in contact with the zinc, and bimolecular reduction (to be discussed subsequently) is minimized. Although the mechanism of this reduction is uncertain,[22] it appears probable that electrons are transferred from the metal surface to the conjugate acid of the ketone as in formula [**18**], and further loss of the hydroxyl group as well as acid hydrolysis of the resultant organozinc compound occur at the metal surface.

$$R\text{—}\overset{\overset{\oplus}{O}\text{—H}}{\overset{\|}{C}}\text{—R (on }\ddot{Zn}\ \ddot{Zn}\ \ddot{Zn}\text{) [18]} \longrightarrow R\text{—}\overset{OH^{\oplus}}{C}\text{—R (on }\oplus\ddot{Zn}\ \ddot{Zn}\ Zn\text{)} \xrightarrow[-Zn^{++}]{H^{\oplus},\ -H_2O} R\text{—C—R (}\|\text{ on }\ddot{Zn}\ Zn\text{)} \xrightarrow[-Zn^{++}]{2H^{\oplus}} \ddot{Zn} + R\text{—}CH_2\text{—R}$$

(21) (a) G. Rosenkranz, O. Mancera, J. Gatica, and C. Djerassi, *J. Am. Chem. Soc.*, **72**, 4077 (1950); (b) W. Cole and P. L. Julian, *J. Org. Chem.*, **19**, 131 (1954); (c) D. H. R. Barton and J. T. Pinhey, *Proc. Chem. Soc.*, **1960**, 279.

(22) (a) E. L. Martin, *Org. Reactions*, **1**, 155 (1942); (b) D. Staschewski, *Angew. Chem.*, **71**, 726 (1959); (c) T. Nakabayashi, *J. Am. Chem. Soc.*, **82**, 3900, 3906, 3909 (1960); (d) J. H. Brewster, *ibid.*, **76**, 6364 (1954); (e) J. H. Brewster, J. Patterson, and D. A. Fidler, *ibid.*, **76**, 6368 (1954).

(23) E. L. Martin, *Org. Syn.*, **Coll. Vol. 2,** 499 (1943).

The reaction of ketones with metals, particularly magnesium (or magnesium plus iodine),[24] magnesium amalgam, zinc, zinc amalgam, or aluminum amalgam, in the absence of protonic solvents, leads to the production of anion radicals in sufficiently high concentration that coupling occurs, as illustrated below by

$$CH_3{-}CO{-}CH_3 \xrightarrow[C_6H_6,\ \text{reflux}]{\text{Mg–Hg}} (CH_3)_2\dot{C}{-}O^{\ominus}\ \tfrac{1}{2}Mg^{++} \longrightarrow \begin{array}{l}(CH_3)_2C{-}O^{\ominus}\ Mg^{++}\\ \quad\ \ |\\ (CH_3)_2C{-}O^{\ominus}\end{array}$$

$$\xrightarrow{H_2O} \underset{(43\text{–}50\%)}{(CH_3)_2C(OH){-}C(OH)(CH_3)_2} \qquad (\textit{Ref. } 25)$$

the reduction of acetone. This process, called bimolecular reduction, is often a competing reaction in other dissolving metal reductions such as the Clemmensen reduction. An analogous reaction is found in the reduction of esters; if an ester such as **[19]** is allowed to react with sodium in the presence of a protonic solvent (e.g., ethanol), the initially formed anion radical **[20]** is protonated and

$$\underset{[19]}{n\text{-}C_{11}H_{23}{-}C(=O){-}OC_2H_5} \xrightarrow[\substack{C_2H_5OH\\ C_6H_5CH_3\\ \text{reflux}}]{\text{Na}} \underset{[20]}{n\text{-}C_{11}H_{23}{-}\overset{\ominus}{C}(\dot{O})\,{-}OC_2H_5\ \ Na^{\oplus}} \xrightarrow{C_2H_5OH} \xrightarrow{\text{Na}} \qquad (\textit{Ref. } 26)$$

$$n\text{-}C_{11}H_{23}{-}CH(O^{\ominus}\,Na^{\oplus}){-}OC_2H_5 \longrightarrow n\text{-}C_{11}H_{23}{-}CH{=}O \xrightarrow[C_2H_5OH]{\text{Na}} \underset{(65\text{–}75\%)}{n\text{-}C_{11}H_{23}{-}CH_2OH}$$

then undergoes the further changes indicated. However, in the absence of a protonic solvent, coupling of two anion radicals occurs to give the dianion **[21]**, which produces a ketol by further reduction and subsequent hydrolysis. This bimolecular reduction of esters, called the acyloin reaction,[27] has proved of special value

(24) M. D. Rausch, W. E. McEwen, and J. Kleinberg, *Chem. Rev.*, **57**, 417 (1957).

(25) (a) R. Adams and E. W. Adams, *Org. Syn.*, **Coll. Vol. 1**, 459 (1944); (b) for examples of bimolecular reduction with metal-ammonia reducing systems see J. Fried and N. A. Abraham, *Tetrahedron Letters*, **No. 28**, 1879 (1964).

(26) S. G. Ford and C. S. Marvel, *Org. Syn.*, **Coll. Vol. 2**, 372 (1943).

(27) S. M. McElvain, *Org. Reactions*, **4**, 256 (1948).

$$n\text{-}C_3H_7\text{—}C(=O)\text{—}OC_2H_5 \xrightarrow[(C_2H_5)_2O,\ \text{reflux}]{Na} n\text{-}C_3H_7\text{—}\dot{C}(O^{\ominus})\text{—}OC_2H_5\ Na^{\oplus} \rightarrow \text{[21]}$$

[21] (*Ref. 28*)

$$\rightarrow \begin{matrix} n\text{-}C_3H_7\text{—}C{=}O \\ n\text{-}C_3H_7\text{—}C{=}O \end{matrix} \xrightarrow{2\,Na} \begin{matrix} n\text{-}C_3H_7\text{—}C\text{—}O^{\ominus} \\ n\text{-}C_3H_7\text{—}C\text{—}O^{\ominus} \end{matrix}\ 2\,Na^{\oplus} \xrightarrow{H_3O^{\oplus}} n\text{-}C_3H_7\text{—}C(=O)\text{—}CH(OH)\text{—}C_3H_7\text{-}n$$

(65–70%)

for the preparation of medium and large rings,[29] as illustrated in

$$CH_3O_2C(CH_2)_8CO_2CH_3 \xrightarrow[C_6H_4(CH_3)_2,\ \text{reflux}]{Na} \xrightarrow{CH_3CO_2H} (CH_2)_8 \text{ ring with } C{=}O \text{ and } CH\text{—}OH$$

(67–74%) (*Ref. 30*)

the equation above. Four-, five-, and six-membered rings have also been obtained by the acyloin reaction, as have products from a mixed ketone-ester coupling (e.g., [**22**]) when the ring size is favorable.

$$\text{cyclohexane-1,2-}(CO_2CH_3)_2 \xrightarrow[C_6H_4(CH_3)_2,\ \text{reflux}]{Na} \text{bicyclic hydroxy ketone (OH, O)} + \text{other products}$$

(12%) (*Ref. 31*)

$$\text{steroid with } CH_3O_2C\text{—}CH_2,\ CH_3O_2C\text{—}CH_2,\ CH_3,\ CH_3,\ C_8H_{17} \xrightarrow[(C_2H_5)_2O,\ \text{liquid } NH_3]{Na} \xrightarrow{H_3O^{\oplus}} \text{HO, O acyloin (82\%)} + \text{HO, O acyloin (5\%)}$$

(82%) (5%)

(*Ref. 32*)

(28) J. M. Snell and S. M. McElvain, *Org. Syn.*, **Coll. Vol. 2,** 114 (1943).

(29) (a) V. Prelog, *J. Chem. Soc.*, **1950**, 420; (b) K. Ziegler in E. Müller (ed.), *Methoden der organischen Chemie* (*Houben-Weyl*), Vol. 4, Part 2, Georg Thieme Verlag, Stuttgart, Germany, 1955, pp. 729–822.

(30) N. L. Allinger, *Org. Syn.*, **Coll. Vol. 4,** 840 (1963).

(31) A. C. Cope and E. C. Herrick, *J. Am. Chem. Soc.*, **72**, 983 (1950).

(32) (a) J. C. Sheehan, R. C. O'Neill, and M. A. White, *ibid.*, **72**, 3376 (1950);

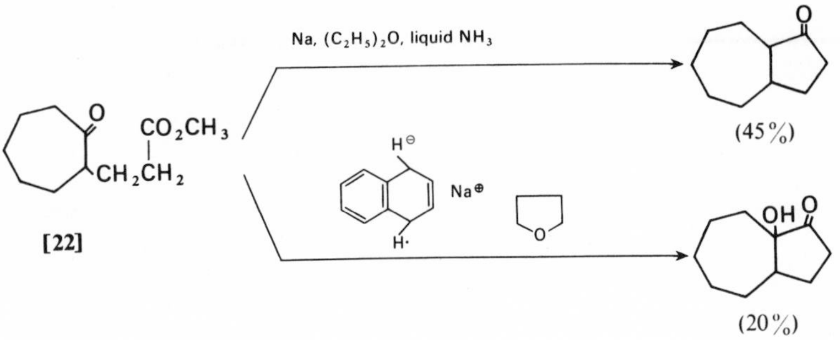

Na, $(C_2H_5)_2O$, liquid NH_3

CO_2CH_3

CH_2CH_2

[22]

$H^{\ominus}$ $Na^{\oplus}$

H·

(45%)

(*Ref. 33*)

OH O

(20%)

Reduction of Conjugated Systems

The most common reactions in this category are the dissolving metal reductions of carbon-carbon double bonds conjugated with carbonyl groups, aromatic systems, or other carbon-carbon multiple bonds; and the dissolving metal reductions of aromatic systems to form dihydro or tetrahydro aromatic systems. Although α,β-unsaturated carbonyl compounds are initially reduced to saturated carbonyl compounds with zinc in acetic acid or with

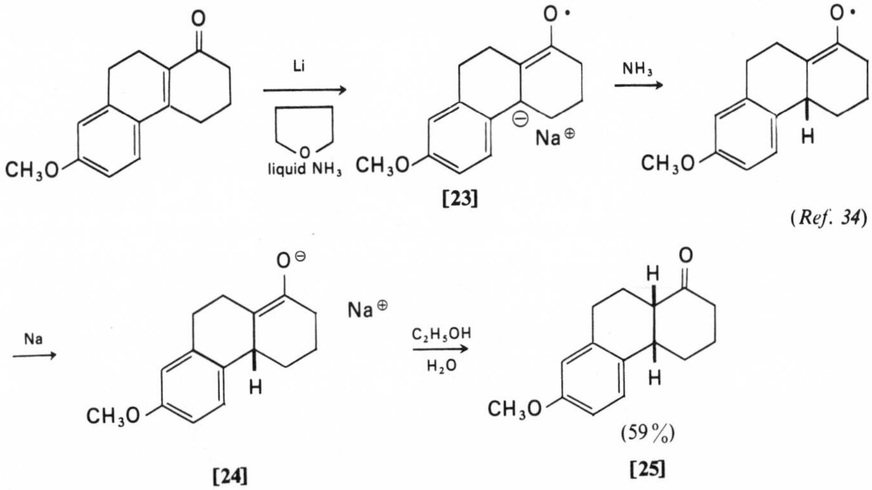

O Li liquid NH_3 CH_3O

O· $Na^{\oplus}$ CH_3O [23]

NH_3 O· H CH_3O

(*Ref. 34*)

Na $O^{\ominus}$ $Na^{\oplus}$ H CH_3O [24]

C_2H_5OH H_2O

O H H CH_3O (59%) [25]

(b) J. C. Sheehan and R. C. Coderre, *ibid.*, **75**, 3997 (1953); (c) J. C. Sheehan and W. F. Erman, *ibid.*, **79**, 6050 (1957).

(33) (a) C. D. Gutsche and I. Y. C. Tao, *J. Org. Chem.*, **28**, 883 (1963); (b) see also E. E. van Tamelen, T. A. Spencer, Jr., D. S. Allen, Jr., and R. L. Orvis, *Tetrahedron*, **14**, 8 (1961).

(34) A. J. Birch, H. Smith, and R. E. Thornton, *J. Chem. Soc.*, **1957**, 1339.

zinc amalgam in aqueous acid (Clemmensen reduction conditions), this type of reduction is more typically accomplished with sodium or lithium in liquid ammonia. Under these conditions the initially formed anion radical [**23**] is a sufficiently strong base to abstract a proton from ammonia and produce, after the addition of a second electron, the enolate anion [**24**]. This intermediate is insufficiently basic to abstract a proton from ammonia and, bearing a full negative charge, it resists addition of another electron, which would correspond to further reduction. When a more acidic proton donor (e.g., ethanol, *t*-butyl alcohol, or ammonium chloride) is added during the isolation process, the enolate is protonated to form the ketonic product [**25**]. The presence of an enolate anion analogous to [**24**] in the reaction mixture prior to the addition of a proton donor has been demonstrated by the addition of methyl iodide to form a C-methylated product.[35] The stereochemical outcome of this reduction has been of particular interest since the beta carbon atom of the α,β-unsaturated carbonyl system is often protonated from the direction that will produce the more stable product,[34,36] frequently not the major product obtained on catalytic hydrogenation. For stereoelectronic reasons, it is only appropriate to consider the protonation of conformations of the intermediate anion radical that permit continuous overlap of the four *p* orbitals[37] involved (i.e., [**26**]). In the reduction of cyclohexanone derivatives this means that the proton introduced at the beta carbon atom will be axial with respect to the six-membered ring containing the ketone. In such cyclohexanone systems there will normally be two conformations that will permit axial protonation at the beta carbon atom. Although the radical ions, such as [**26**], derived from $\Delta^{1,9}$-octal-2-one systems are usually protonated

(35) (a) G. Stork, P. Rosen, and N. L. Goldman, *J. Am. Chem. Soc.*, **83**, 2965 (1961); (b) R. E. Schaub and M. J. Weiss, *Chem. Ind.* (*London*), **1961**, 2003; (c) M. J. Weiss, R. E. Schaub, J. F. Poletto, G. R. Allen, Jr., and C. J. Coscia, *ibid.*, **1963**, 118; (d) M. J. Weiss and co-workers, *Tetrahedron*, **20**, 357 (1964).

(36) (a) D. H. R. Barton and C. H. Robinson, *J. Chem. Soc.*, **1954**, 3045; (b) in some cases, the composition of stereoisomeric mixtures obtained from the dissolving metal reduction of conjugated systems can be varied by changing the metal and the proton donor used; for example, see G. E. Arth and co-workers, *J. Am. Chem. Soc.*, **76**, 1715 (1954).

(37) (a) G. Stork and S. D. Darling, *ibid.*, **82**, 1512 (1960); **86**, 1761 (1964); (b) for other examples, see H. Bruderlein, N. Dufort, H. Favre, and A. J. Liston, *Can. J. Chem.*, **41**, 2908 (1963); L. Velluz, J. Valls, and G. Nominé, *Angew. Chem., Intern. Ed. Engl.*, **4**, 181 (1965).

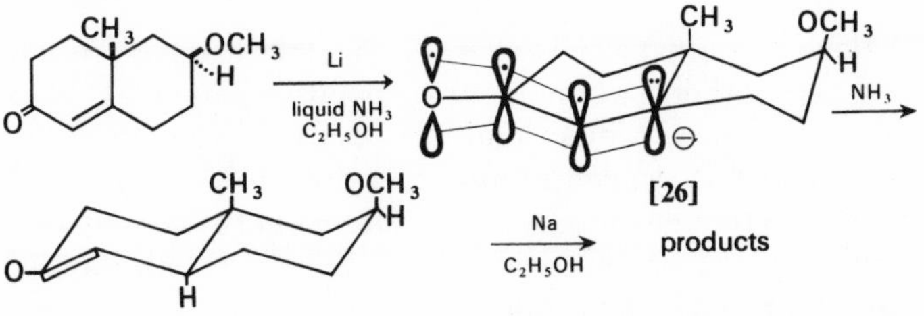

[26]

products

(*Ref. 37*)

at the beta carbon atom from the direction that leads to a *trans*-decalone system, it has not been established whether this represents thermodynamic control of the reaction (to form the more stable product)[36a] or whether the direction of protonation is determined by other factors.[37]

The final protonation at the alpha carbon atom of the enolate anion (e.g., **[24]**) to form the product is usually a kinetically controlled process. The kinetic protonation of an enolate anion at carbon must, for stereoelectronic reasons, occur from a direction perpendicular to the plane of the enolate anion. Although this protonation frequently occurs from the less hindered side of the enolate anion, no such generalization always is valid since other factors may influence the direction from which the proton is added.[38] In a number of cases (e.g., **[25]** and **[27]**) kinetic protonation leads to a product that does not have the more stable configuration at the alpha carbon atom. However, the initial product may be subsequently equilibrated in the presence of acid or base to produce the diastereoisomer which does have the more stable configuration at the alpha carbon.

(84%)

[27]

(94%)

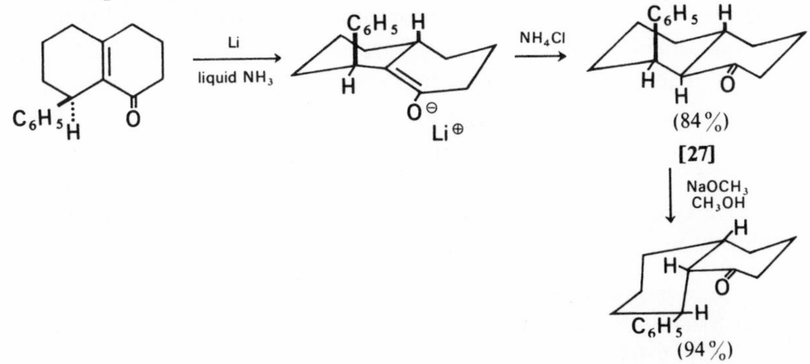

(*Ref. 39*)

(38) (a) H. E. Zimmerman in P. deMayo (ed.), *Molecular Rearrangements*, Vol. 1, Wiley-Interscience, New York, 1963, p. 345; (b) E. J. Corey and R. A. Sneen, *J. Am. Chem. Soc.*, **78**, 6269 (1956).

(39) H. O. House and H. W. Thompson, *J. Org. Chem.*, **28**, 360 (1963).

An analogous mechanism is operative in the dissolving metal reductions of carbon-carbon double bonds conjugated with aromatic systems or with other multiple bonds. The nature of the reduction product is dependent on the availability of a proton donor in the reaction medium, a fact illustrated in the accompanying examples. In the absence of a proton donor, dimerization of the initially formed anion radical is observed.

$$(C_6H_5)_2C{=}CH_2 \xrightarrow[\text{liquid } NH_3,\ (C_2H_5)_2O]{Na} \xrightarrow{NH_4Cl} \underset{(67\%)}{(C_6H_5)_2CHCH_3} + \underset{(17\%)}{(C_6H_5)_2CHCH_2CH_2CH(C_6H_5)_2} \quad (Ref.\ 40)$$

$$CH_2{=}CH{-}CH{=}CH_2 \xrightarrow[p\text{-}(C_6H_5)_2C_6H_4,\ (CH_3)_2O]{Na} {}^{\ominus}CH_2{-}CH{=}CH{-}\dot{C}H_2 \rightarrow [{}^{\ominus}CH_2{-}CH{=}CH{-}CH_2{-}]_2$$

$$\xrightarrow{CO_2} \text{unsaturated acids} \xrightarrow[\text{catalyst}]{H_2} \underset{(23\%)}{HO_2C(CH_2)_8CO_2H} + \underset{(36\%)}{HO_2CCH(C_2H_5)(CH_2)_5CO_2H} + \underset{(8\%)}{HO_2CCH(C_2H_5)(CH_2)_2CH(C_2H_5)CO_2H} \quad (Ref.\ 41)$$

$$CH_2{=}CH{-}CH{=}CH_2 \xrightarrow[\text{liquid } NH_3]{Na} \text{cis-}CH_3CH{=}CHCH_3 + \text{trans-}CH_3CH{=}CHCH_3 \quad (Ref.\ 42)$$

(cis isomer: at −33°, 13% of mixture; at −78°, 50% of mixture)

The ability of alkali metals to partially reduce aromatic systems has proved especially useful in organic synthesis. Illustrative is the reduction of benzene to 1,4-dihydrobenzene [**31**] with lithium and ethanol in liquid ammonia. In reductions of benzene derivatives, the anion radical [**28**] is formed reversibly in low concentration and then reacts further with the protonic solvent to form the radical [**29**] and, subsequently, the anion [**30**] and the dihydro derivatives.[43] Thus, one important function of the alcohol in the reduction of benzene derivatives is to provide a proton source

(40) H. Gilman and J. C. Bailie, *J. Am. Chem. Soc.*, **65**, 267 (1943).

(41) National Distillers and Chemical Corp., Brit. Pat. No. 756,385 dated Sept. 5, 1956; *CA*, **51**, 15557 (1957).

(42) N. L. Bauld, *J. Am. Chem. Soc.*, **84**, 4345, 4347 (1962).

(43) (a) A. P. Krapcho and A. A. Bothner-By, *ibid.*, **81**, 3658 (1959); **82**, 751 (1960); (b) J. F. Eastham and D. R. Larkin, *ibid.*, **81**, 3652 (1959); (c) A. P. Krapcho and M. E. Nadel, *ibid.*, **86**, 1096 (1964).

that is more acidic than ammonia. A number of polycyclic aromatic systems are reduced with an alkali metal in liquid ammonia even in the absence of an alcohol. Whether the success of these reductions is to be attributed to the presence of a higher concentration of the anion radical, permitting a more rapid rate of proton abstraction from ammonia, or to the formation of a dianion by the addition of a second electron to the anion radical is uncertain.

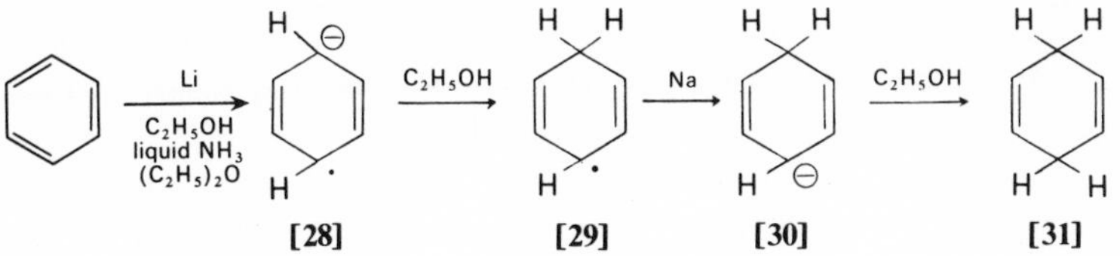

Since the reduction of benzene derivatives occurs only very slowly in the absence of an alcohol (or some other relatively acidic proton donor) in the reaction medium, it is possible to effect the selective reduction of an α,β-unsaturated carbonyl system (e.g., **[32]**) in the presence of a benzene ring if no alcohol is added. It should

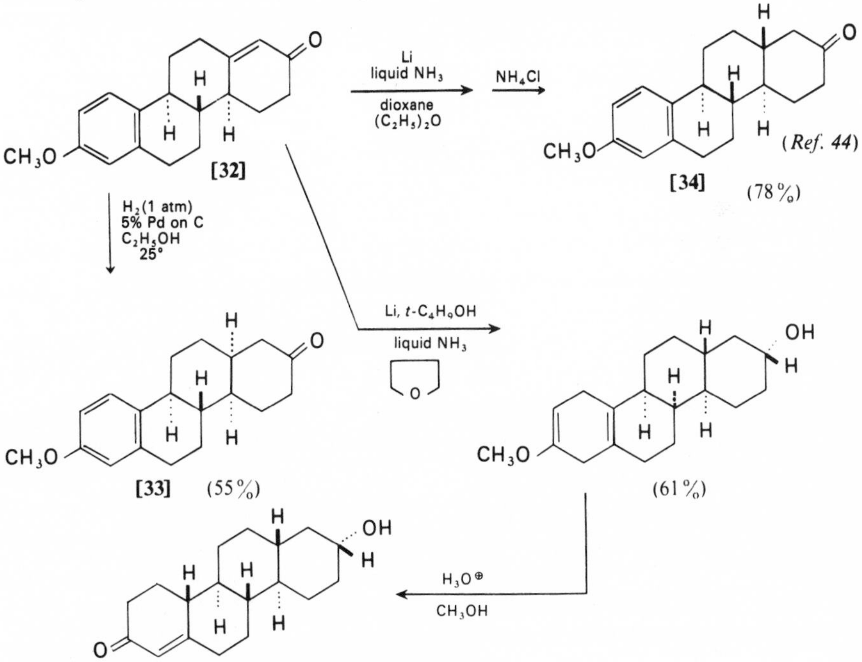

(44) W. F. Johns, *J. Org. Chem.*, **28**, 1856 (1963).

be noted that catalytic reduction of the unsaturated ketone [**32**] leads to a diastereoisomer [**33**] of the product [**34**] produced by a dissolving metal reduction.

The kinetically controlled protonation of the anion [**30**] to form the nonconjugated diene [**31**] rather than the conjugated isomer is representative of a general phenomenon observed in the kinetic protonation of conjugated anions of the type [**35**].[34,38a,45] The reaction course indicates that the energy barrier for proton addition (or proton removal) at the center of the system [**35**] to form the nonconjugated isomer [**36**] is lower than the energy barrier for the addition (or removal) of a proton to the terminal carbon atom to form the conjugated isomer [**37**], even though the latter is frequently more stable.

$$—CH{=}CH—\overset{\ominus}{C}H—CH{=}X \longleftrightarrow \overset{\ominus}{—CH}—CH{=}CH—CH{=}X$$

[**35**] ($X = CH_2$ or O)

(relatively rapid) $H^{\oplus}$ / $-H^{\oplus}$ ⇅ $H^{\oplus}$ / $-H^{\oplus}$ (relatively slow)

$—CH{=}CH—CH_2—CH{=}X$
[**36**]
(usually less stable)

$—CH_2—CH{=}CH—CH{=}X$
[**37**]
(usually more stable)

For the reduction of an aromatic system to be stopped at the dihydro stage it is necessary that the nonconjugated diene (e.g., [**31**]) initially formed not be reconverted to the anion (e.g., [**30**]). Such reconversion would allow the nonconjugated diene to be in equilibrium with the conjugated diene, which would be reduced further to the tetrahydro stage. Because bases such as $NH_2^{\ominus}$ and $R—NH^{\ominus}$ are sufficiently strong to effect this equilibration, a second function of the alcohol present in metal-ammonia reduction mixtures is to ensure the absence of an appreciable concentration of amide ion ($NH_2^{\ominus}$), a substantially stronger base than alkoxide

(45) (a) H. J. Ringold and S. K. Malhotra, *Tetrahedron Letters*, **No. 15,** 669 (1962); (b) H. J. Ringold and S. K. Malhotra, *J. Am. Chem. Soc.*, **84**, 3402 (1962); (c) H. J. Ringold and S. K. Malhotra, *ibid.*, **85**, 1538 (1963); (d) R. B. Bates, R. H. Carnighan, and C. E. Staples, *ibid.*, **85**, 3030–3032 (1963); (e) this phenomenon has been discussed in a more general way by G. S. Hammond, *ibid.*, **77**, 334 (1955).

ion (R—O$^{\ominus}$). The presence of alcohol has the same effect on reductions of aromatic systems by solutions of sodium or lithium in low-molecular-weight amines (e.g., methylamine, b.p. −6°, or ethylamine, b.p. 17°), as illustrated in the accompanying equations.

C_2H_5-benzene $\xrightarrow[C_2H_5NH_2,\ -78°]{Li}$ 1-ethylcyclohexene (75%)

C_2H_5-benzene $\xrightarrow[CH_3NH_2,\ CH_3CH_2CH_2OH]{Li}$ 1-ethyl-1,4-cyclohexadiene (46%)

(*Ref. 46*)

As would be anticipated from the previous discussion, electron-withdrawing substituents (e.g., —COONa) on an aromatic system will favor the acceptance of an electron to form an anion radical and accelerate reduction, whereas electron-donating substituents (e.g., —CH_3, —NH_2, —O$^{\ominus}$) will retard reduction.[1,43a] Also, the presence of bulky substituents on an aromatic ring retards reduction, presumably because of steric interference with solvation of the radical anion.[43a] The reduction indicated in the accompanying equation illustrates this selectivity.

1-naphthol (OH) $\xrightarrow[\text{liquid } NH_3,\ C_2H_5OH]{Li}$ 5,8-dihydro-1-naphthol (OH) (97–99%)

(*Ref. 47*)

The dihydrobenzenes produced from benzene derivatives having an electron-withdrawing substituent (e.g., [**38**]) have been found to be 1-substituted-1,4-dihydrobenzenes, whereas the products from benzene derivatives having electron-donating substituents

(46) (a) R. A. Benkeser, R. E. Robinson, D. M. Sauve, and O. H. Thomas, *J. Am. Chem. Soc.*, **77**, 3230 (1955); (b) R. A. Benkeser, M. L. Burrous, J. J. Hazdra, and E. M. Kaiser, *J. Org. Chem.*, **28**, 1094 (1963); R. A. Benkeser and co-workers, *ibid.*, **29**, 1313 (1964); (c) for examples of reductions with lithium in ethylenediamine, see L. Reggel, R. A. Friedel, and I. Wender, *ibid.*, **22**, 891 (1957).

(47) C. D. Gutsche and H. H. Peter, *Org. Syn.*, **Coll. Vol. 4,** 887 (1963).

(e.g., [**39**]) are 1-substituted-2,5-dihydrobenzenes.[1] Within the latter category, the directive effects of $—O—CH_3$ and $—N(CH_3)_2$ substituents outweigh the directive effect of an alkyl group.[1] These directive effects have been rationalized[1] by suggesting that in an

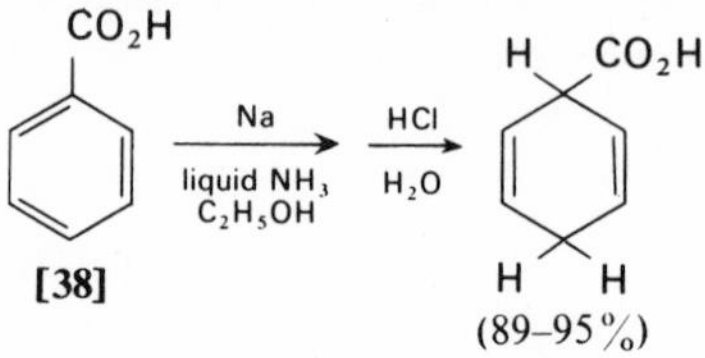

CO_2H [38] → (Na, liquid NH_3, C_2H_5OH; HCl, H_2O) → H CO_2H H H (89–95%) (*Ref. 48*)

OCH_3 [39] → (Li, liquid NH_3, $(C_2H_5)_2O$, C_2H_5OH) → H H OCH_3 H H (80% of product) + H H H OCH_3 H (20% of product) (*Ref. 49*)

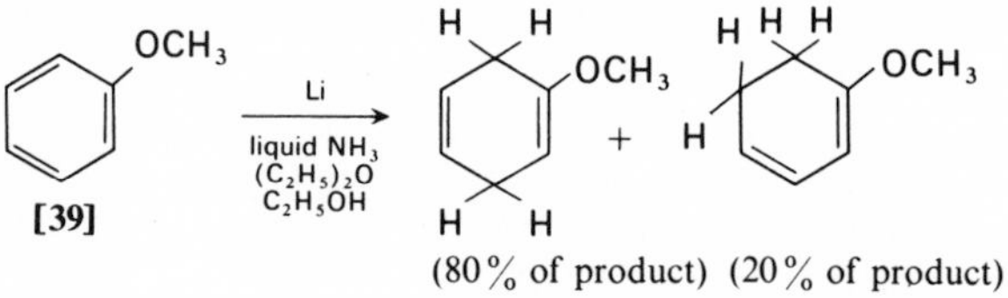

anion radical the electron density is greatest at a position *para* to an electron-withdrawing group and at a position *ortho* or *meta* to an electron-donating group. The latter suggestion has received experimental support from the e.s.r. spectrum of the anion radical

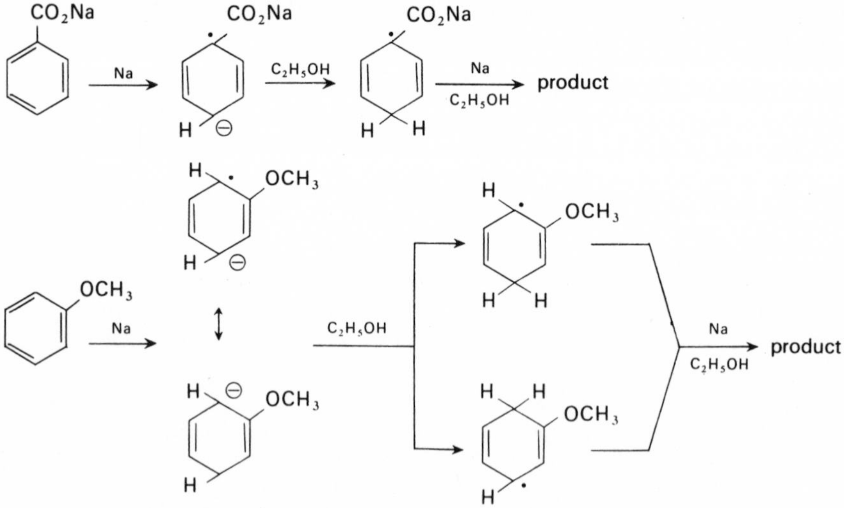

CO_2Na → (Na) → CO_2Na H ⊖ → (C_2H_5OH) → CO_2Na H H → (Na, C_2H_5OH) → product

OCH_3 → (Na) → H OCH_3 H ⊖ ↕ H ⊖ OCH_3 H → (C_2H_5OH) → H OCH_3 H H + H H OCH_3 H → (Na, C_2H_5OH) → product

(48) (a) M. E. Kuehne and B. F. Lambert, *Org. Syn.*, **43**, 22 (1963); (b) M. E. Kuehne and B. F. Lambert, *J. Am. Chem. Soc.*, **81**, 4278 (1959).

(49) A. L. Wilds and N. A. Nelson, *ibid.*, **75**, 5360, 5366 (1953).

derived from toluene.[50] Such radical anions are presumably protonated initially at the suggested sites of highest electron density, leading, after further electron transfer and protonation, to the observed products. Molecular orbital calculations[51] of the sites of highest electron density in anion radicals have successfully explained the orientation effects observed in dissolving metal reductions of aromatic systems.

Two frequently encountered problems in the usual procedure for Birch reductions (addition of sodium to a solution of the aromatic compound and an alcohol in liquid ammonia[1]) have been the insolubility of the aromatic compounds in the reaction medium and the failure of this reaction system to reduce aromatic compounds having several electron-donating or bulky substituents. Solubility problems have been overcome by the use of co-solvents such as ether, tetrahydrofuran, ethanol, or *t*-butyl alcohol; by the use of low-molecular-weight amines; or by conversion of the aromatic compounds to the more soluble *β*-hydroxyethyl ethers or glyceryl ethers.[1]

A modification[49] of this reduction procedure, which consists of adding the aromatic compound to a solution of lithium and a nonprotonic solvent (e.g., ether, tetrahydrofuran, dioxane, or 1,2-dimethoxyethane) in liquid ammonia and then adding an alcohol (ethanol, isopropyl alcohol, *t*-butyl alcohol), was found to facilitate the reduction of difficultly reduced aromatic systems. The use of a larger excess of alcohol, accompanied by the continuous addition of lithium to provide a high metal concentration in the reaction medium,[52] has permitted the successful reaction of systems

[40]

(*Ref. 52*)

(50) T. R. Tuttle, Jr., and S. I. Weissman, *ibid.*, **80**, 5342 (1958).

(51) (a) A. Streitwieser, Jr., *Molecular Orbital Theory for Organic Chemists*, Wiley, New York, 1962, pp. 425–431; (b) H. E. Zimmerman, *Tetrahedron*, **16**, 169 (1961).

(52) (a) W. S. Johnson, B. Bannister, and R. Pappo, *J. Am. Chem. Soc.*, **78**, 6331 (1956); (b) W. S. Johnson, R. Pappo, and W. F. Johns, *ibid.*, **78**, 6339 (1956).

(e.g., [**40**]) that are essentially inert to the usual conditions of the Birch reduction. The enhanced reducing power of such reaction systems employing lithium rather than sodium was originally attributed[49] to the greater solubility of lithium in liquid ammonia and to a higher reduction potential for lithium than for sodium. More recently, at least part of the advantage of lithium over sodium or potassium has been found to arise from the fact that traces of iron (present in undistilled liquid ammonia) catalyze the unwanted reaction of sodium or potassium with an alcohol (to form hydrogen) to a much greater extent than the corresponding reaction with lithium.[53] In the absence of iron, lithium, sodium, and potassium are all effective reducing agents. Although the relative rates of reduction of benzene with the alkali metals and ethanol in liquid ammonia follow the order lithium > sodium > potassium,[43a] all three are sufficiently rapid to be synthetically useful. In certain difficult cases, the selection of an alcohol of the correct acidity to serve as a proton donor may be important for successful reduction.[12c,53] Utilizing these facts, a procedure has been developed[53] employing a solution of the aromatic compound (e.g., [**41**]) in a mixture of distilled liquid ammonia (2 parts), tetrahydrofuran (1 part), and *t*-butyl alcohol (1 part), to which either sodium or lithium metal is added.

CH_3O [**41**] —(Li or Na; liquid NH_3, $t\text{-}C_4H_9OH$, THF)→ (79% with Li) (88% with Na) (*Ref.* 53)

Pyridine and its derivatives readily accept an electron from a metal to form an anion radical, and consequently these materials

Pyridine —(Na; C_2H_5OH, reflux)→ piperidine —(C_6H_5COCl; NaOH)→ N-$CO—C_6H_5$ (77–81%) (*Ref.* 54)

(53) H. L. Dryden, Jr., G. M. Webber, R. R. Burtner, and J. A. Cella, *J. Org. Chem.*, **26**, 3237 (1961).

(54) C. S. Marvel and W. A. Lazier, *Org. Syn.*, **Coll. Vol. 1,** 99 (1944).

are easily reduced with metals in protonic solvents. However, if the pyridine anion radical is formed in the absence of a protonic solvent, it very rapidly dimerizes,[55] as illustrated by the reduction of pyridine with zinc and acetic anhydride.

$$\text{C}_5\text{H}_5\text{N} \xrightarrow[\text{25–30°}]{\text{Zn, (CH}_3\text{CO)}_2\text{O}} \text{CH}_3\text{CO—N}\langle\text{H}\rangle\text{—}\langle\text{H}\rangle\text{N—COCH}_3$$ (*Ref. 56*)

Reduction of Other Functional Groups

Although nonconjugated, nonterminal[43c] olefins are normally stable to solutions of alkali metals in liquid ammonia, disubstituted acetylenes (e.g., **[42]**) are readily reduced to form *trans*-olefins. This reduction, which serves as a useful synthesis for *trans*-olefins, is in contrast to the catalytic hydrogenation of acetylenes, which yields *cis*-olefins. The reaction presumably proceeds by addition

$$n\text{-C}_3\text{H}_7\text{—C}{\equiv}\text{C—C}_3\text{H}_7\text{-}n \;\textbf{[42]} \xrightarrow[\text{liquid NH}_3]{\text{Na}} n\text{-C}_3\text{H}_7\text{—}\overset{\ominus}{\text{C}}{=}\dot{\text{C}}\text{—C}_3\text{H}_7\text{-}n \;\textbf{[43]} \xrightarrow{\text{NH}_3}$$ (*Ref. 57*)

$$\text{H(}n\text{-C}_3\text{H}_7\text{)C}{=}\dot{\text{C}}\text{(C}_3\text{H}_7\text{-}n\text{)} \;\textbf{[44]} \xrightarrow{\text{Na}} \text{H(}n\text{-C}_3\text{H}_7\text{)C}{=}\overset{\ominus}{\text{C}}\text{(C}_3\text{H}_7\text{-}n\text{)} \;\textbf{[45]} \xrightarrow{\text{NH}_3} \text{H(}n\text{-C}_3\text{H}_7\text{)C}{=}\text{C(H)(C}_3\text{H}_7\text{-}n\text{)} \;(80\text{–}90\%)$$

of one electron to form an anion radical **[43]**, which is protonated to give **[44]**. Subsequent electron transfer to form the anion **[45]**,

(55) (a) R. L. Ward, *J. Am. Chem. Soc.*, **83**, 3623 (1961); (b) J. W. Dodd, F. J. Hopton, and N. S. Hush, *Proc. Chem. Soc.*, **1962**, 61.

(56) (a) R. L. Frank and P. V. Smith, *Org. Syn.*, **Coll. Vol. 3,** 410 (1955); (b) A. T. Nielsen, D. W. Moore, G. M. Muha and K. H. Berry, *J. Org. Chem.*, **29**, 2175 (1964).

(57) (a) K. N. Campbell and L. T. Eby, *J. Am. Chem. Soc.*, **63**, 216, 2683 (1941); (b) A. L. Henne and K. W. Greenlee, *ibid.*, **65**, 2020 (1943).

followed by protonation, leads to the olefin. The preference for producing the *trans*-radical **[44]** on protonation of the anion radical **[43]** could be considered analogous to the *trans* addition of electrophilic reagents to acetylenes. Presumably the further reduction of the radical **[44]** to the anion **[45]** and the formation of the olefinic product occur more rapidly than inversion of the vinylic radical and the vinylic carbanion. Alternatively, the addition of the proton and a second electron from the metal to the anion radical may be concerted processes leading directly from the anion radical **[43]** to the anion **[45]**. Although terminal acetylenes may be reduced to terminal olefins with sodium in liquid ammonia,[57b] the acetylide anions produced from terminal acetylenes are inert to these reducing conditions because of the difficulty of adding an electron to the multiple bond, which already carries a full negative charge. This fact permits the selective reduction of a disubstituted acetylene in the presence of a terminal acetylene, as illustrated in the accompanying equation. Allenes (e.g., **[46]**) are also reduced by sodium in liquid ammonia and have been shown to be intermediates in the reduction of certain cyclic acetylenes

$$CH_3(CH_2)_2—C{\equiv}C—(CH_2)_4—C{\equiv}C—H \xrightarrow[\text{liquid } NH_3]{NaNH_2} CH_3(CH_2)_2—C{\equiv}C—(CH_2)_4—C{\equiv}C^{\ominus}\ Na$$

(*Ref. 58*)

$$\xrightarrow[\text{liquid } NH_3]{Na} \xrightarrow{NH_4Cl} \underset{(75\%)}{\overset{H\qquad\quad (CH_2)_4C{\equiv}CH}{CH_3(CH_2)_2\ \ C{=}C\ \ H}}$$

$$\underset{[46]}{(CH_3)_2C{=}C{=}CH—CH_3} \xrightarrow[\text{liquid } NH_3]{Na} \underset{(34\%)}{\overset{(CH_3)_2CH\qquad CH_3}{H\ \ C{=}C\ \ H}} + \underset{(48\%)}{\overset{(CH_3)_2CH\qquad H}{H\ \ C{=}C\ \ CH_3}}$$

$$+ \underset{(18\%)}{(CH_3)_2C{=}CHCH_2CH_3}$$

(*Ref. 59*)

with sodium and liquid ammonia to form *cis*-olefins rather than the expected *trans*-olefins.[59b]

(58) N. A. Dobson and R. A. Raphael, *J. Chem. Soc.*, **1955**, 3558.

(59) (a) D. Devaprabhakara and P. D. Gardner, *J. Am. Chem. Soc.*, **85**, 648 (1963); (b) M. Svoboda, J. Sicher, and J. Zavada, *Tetrahedron Letters*, **No. 1,** 15 (1964); (c) J. M. Brown, *Chem. Ind.* (*London*), **No. 42,** 1689 (1963).

Certain other functional groups—nitro groups, nitroso groups, and oximes, among them—may be reduced by reaction with metals in protonic solvents; examples are provided in the accompanying equations. Both from e.s.r. studies with aromatic nitro

$$\text{2-}CH_3\text{-1,4-}(NO_2)_2C_6H_3 \xrightarrow[\text{HCl, } H_2O,\ C_2H_5OH,\ \text{reflux}]{\text{Fe}} \text{2-}CH_3\text{-1,4-}(NH_2)_2C_6H_3 \ (74\%) \qquad (\textit{Ref. 60})$$

$$C_6H_5{-}NO_2 \xrightarrow[H_2O,\ 60\text{–}65^\circ]{\text{Zn, } NH_4Cl} C_6H_5{-}NHOH \ (62\text{–}68\%) \qquad (\textit{Ref. 61})$$

$$C_6H_5{-}NO_2 \xrightarrow[H_2O,\ CH_3OH,\ \text{reflux}]{\text{Zn, NaOH}} C_6H_5{-}N{=}N{-}C_6H_5 \ (84\text{–}86\%) \qquad (\textit{Ref. 62})$$

$$C_6H_5{-}N(CH_3){-}N{=}O \xrightarrow[H_2O,\ CH_3CO_2H,\ 80^\circ]{\text{Zn}} C_6H_5{-}N(CH_3){-}NH_2 \ (52\text{–}56\%) \qquad (\textit{Ref. 63})$$

$$n\text{-}C_6H_{13}{-}CH{=}NOH \xrightarrow[C_2H_5OH,\ \text{reflux}]{\text{Na}} n\text{-}C_6H_{13}{-}CH_2{-}NH_2 \ (60\text{–}73\%) \qquad (\textit{Ref. 64})$$

$$HO{-}N{=}C(CO_2C_2H_5)_2 \xrightarrow[CH_3CO_2H,\ (CH_3CO)_2O,\ 40\text{–}50^\circ]{\text{Zn}} CH_3CO{-}NH{-}CH(CO_2C_2H_5)_2 \ (77\text{–}78\%) \qquad (\textit{Ref. 65})$$

compounds[7] and from other observations[66] there is reason to believe that these compounds form relatively stable anion radicals such as **[47]**. The further protonation and reduction of such intermediates are presumably analogous to the dissolving metal

(60) S. A. Mahood and P. V. L. Schaffner, *Org. Syn.*, **Coll. Vol. 2,** 160 (1943).

(61) O. Kamm, *Org. Syn.*, **Coll. Vol. 1,** 445 (1944).

(62) H. E. Bigelow and D. B. Robinson, *Org. Syn.*, **Coll. Vol. 3,** 103 (1955).

(63) W. W. Hartman and L. J. Roll, *Org. Syn.*, **Coll. Vol. 2,** 418 (1943).

(64) W. H. Lycan, S. V. Puntambeker, and C. S. Marvel, *ibid.*, **Coll. Vol. 2,** 318 (1943).

(65) A. J. Zambito and E. E. Howe, *Org. Syn.*, **40**, 21 (1960).

(66) (a) G. A. Russell and E. G. Janzen, *J. Am. Chem. Soc.*, **84**, 4153 (1962); (b) G. A. Russell, E. G. Janzen, and E. T. Strom, *ibid.*, **84**, 4155 (1962); *ibid.*, **86**, 1807 (1964); (c) A. K. Hoffmann and co-workers, *ibid.*, **86**, 631, 639, 646 (1964); (d) P. L. Kolker and W. A. Waters, *J. Chem. Soc.*, **1964**, 1136.

reductions previously discussed. A possible reaction path is indicated below. The final step, involving cleavage of the N—O bond, is analogous to the subsequently discussed cleavage of other

$$C_6H_5-\overset{\oplus}{N}(=O)-O^{\ominus} \xrightarrow{\text{metal}} C_6H_5-\dot{N}^{\oplus}(O^{\ominus})-O^{\ominus}\ [47] \xrightarrow{H^{\oplus}} C_6H_5-\dot{N}^{\oplus}(OH)-O^{\ominus} \xrightarrow{\text{metal}}$$

$$C_6H_5-\ddot{N}(OH)-O^{\ominus} \longrightarrow C_6H_5-\ddot{N}=\ddot{O} \xrightarrow{\text{metal}} C_6H_5-\dot{\ddot{N}}-\ddot{O}:^{\ominus} \xrightarrow{H^{\oplus}} C_6H_5-\dot{\ddot{N}}-OH$$

$$\xrightarrow{\text{metal}} C_6H_5-\ddot{N}^{\ominus}-OH \xrightarrow{H^{\oplus}} C_6H_5-\ddot{N}H-OH \xrightarrow[H^{\oplus}]{\text{metal}} C_6H_5NH_2$$

single bonds in dissolving metal reductions. The complete reduction of these functional groups to amino groups is generally more easily accomplished by catalytic hydrogenation. However, the partial reduction of nitro groups to azo compounds or hydroxylamine derivatives is best accomplished with metals such as zinc in neutral or basic media.

Various single bonds may be cleaved by dissolving metal reductions. The cleavage of benzyl or allyl alcohol derivatives (e.g., **[48]** and **[49]**), quaternary ammonium salts (e.g., **[50]**), and thioethers occurs with particular ease, making this reductive cleavage valuable for the removal of benzyl protecting groups.

$$m\text{-}CH_3O-C_6H_4-C(CH_3)_2-OH\ [48] \xrightarrow[\text{liquid } NH_3,\ C_2H_5OH]{Na} [51] \longrightarrow m\text{-}CH_3O-C_6H_4-\dot{C}(CH_3)_2$$

(*Ref.* 67)

$$\xrightarrow{Na} m\text{-}CH_3O-C_6H_4-C^{\ominus}(CH_3)_2 \xrightarrow{C_2H_5OH} m\text{-}CH_3O-C_6H_4-CH(CH_3)_2\ (81\%)$$

(67) (a) A. J. Birch, *J. Chem. Soc.*, **1945**, 809; (b) A. J. Birch and S. M. Mukherji, *ibid.*, **1949**, 2531.

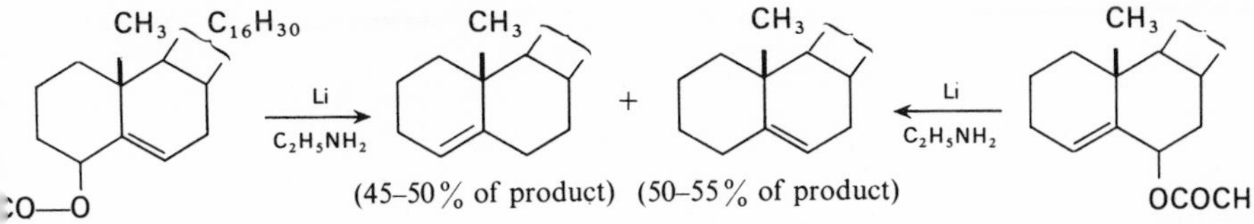

[49] $\xrightarrow[C_2H_5NH_2]{Li}$ (45–50% of product) + (50–55% of product) $\xleftarrow[C_2H_5NH_2]{Li}$ ($OCOCH_3$) (*Ref. 68*)

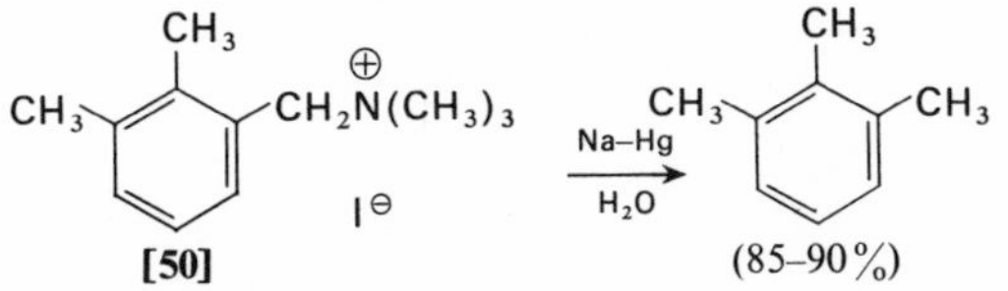

[50] $\xrightarrow[H_2O]{Na\text{–}Hg}$ (85–90%) (*Ref. 69*)

All such reactions are believed to proceed by formation of a radical anion (e.g., **[51]**) followed by elimination of a stable anion. Further reaction of the resulting radical with the metal and subsequent protonation give the product.

Aryl ethers (e.g., **[52]** and **[53]**) and aryl thioethers (e.g., **[54]**) are also cleaved by reaction with metals, although with more difficulty than benzyl and allyl systems. In these cases it is not certain whether the anion radical undergoes cleavage or whether a second electron is added and the resulting dianion then cleaves.[70] Alternatively, the dimer derived from the anion radical may be cleaved in certain cases.[70b] The cleavage of aryl diethyl phosphates with sodium or lithium in liquid ammonia to form aromatic hydrocarbons[71] is also worthy of note.

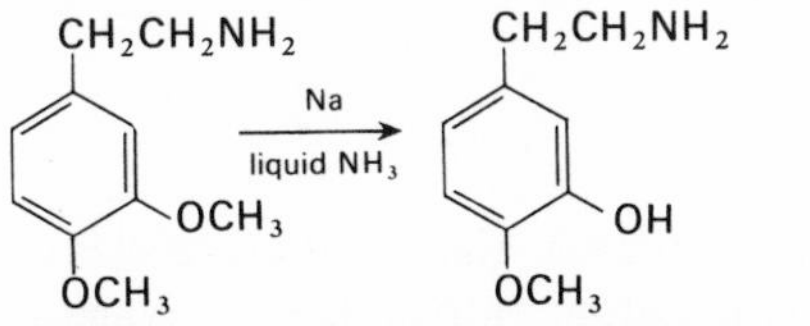

[52] $\xrightarrow[\text{liquid } NH_3]{Na}$ (85% as the hydrochloride) (*Ref. 72*)

(68) A. S. Hallsworth, H. B. Henbest, and T. I. Wrigley, *ibid.*, **1957**, 1969.

(69) W. R. Brasen and C. R. Hauser, *Org. Syn.*, **Coll. Vol. 4,** 508 (1963).

(70) (a) D. H. Eargle, Jr., *J. Org. Chem.*, **28**, 1703 (1963); (b) H. O. House and V. Kramar, *ibid.*, **27**, 4146 (1962).

(71) G. W. Kenner and N. R. Williams, *J. Chem. Soc.*, **1955,** 522.

(72) K. E. Hamlin and F. E. Fischer, *J. Am. Chem. Soc.*, **75**, 5119 (1953).

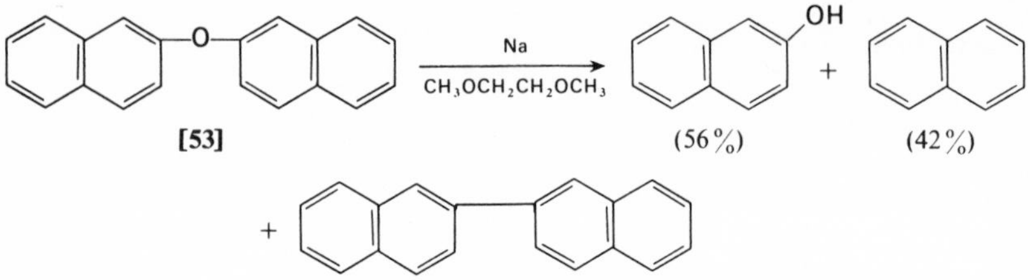

[53] —Na, $CH_3OCH_2CH_2OCH_3$→ 2-naphthol (56%) + naphthalene (42%) + 2,2'-binaphthyl (14%) (*Ref. 70a*)

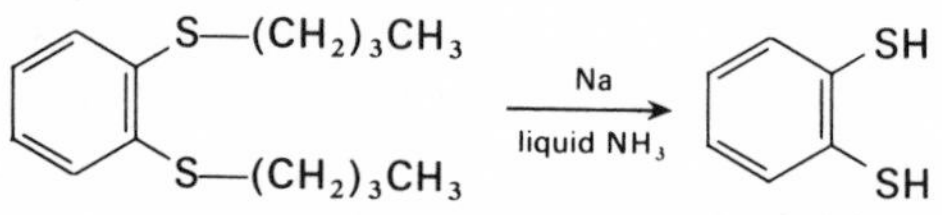

[54] $S—(CH_2)_3CH_3$, $S—(CH_2)_3CH_3$ —Na, liquid NH_3→ SH, SH (56–85%) (*Ref. 73*)

Similarly, carbon-halogen bonds may be reductively cleaved by reaction with metals in protonic solvents, as shown in the accompanying examples. Such reactions are probably related to the formation of organometallic derivatives (or dimeric products) when

$$n\text{-}C_{15}H_{31}—CH_2—I \xrightarrow[CH_3CO_2H,\ 100^\circ]{Zn,\ HCl} n\text{-}C_{15}H_{31}—CH_3 \quad (85\%)$$ (*Ref. 74*)

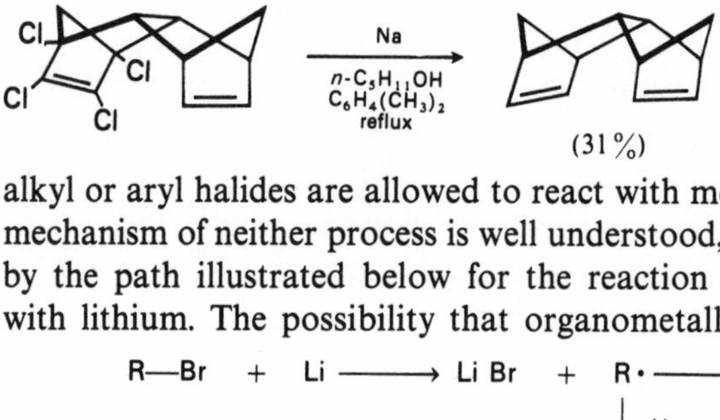

Cl, Cl, Cl, Cl —Na, $n\text{-}C_5H_{11}OH$, $C_6H_4(CH_3)_2$, reflux→ (31%) (*Ref. 75a*)

alkyl or aryl halides are allowed to react with metals. Although the mechanism of neither process is well understood, both may proceed by the path illustrated below for the reaction of an alkyl halide with lithium. The possibility that organometallic derivatives may

$$R—Br + Li \longrightarrow Li\,Br + R\cdot \longrightarrow R—R$$

$$R\cdot \xrightarrow{Li} R—Li$$

$$R—H + LiOC_2H_5 \xleftarrow{C_2H_5OH} R—Li$$

be short-lived intermediates in these reductive cleavage reactions is suggested, since elimination rather than cleavage is observed if

(73) A. Ferretti, *Org. Syn.*, **42**, 54 (1962).

(74) P. A. Levens, *Org. Syn.*, **Coll. Vol. 2,** 320 (1943).

(75) (a) S. B. Soloway, A. M. Damiana, J. W. Sims, H. Bluestone, and R. E. Lidov, *J. Am. Chem. Soc.*, **82**, 5377 (1960); (b) for the reduction of alkyl halides with magnesium in the presence of a secondary or tertiary alcohol, see D. Bryce-Smith, B. J. Wakefield, and E. T. Blues, *Proc. Chem. Soc.*, 219 (1963); (c) P. E. Verkade, K. S. de Vries, and B. M. Wepster, *Rec. trav. chim.*, **83**, 367 (1964); (d) C. F. Wilcox, Jr., and J. G. Zajacek, *J. Org. Chem.*, **29**, 2209 (1964).

a substituent (halogen, —OH, —OR, —O—CO—R) that can be lost as a stable anion is present at an adjacent carbon atom (e.g., **[55]**).

$$n\text{-}C_3H_7\text{—}\underset{\text{Br}}{\underset{|}{CH}}\text{—}\underset{OCH_3}{\underset{|}{CH}}\text{—}C_3H_7\text{-}n \xrightarrow[\substack{C_2H_5OH\\H_2O\\\text{reflux}}]{\text{Zn}} n\text{-}C_3H_7\text{—}\overset{\oplus ZnBr}{\overset{\ominus}{CH}}\text{—}\underset{OCH_3}{\underset{|}{CH}}\text{—}C_3H_7\text{-}n \longrightarrow$$

[55]

(either *erythro* or *threo*)

$$\underset{(55\%\text{ of product})}{(n\text{-}C_3H_7)(H)C{=}C(C_3H_7\text{-}n)(H)} + \underset{(45\%\text{ of product})}{(n\text{-}C_3H_7)(H)C{=}C(H)(C_3H_7\text{-}n)}$$

(*Ref.* 76)

Although the reductive cleavage of alkyl halides may[75c] or may not[36] occur with retention of configuration, the cleavage of vinyl chlorides with sodium in liquid ammonia has been found to yield olefins having the same configuration as the starting halide.[77] This observation, which reflects the fact that vinyl carbanions are conformationally more stable than alkyl carbanions, has been used to design a reaction sequence for the conversion of one geometric isomer of an olefin to the other:

$$(CH_3CH_2)(H)C{=}C(H)(CH_2CH_3) \xrightarrow[\substack{SbCl_5\\CHCl_3\\-78^\circ}]{Cl_2} \underset{\text{(from } trans \text{ addition)}}{CH_3CH_2\text{—}CHCl\text{—}CHCl\text{—}CH_2CH_3} \xrightarrow[\substack{CH_3CH_2CH_2OH\\\text{reflux}}]{KOH}$$

$$\underset{\text{(from } trans \text{ elimination)}}{(CH_3CH_2)(H)C{=}C(CH_2CH_3)(Cl)} \xrightarrow[\substack{\text{liquid } NH_3\\\text{methylcyclohexane}}]{Na} (CH_3CH_2)(H)C{=}C(CH_2CH_3)(H)$$

(*Ref.* 77)

(76) H. O. House and R. S. Ro, *J. Am. Chem. Soc.*, **80**, 182 (1958).
(77) M. C. Hoff, K. W. Greenlee, and C. E. Boord, *ibid.*, **73**, 3329 (1951).

4

OXIDATIONS WITH CHROMIUM AND MANGANESE COMPOUNDS

AMONG THE VARIETY OF AGENTS AVAILABLE for the oxidation of organic compounds,[1] the most commonly used are derivatives of hexavalent chromium (Cr^{VI}) or heptavalent manganese (Mn^{VII}). Chromium trioxide (CrO_3) and sodium dichromate ($Na_2Cr_2O_7$) are converted to the trivalent chromic ion (Cr^{3+}) in the course of such oxidations, for a net transfer of three electrons to each chromium atom. The oxidation of organic compounds with potassium permanganate ($KMnO_4$) in acidic media produces the divalent manganous ion (Mn^{++}), for a net transfer of five electrons to each manganese atom; in neutral or basic media, manganese dioxide (MnO_2) is formed, with a corresponding net transfer of three electrons. The over-all stoichiometry for the oxidation of a secondary alcohol to a ketone (transfer of two electrons) with these reagents is illustrated in the accompanying equations. It will be

(1) W. A. Waters in H. Gilman (ed.), *Organic Chemistry*, Vol. IV, Wiley, New York, 1953, pp. 1120–1245; (b) R. Stewart, *Oxidation Mechanisms*, Benjamin, New York, 1964; (c) K. B. Wiberg in A. F. Scott, ed., *Survey of Progress in Chemistry*, Vol. I, Academic Press, New York, 1963, pp. 211–248.

noted that in each case acid is consumed (or hydroxide ion is

$$2\,CrO_3 + 3\,R_2CHOH + 6\,H^{\oplus} \longrightarrow 3\,R_2C{=}O + 2\,Cr^{3+} + 6\,H_2O$$

$$2\,MnO_4^{\ominus} + 5\,R_2CHOH + 6\,H^{\oplus} \longrightarrow 5\,R_2C{=}O + 2\,Mn^{2+} + 8\,H_2O$$

$$2\,MnO_4^{\ominus} + 3\,R_2CHOH \longrightarrow 3\,R_2C{=}O + \underset{\text{(ppt.)}}{2\,MnO_2} + 2\,H_2O + 2\,OH^{\ominus}$$

produced) during the reaction. Potassium permanganate is normally employed as a neutral or alkaline aqueous solution. If the organic compound to be oxidized is not soluble in water, it may be oxidized as a suspension in the aqueous permanganate solution, or a co-solvent such as *t*-butyl alcohol or acetic acid may be employed; ethanol or acetone are less desirable co-solvents since they are rapidly attacked by permanganate in aqueous alkaline solution. Solutions of potassium permanganate in dry acetone or in pyridine have also been used. Chromium trioxide, a polymer, is insoluble in glacial acetic acid but dissolves (with reaction leading to depolymerization) in water, acetic anhydride, pyridine, and *t*-butyl alcohol.[2] Although a suspension of this reagent in glacial acetic acid has been used for oxidations, a solution in aqueous sulfuric acid is more commonly employed. A comparable solution may be prepared by adding sodium or potassium dichromate to aqueous sulfuric acid. Co-solvents most frequently used are acetic acid or acetone. Oxidations have also been run in a two-phase system consisting of the aqueous chromic acid layer and a second layer which is either the pure organic reactant or a solution of the organic reactant in benzene, methylene chloride, or ether. Alternatively, hexavalent chromium oxidations have been run with a solution of sodium dichromate dihydrate in glacial acetic acid,[3] with a solution of chromium trioxide in acetic anhydride, with a solution of the chromium trioxide–pyridine complex in excess pyridine, and with a solution of chromyl chloride (CrO_2Cl_2) in carbon tetrachloride or carbon disulfide.[4]

Solutions of hexavalent chromium compounds in aqueous mineral acid or in mixtures of acetic acid and aqueous mineral

(2) K. B. Wiberg in K. B. Wiberg, ed., *Oxidation and Reduction*, Vol. I, Academic Press, to be published

(3) L. F. Fieser, *J. Am. Chem. Soc.*, **75**, 4377 (1953).

(4) W. H. Hartford and M. Darrin, *Chem. Rev.*, **58**, 1 (1958).

acid contain an equilibrating mixture of the acid chromate ion and the dichromate ion, as indicated in the equation below.[2,5] In aqueous acetic acid solutions the acetylchromic anion

$$2\ HCrO_4^{\ominus} \rightleftharpoons H_2O + Cr_2O_7^{\ominus}$$

($CH_3CO_2CrO_3^{\ominus}$) may also be present.[5c] The predominant species in solutions of chromium trioxide in acetic acid is chromyl acetate [$CrO_2(OCOCH_3)_2$, the analog of CrO_2Cl_2].[2,4,6] The same material may be formed by solution of sodium dichromate in acetic acid.

Studies of the mechanisms of oxidations with chromium and manganese compounds[2,5,7,8] have been complicated by the fact that each stage in the oxidation of most organic compounds is accompanied by the net transfer of two electrons although the oxidizing agents normally accept a total of three or five electrons. It is therefore evident that intermediate valence states of chromium and manganese are important in the over-all process. The problem is well illustrated by the oxidation of a secondary alcohol with a hexavalent chromium compound, one of the many possible reaction schemes for which is presented in the accompanying equations. Both the Cr^{V} and the Cr^{IV} species are more powerful oxidizing

$$Cr^{VI} + R_2CHOH \longrightarrow R_2C{=}O + 2\ H^{\oplus} + Cr^{IV}$$

$$Cr^{IV} + Cr^{VI} \longrightarrow 2\ Cr^{V}$$

$$Cr^{V} + R_2CHOH \longrightarrow R_2C{=}O + 2\ H^{\oplus} + Cr^{III}$$

agents than Cr^{VI}.[5] It is evident from the equations that these intermediate valence states may be responsible for as much as two-thirds of the total oxidation and in some cases may lead to unwanted side reactions. Although the presence of intermediate valence states of chromium in a reaction mixture can be minimized if manganous or cerous ion is added to the solution,[5] such a procedure has not yet been utilized to a significant extent in synthetic work.

(5) F. H. Westheimer, *ibid.*, **45**, 419 (1949); (b) K. B. Wiberg and T. Mill, *J. Am. Chem. Soc.*, **80**, 3022 (1958); (c) G. T. E. Graham and F. H. Westheimer, *ibid.*, **80**, 3030 (1958); (d) K. B. Wiberg and P. A. Lepse, *ibid.*, **86**, 2612 (1964); (e) D. G. Lee and R. Stewart, *ibid.*, **86**, 3051 (1964).

(6) H. L. Krauss, *Angew. Chem.*, **70**, 502 (1958).

(7) (a) J. W. Ladbury and C. F. Cullis, *Chem. Rev.*, **58**, 403 (1958); (b) W. A. Waters, *Quart. Rev. (London)*, **12**, 277 (1958).

(8) K. B. Wiberg and R. J. Evans, *Tetrahedron*, **8**, 313 (1960).

Oxidation of Alcohols

The oxidation of a secondary alcohol to a ketone is usually accomplished either with a solution of the alcohol and aqueous acidic chromic acid in acetic acid or by reaction of the alcohol (e.g., [**1**]) with aqueous acidic chromic acid as a heterogeneous system. Alternatively, the oxidation may be effected by stirring a

CH_3 / $(CH_3)_2CH$ — H, OH — [**1**] $\xrightarrow[\text{H}_2\text{O, 65–72°}]{\text{Na}_2\text{Cr}_2\text{O}_7,\ \text{H}_2\text{SO}_4}$ CH_3 / $(CH_3)_2CH$ — O (94%) (*Ref. 9*)

solution of the compound to be oxidized (e.g., [**2**], [**3**], or [**4**]) in benzene, methylene chloride, or ether with an acidic aqueous solution of chromic acid. When the oxidation is relatively slow, the use of ether as a solvent is undesirable because the latter is slowly oxidized, consuming the chromic acid. The course of these

H, OH, CH_3 — [**2**] $\xrightarrow[\text{H}_2\text{O, C}_6\text{H}_6,\ \text{CH}_3\text{CO}_2\text{H, 10°}]{\text{Na}_2\text{Cr}_2\text{O}_7,\ \text{H}_2\text{SO}_4}$ O, CH_3 (85–88%) (*Ref. 10*)

HO, OH — [**3**] $\xrightarrow[\text{H}_2\text{O, CH}_2\text{Cl}_2,\ -5\text{–}0°]{\text{CrO}_3,\ \text{H}_2\text{SO}_4}$ O, O (67–79%) (*Ref. 11*)

(9) (a) A. S. Hussey and R. H. Baker, *J. Org. Chem.*, **25**, 1434 (1960); (b) L. T. Sandborn, *Org. Syn.*, **Coll. Vol. 1,** 340 (1944); (c) an alternative, convenient procedure for the oxidation of secondary alcohols to ketones consists of reaction of the alcohol with ruthenium tetroxide in carbon tetrachloride solution; H. Nakata, *Tetrahedron*, **19**, 1959 (1963); (d) a solution of lead tetracetate in pyridine is a useful reagent for the oxidation of primary and secondary alcohols to aldehydes and ketones; R. E. Partch, *Tetrahedron Letters*, **No. 41,** 3071 (1964).

(10) (a) E. W. Warnhoff, D. G. Martin, and W. S. Johnson, *Org. Syn.*, **Coll. Vol. 4,** 162 (1963); (b) for similar procedures where benzene is used as a co-solvent, see W. F. Bruce, *Org. Syn.*, **Coll. Vol. 2,** 139 (1943); W. S. Johnson, C. D. Gutsche, and D. K. Banerjee, *J. Am. Chem. Soc.*, **73**, 5464 (1951).

(11) G. H. Rasmusson, H. O. House, E. F. Zaweski, and C. H. DePuy, *Org. Syn.*, **42**, 36 (1962).

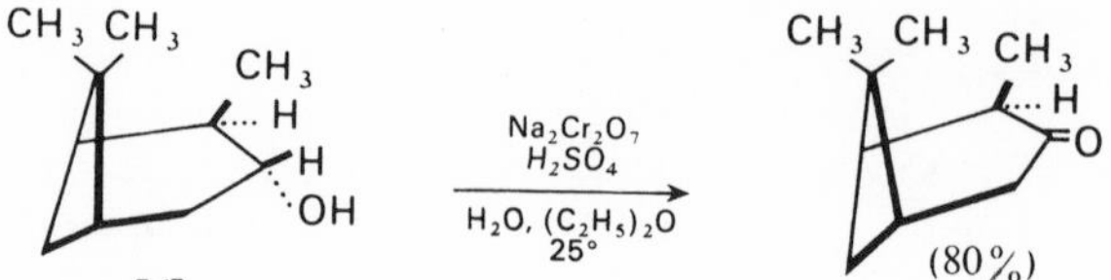

[4] $\xrightarrow[\text{H}_2\text{O, (C}_2\text{H}_5)_2\text{O, }25°]{\text{Na}_2\text{Cr}_2\text{O}_7,\ \text{H}_2\text{SO}_4}$ (80%) (*Ref. 12*)

oxidations may be followed spectrophotometrically as the yellow-orange absorption at 350 mμ of the Cr^{VI} reactants is converted to the green of the hydrated chromic ion.[13] The presence of unchanged Cr^{VI} species may be detected by adding a few drops of the reaction mixture to an aqueous solution of sodium diphenylaminesulfonate; a blue-violet color develops. Excess oxidant remaining in an oxidation reaction mixture may be destroyed by the dropwise addition of methanol. For homogeneous oxidations in aqueous acetic acid solution, the rate of reaction may be increased by decreasing the concentration of water and by increasing the concentration of acid.

The probable mechanism of oxidation of alcohols by Cr^{VI} species is outlined in the accompanying equations.[2,5,7,8] With unhindered alcohols the initial equilibrium to form the chromate ester **[5]** is fast and the subsequent decomposition of the chromate ester is the rate-limiting step. However, if the formation of the

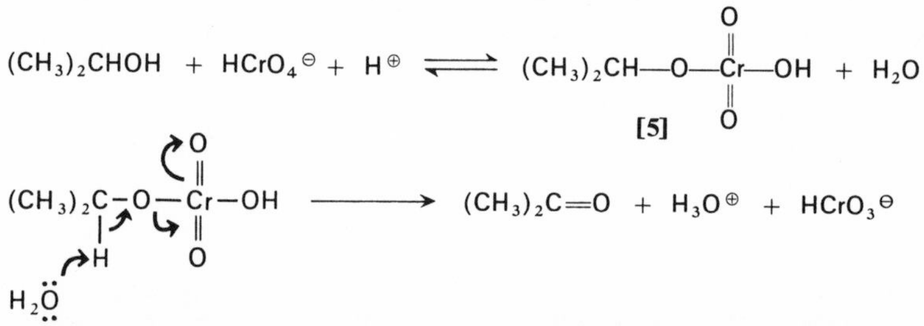

$$(CH_3)_2CHOH + HCrO_4^{\ominus} + H^{\oplus} \rightleftharpoons (CH_3)_2CH{-}O{-}CrO_2{-}OH + H_2O$$

[5]

$$(CH_3)_2C(H){-}O{-}CrO_2{-}OH \;(+\ H_2\ddot{O}) \longrightarrow (CH_3)_2C{=}O + H_3O^{\oplus} + HCrO_3^{\ominus}$$

chromate ester results in a serious steric interaction (e.g., **[6]**), then its decomposition rate is accelerated because steric strain is relieved in going from the reactant to the product.[13b,14] In extreme

(12) H. C. Brown and C. P. Garg, *J. Am. Chem. Soc.*, **83**, 2952 (1961).

(13) (a) F. H. Westheimer and N. Nicolaides, *ibid.*, **71**, 25 (1949); (b) J. Schreiber and A. Eschenmoser, *Helv. Chim. Acta*, **38**, 1529 (1955).

(14) (a) J. Rocek, F. H. Westheimer, A. Eschenmoser, L. Moldovanyi, and J. Schreiber, *Helv. Chim. Acta*, **45**, 2554 (1962); (b) H. Kwart and P. S. Francis, *J. Am. Chem. Soc.*, **81**, 2116 (1959); (c) C. F. Wilcox, Jr., M. Sexton, and M. F. Wilcox, *J. Org. Chem.*, **28**, 1079 (1963); (d) L. F. Fieser and M. Fieser, *Steroids*, Reinhold, New York, 1959, pp. 202–225.

cases such as [7], the initial esterification step becomes the rate-limiting step in the oxidation. Measurement of the relative rates

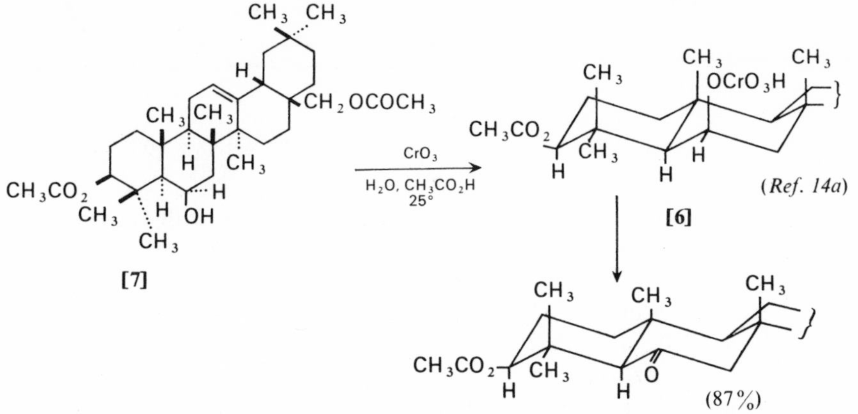

[7] $\xrightarrow[\text{H}_2\text{O, CH}_3\text{CO}_2\text{H, }25^\circ]{\text{CrO}_3}$ [6] (*Ref. 14a*) → (87%)

of chromic acid oxidations of epimeric alcohols to their corresponding ketones has proved useful for making stereochemical assignments since, *in the absence of competing side reactions*, the alcohol with the more hindered hydroxyl group is oxidized more rapidly. Examples of relative oxidation rates for epimeric pairs of alcohols are provided in the accompanying formulas. The rate of oxidation of benzylic secondary alcohols (e.g., [8]) has been found to be accelerated by electron-donating substituents.[15]

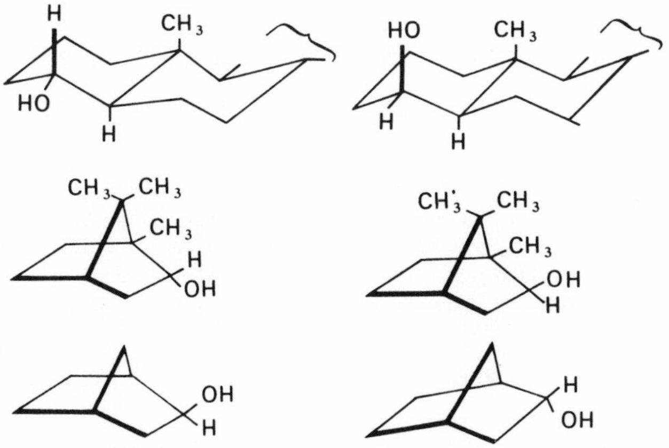

	relative rates of chromic acid oxidation	
	1:18	(*Ref. 13b*)
	1:2	(*Ref. 14b*)
	1:2.5	(*Ref. 14b*)

(15) H. Kwart and P. S. Francis, *J. Am. Chem. Soc.*, 77, 4907 (1955).

$$X-C_6H_4-CH(OH)-CH_3 \xrightarrow[H_2O,\ CH_3CO_2H,\ 30^\circ]{CrO_3,\ HClO_4} X-C_6H_4-CO-CH_3$$

[8]

X	*relative rates of oxidation*	
—OCH_3	2.7	
—H	1.0	(*Ref. 15*)
—NO_2	0.2	

The previously discussed reaction conditions with chromic acid are sufficiently vigorous to effect the slow oxidation of ethers,[16] amines,[17] carbon-carbon multiple bonds, enolizable ketones, and benzylic and allylic C—H bonds. Hydroxyl groups may be protected from oxidation by acetylation (e.g., **[7]**), and acylation or salt formation may be used to protect primary and secondary amines.[18] However, a milder method of oxidation, which at least in part avoids these complications, consists of adding, dropwise, an aqueous chromic acid solution (the Jones reagent) to an acetone solution of the compound to be oxidized. A stoichiometric amount of the aqueous chromic acid solution (which is 8 *N* in chromic acid and contains the calculated amount of sulfuric acid) is normally utilized. The reaction is run at or below room temperature[19] and has permitted the oxidation of alcohols (e.g., **[9]**) to ketones without appreciable oxidation or rearrangement of double bonds. It has also permitted the oxidation of β, γ-unsaturated alcohols such as **[10]** to β, γ-unsaturated ketones without subsequent isomerization to the more stable α, β-unsaturated ketones.[20a] The same procedure has been used for the oxidation of alcohols to enolizable

(16) R. Brownell, A. Leo, Y. W. Chang, and F. H. Westheimer, *ibid.*, **82,** 406 (1960).

(17) A. T. Bottini and R. E. Olsen, *J. Org. Chem.*, **27**, 452 (1962).

(18) (a) J. F. W. McOmie in R. A. Raphael, E. C. Taylor, and H. Wynberg (eds.), *Advances in Organic Chemistry; Methods and Results*, Vol. 3, Wiley-Interscience, New York, 1963, pp. 191–294; (b) the rate of oxidation of a secondary alcohol with chromic acid appears to be retarded by the presence of a tertiary amine function in the same molecule: see G. I. Poos and M. M. Lekman, *J. Org. Chem.*, **26**, 2576 (1961).

(19) A. Bowers, T. G. Halsall, E. R. H. Jones, and A. J. Lemin, *J. Chem. Soc.*, **1953,** 2548.

(20) (a) C. Djerassi, R. R. Engle, and A. Bowers, *J. Org. Chem.*, **21,** 1547 (1956); (b) C. Djerassi, P. A. Hart, and E. J. Warawa, *J. Am. Chem. Soc.*, **86,** 78 (1964).

ketones without epimerization of an asymmetric center alpha to the ketone function.[20b] Alternatively, epimerization has been avoided by oxidizing an alcohol to a ketone in a two-phase reaction mixture consisting of benzene and aqueous chromic acid.[10b]

CH_3O_2C $CH_2CH_2C(=CH_2)—CH(CH_3)_2$ CH CH_3 CH_3 OH O CH_3 CH_3 [9] $\xrightarrow[H_2O,\ CH_3COCH_3]{CrO_3,\ H_2SO_4}$ CH_3O_2C $CH_2CH_2C(=CH_2)—CH(CH_3)_2$ CH_3 CH CH_3 =O O CH_3 CH_3 (70%) (*Ref. 19*)

CH_3 $COCH_3$ CH_3 HO [10] $\xrightarrow[H_2O,\ CH_3COCH_3]{CrO_3,\ H_2SO_4}$ CH_3 $COCH_3$ CH_3 O (89%) (*Ref. 20*)

For compounds that contain acid-sensitive functions (e.g., acetals or ketals), oxidation has been effected with the chromium trioxide–pyridine complex ($CrO_3 \cdot 2C_5H_5N$).[21] This reagent is prepared by *adding chromium trioxide to pyridine* (adding pyridine to chromium trioxide frequently starts a fire) to form a pyridine solution (or partial solution–partial suspension) of the complex. (The complex has also been prepared by the addition of a concentrated aqueous solution of chromic acid to pyridine.[21c]) The alcohol to be oxidized is then introduced and the mixture is

(21) (a) G. I. Poos, G. E. Arth, R. E. Beyler, and L. H. Sarett, *ibid.*, **75,** 422 (1953); (b) J. R. Holum, *J. Org. Chem.*, **26,** 4814 (1961); (c) R. H. Cornforth, J. W. Cornforth, and G. Popjak, *Tetrahedron*, **18,** 1351 (1962); (d) the Jones oxidation procedure (aqueous chromic acid in acetone) has also been used successfully for the oxidation of alcohols to ketones in the presence of ketal functions: see R. F. Church, R. E. Ireland, and D. R. Shridhar, *J. Org. Chem.*, **27,** 707 (1962).

allowed to stand at room temperature. The crude product may be isolated by diluting the reaction mixture with water and extracting with an organic solvent; but because this extraction is made difficult by the presence of insoluble basic chromium salts, two alternative isolation procedures have been developed: dilution of the pyridine solution with ether followed by filtration of the insoluble chromium-pyridine complex prior to the addition of water, and dilution of the reaction mixture with ethyl acetate followed by filtration through an alumina-celite column.[23]

HO, CH_3, H, H, O —CrO_3, pyridine, 25°→ O, CH_3, H, H, O (89%) (*Ref. 21a*)

C_6H_5, OH, $CH—C_6H_5$, H, O, H —CrO_3, pyridine, 25°→ C_6H_5, O, $C—C_6H_5$, H, O, H (65%) (*Ref. 22*)

Many allylic alcohols may be oxidized to α, β-unsaturated ketones with chromic acid (especially in acetone solution at low temperature). A milder, more selective method for the oxidation of allylic and benzylic alcohols, however, consists of stirring a pentane solution of the alcohol with a large excess of specially prepared manganese dioxide.[24] Whether the actual oxidizing agent is manganese dioxide or some other manganese compound adsorbed on the surface of the manganese dioxide is not clear. In any event the procedure offers an unusually mild method for the preparation of unsaturated aldehydes and ketones, as is illustrated by the oxidations of alcohols **[11]** and **[12]**. The major disadvantages of the method are that it is general only for allylic

(22) H. H. Wasserman and N. E. Aubrey, *J. Am. Chem. Soc.*, **77,** 590 (1955).

(23) R. K. Hill, J. A. Joule, and L. J. Loeffler, *ibid.*, **84,** 4951 (1962).

(24) (a) R. J. Gritter and T. J. Wallace, *J. Org. Chem.*, **24,** 1051 (1959); (b) R. M. Evans, *Quart. Rev.* (*London*), **13,** 61 (1959).

$$\text{[11] (1,3,3-trimethylcyclohexenyl)}-CH{=}CH-C(CH_3){=}CH-CH_2OH \xrightarrow[\text{pentane, }25^\circ\text{, 7 days}]{MnO_2} \text{(1,3,3-trimethylcyclohexenyl)}-CH{=}CH-C(CH_3){=}CH-CHO$$

(*Ref.* 25a)

$$\text{[12] } (CH_3)(H)C{=}C(CH_3)-CH(OH)-CH_3 \xrightarrow[\text{pentane, }25^\circ\text{, 12 hr}]{MnO_2} (CH_3)(H)C{=}C(CH_3)-C(=O)-CH_3 \quad (72\%)$$

(*Ref.* 25b)

and benzylic alcohols[26] and that large excesses of oxidant and relatively long reaction times are often required. Manganese dioxide has also been found to oxidize N-alkylanilines to form various products, depending on the nature of the N-alkyl group.[27]

Although the oxidation of primary alcohols to aldehydes may be accomplished with chromic acid, the reaction is complicated by the fact that the aldehyde formed can be further oxidized to the corresponding carboxylic acid, though at a rate slower than that of the oxidation of the alcohol.[28] A more serious complication is the reaction of the aldehyde and the alcohol in the reaction mixture to form a hemiacetal (e.g., **[13]**), which is oxidized rapidly (cf. the effect of electron-donating groups in Ref. 15) to an ester. However, moderate yields of aldehydes have been obtained from

$$n\text{-}C_3H_7-CH_2OH \xrightarrow[H_2O,\ 35^\circ]{Na_2Cr_2O_7,\ H_2SO_4} n\text{-}C_3H_7-CHO \overset{n\text{-}C_3H_7CH_2OH}{\rightleftharpoons}$$

$$n\text{-}C_3H_7-CH(OH)-OCH_2-C_3H_7\text{-}n \ \textbf{[13]} \xrightarrow{H_2CrO_4} n\text{-}C_3H_7-C(=O)-O-CH_2-C_3H_7\text{-}n \quad (41\text{–}47\%)$$

(*Ref.* 29)

(25) (a) N. L. Wendler, H. L. Slates, N. R. Trenner, and M. Tishler, *J. Am. Chem. Soc.*, **73,** 719 (1951); (b) H. O. House and R. S. Ro, *ibid.*, **80,** 2428 (1958).

(26) For examples of the oxidation of saturated alcohols with manganese dioxide, see (a) M. Z. Barakat, M. F. Abdel-Wahab, and M. M. El-Sadr, *J. Chem. Soc.*, **1956,** 4685; (b) L. Crombie and J. Crossley, *ibid.*, **1963,** 4983; (c) I. T. Harrison, *Proc. Chem. Soc.*, **1964,** 110.

(27) H. B. Henbest and A. Thomas, *ibid.*, **1957,** 3032.

(28) W. A. Mosher and D. M. Preiss, *J. Am. Chem. Soc.*, **75,** 5605 (1953).

(29) G. R. Robertson, *Org. Syn.*, **Coll. Vol. 1,** 138 (1944).

oxidations of primary alcohols with chromic acid, especially in such cases as **[14]** and **[15]** where the volatile aldehyde can be distilled from the reaction mixture as it is formed. This oxidation procedure is also satisfactory for the preparation of sterically hindered aldehydes such as those obtained from alcohols of the neopentyl type.[30]

Reasonable yields of aldehydes have been obtained by the oxidation of primary alcohols with chromium trioxide in pyridine,

$$C_2H_5{-}CH_2OH \xrightarrow[H_2O]{Na_2Cr_2O_7,\ H_2SO_4} C_2H_5{-}CHO \quad (\textit{Ref. 31a})$$

[14] (45–49%, distilled from mixture as formed)

$$HC{\equiv}C{-}CH_2OH \xrightarrow[H_2O]{CrO_3,\ H_2SO_4} HC{\equiv}C{-}CHO \quad (\textit{Ref. 31b})$$

[15] (35–41%, distilled from mixture as formed)

especially in cases where the alcohol is allylic or benzylic. The success of this procedure may be attributable in part to the

$$C_6H_5{-}CH{=}CH{-}CH_2OH \xrightarrow[\text{pyridine, } 25^\circ]{CrO_3} C_6H_5{-}CH{=}CH{-}CHO \quad (\textit{Ref. 21b})$$

(81%)

fact that the oxidation is done in the absence of an appreciable concentration of water, a necessary reactant for at least one of the mechanistic pathways for the conversion of an aldehyde to an acid.

Tertiary alcohols are relatively inert to oxidation by chromic acid; failure of an alcohol to be oxidized by chromic acid is often cited as evidence that it is tertiary. However, tertiary 1,2-diols are very rapidly cleaved by chromic acid, provided they are sterically capable of forming cyclic chromate esters such as **[16]**.[32] Although this cleavage reaction appears similar to that of 1,2-diols with lead

(30) For example, see R. E. Ireland and P. W. Schiess, *J. Org. Chem.*, **28,** 6 (1963).

(31) (a) C. D. Hurd and R. N. Meinert, *Org. Syn.*, **Coll. Vol. 2,** 541 (1943); (b) J. C. Sauer, *Org. Syn.*, **Coll. Vol. 4,** 813 (1963).

(32) J. Rocek and F. H. Westheimer, *J. Am. Chem. Soc.*, **84,** 2241 (1962).

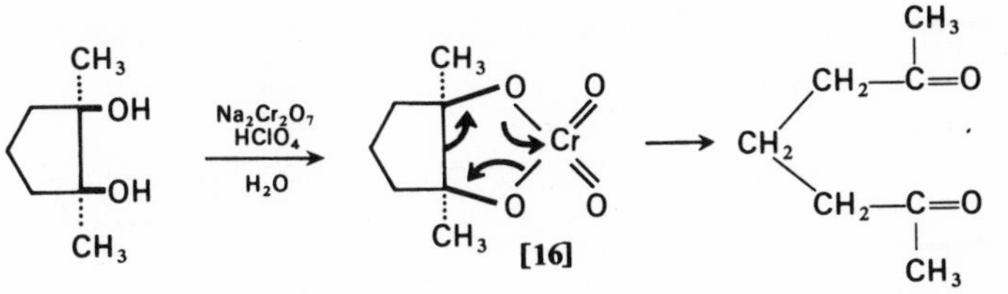

(*Ref. 32*)

[16]

[85% as bis (2,4-dinitrophenylhydrazone)]

tetraacetate[33] and periodic acid,[34] the cleavage with chromic acid is not completely analogous because 1,2-diols, having at least one alpha hydrogen atom (e.g., **[17]**), are normally oxidized by chromic acid to form α-hydroxyketones.

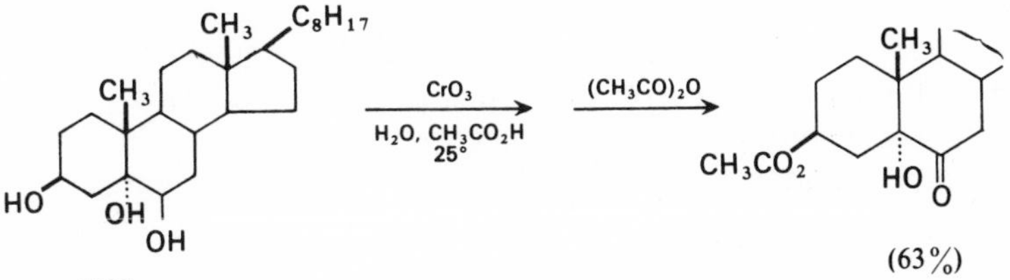

[17] (63%) (*Ref. 35*)

Carbon-carbon bond cleavage has also been observed during the chromic acid oxidation of certain secondary alcohols such as **[18]**, which contain an alpha substituent (*t*-butyl group in **[18]**) that can be eliminated as a relatively stable carbonium ion (or free radical). This cleavage reaction is of particular interest because it provides an example of an alcohol that is oxidized normally with Cr^{VI} species to form the ketone **[19]**, whereas reaction of the same alcohol with Cr^{IV} and/or Cr^{V} species results in cleavage. As would be anticipated from the previous discussion, the yield of cleavage products can be substantially reduced by performing the oxidation in the presence of manganous or cerous ion.[36]

(33) (a) R. Criegee in *Newer Methods of Preparative Organic Chemistry*, Wiley-Interscience, New York, 1948, pp. 1–20; (b) R. Criegee in W. Foerst (ed.), *Newer Methods of Preparative Organic Chemistry*, Vol. 2, Academic, New York, 1963, pp. 367–388.

(34) E. L. Jackson, *Org. Reactions*, **2,** 341 (1944).

(35) B. Ellis and V. Petrow, *J. Chem. Soc.*, **1939,** 1078.

(36) (a) J. Hampton, A. Leo, and F. H. Westheimer, *J. Am. Chem. Soc.*, **78,** 306 (1956); (b) J. J. Cawley and F. H. Westheimer, *ibid.*, **85,** 1771 (1963).

$$C_6H_5\text{—}CH(OH)\text{—}C(CH_3)_3 \xrightarrow[H_2O,\ CH_3CO_2H]{CrO_3} C_6H_5\text{—}CO\text{—}C(CH_3)_3 + Cr^{V}$$

[18] [19] (47%)

Cr^{V} + $C_6H_5\text{—}CH(OH)\text{—}C(CH_3)_3$ → $C_6H_5\text{—}CH(\text{—}O\text{—}Cr(=O)(OH)_2)\text{—}C(CH_3)_3$

$$C_6H_5\text{—}CH(OCr(=O)(OH)_2)\text{—}C(CH_3)_3 \longrightarrow C_6H_5\text{—}CHO + (CH_3)_3C^{\oplus} + Cr^{III}$$

$C_6H_5\text{—}CHO$ (14%) $\xrightarrow{H_2CrO_4}$ $C_6H_5\text{—}CO_2H$ (5%)

$(CH_3)_3C^{\oplus} \xrightarrow{H_2O} (CH_3)_3COH$

Oxidation of Aldehydes

Although both chromium and manganese compounds can be used for the oxidation of aldehydes to carboxylic acids,[2,5,7,8,37] an aqueous solution of potassium permanganate under either acidic or basic conditions is the more commonly employed reagent.

$$n\text{-}C_6H_{13}\text{—}CHO \xrightarrow[H_2O,\ 20°]{KMnO_4,\ H_2SO_4} n\text{-}C_6H_{13}\text{—}CO_2H \quad (76\text{–}78\%) \qquad (\textit{Ref. 38})$$

$$3,4\text{-}(OCH_2O)C_6H_3\text{—}CHO \xrightarrow[H_2O,\ 70\text{–}80°]{KMnO_4} \xrightarrow{H_3O^{\oplus}} 3,4\text{-}(OCH_2O)C_6H_3\text{—}CO_2H \quad (78\text{–}84\%) \qquad (\textit{Ref. 39})$$

Permanganate oxidations in neutral or acidic media are catalyzed by acid, and the reaction is accelerated slightly by the presence of electron-donating groups.[37] The oxidation mechanism is believed to involve the formation and subsequent decomposition of the permanganate ester **[20]**. Oxidation in basic media is

(37) (a) K. B. Wiberg and R. Stewart, *J. Am. Chem. Soc.*, **77,** 1786 (1955); (b) for an example utilizing the chromium trioxide–pyridine complex with added water for the oxidation of an aldehyde to a carboxylic acid, see W. S. Johnson and co-workers, *ibid.*, **85,** 1409 (1963).

(38) J. R. Ruhoff, *Org. Syn.* **Coll. Vol. 2,** 315 (1943).

(39) R. L. Shriner and E. C. Kleiderer, *ibid.*, **Coll. Vol. 2,** 538 (1943).

$$C_6H_5{-}CHO + H_3O^{\oplus} \rightleftharpoons H_2O + C_6H_5{-}CH^{\oplus}{-}OH \xrightarrow{MnO_4^{\ominus}} C_6H_5{-}CH(OH){-}OMnO_3 \quad [20]$$

$$C_6H_5{-}C(OH)(H){-}O{-}MnO_3 \xrightarrow{H_2\ddot{O}} C_6H_5CO_2H + MnO_3^{\ominus}$$

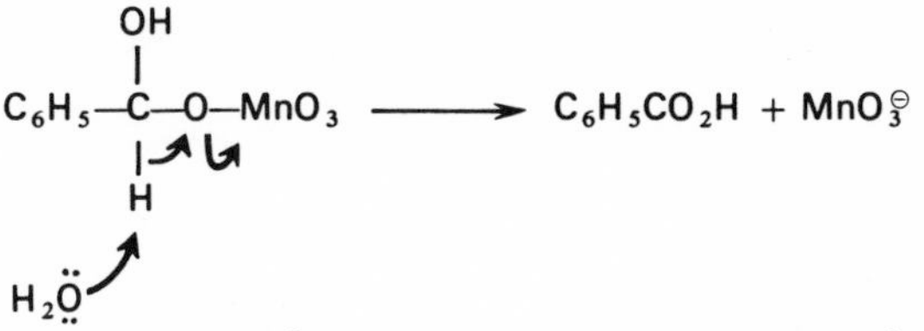

$$3\,MnO_3^{\ominus} + H_2O \longrightarrow 2\,MnO_2 + MnO_4^{\ominus} + 2\,OH^{\ominus}$$

apparently more complex. Under these conditions the reaction, which is accelerated by electron-withdrawing groups, appears to be a free-radical chain process, possibly proceeding as indicated in the following equations[37]:

Initiation:

$$MnO_4^{\ominus} + OH^{\ominus} \longrightarrow MnO_4^{\ominus} + HO\cdot$$

Propagation:

$$C_6H_5{-}CHO + HO\cdot \longrightarrow C_6H_5{-}CH(OH){-}O\cdot$$

$$C_6H_5{-}C(H)(OH){-}O\cdot + MnO_4^{\ominus} \longrightarrow C_6H_5CO_2H + MnO_3^{\ominus} + HO\cdot$$

The oxidation of aldehydes with chromic acid, a reaction catalyzed by acid and accelerated by electron-withdrawing groups, is believed to involve the formation and decomposition of the chromate ester of the aldehyde hydrate, as illustrated below.[5b–d]

$$C_6H_5{-}CHO + H^{\oplus} + HCrO_4^{\ominus} \rightleftharpoons C_6H_5{-}CH(OH){-}O{-}CrO_3H$$

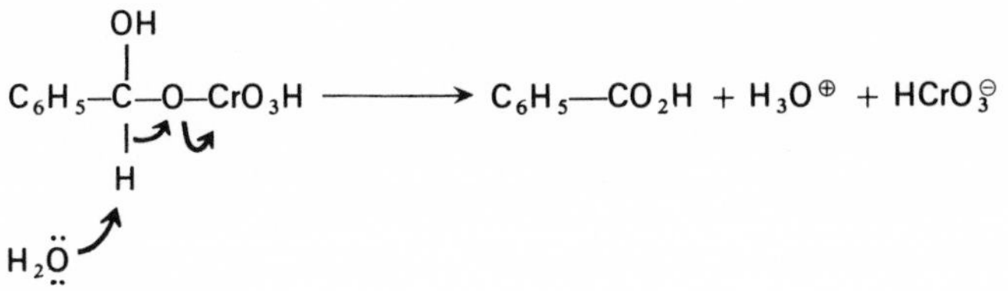

$$C_6H_5{-}C(OH)(H){-}O{-}CrO_3H \xrightarrow{H_2\ddot{O}} C_6H_5{-}CO_2H + H_3O^{\oplus} + HCrO_3^{\ominus}$$

Other agents that have been used for the oxidation of aldehydes include fuming nitric acid (e.g., **[21]**) and a suspension of silver oxide in aqueous alkali (e.g., **[22]**). The use of the latter provides a very mild and selective method for this type of oxidation.

$$ClCH_2CH_2CHO \xrightarrow[30\text{–}35°]{\text{fuming } HNO_3} ClCH_2CH_2CO_2H \quad (60\text{–}65\%)$$ (*Ref. 40*)

[21]

$$\text{3-thiophenecarboxaldehyde} \xrightarrow[H_2O]{Ag_2O,\ NaOH} \xrightarrow{H_3O^{\oplus}} \text{3-thiophenecarboxylic acid } (CO_2H) \quad (95\text{–}97\%)$$ (*Ref. 41*)

[22]

Oxidation of Carbon-Carbon Double Bonds

An aqueous solution of potassium permanganate reacts with olefins to add two hydroxyl functions to the double bond in a *cis* manner, provided the reaction mixture is alkaline. If the reaction mixture is kept neutral, either by the continuous addition of acid or by adding magnesium sulfate (hydroxide ion is removed by the precipitation of magnesium hydroxide), the permanganate oxidation results in cleavage or in the formation of α-hydroxyketones.[42] These reactions, illustrated by the following equations, are believed to proceed with the initial formation of a cyclic manganese ester

$$\underset{CH_3(CH_2)_7}{H}\!\!>C{=}C<\!\!\underset{(CH_2)_7CO_2H}{H} \xrightarrow[H_2O]{KMnO_4,\ NaOH\ (excess)} CH_3(CH_2)_7\text{–}CH(OH)\text{–}CH(OH)\text{–}(CH_2)_7CO_2H \quad (81\%)$$ (*Ref*

$$\xrightarrow[H_2SO_4 \text{ added to maintain pH at } 9.0\text{–}9.5]{KMnO_4,\ H_2O} CH_3(CH_2)_7\text{–}CH(OH)\text{–}C(=O)\text{–}(CH_2)_7CO_2H \quad (75\% \text{ of mixture})$$ (*Ref*

(40) C. Moureu and R. Chaux, *Org. Syn.*, **Coll. Vol. 1,** 166 (1944).

(41) (a) E. Campaigne and W. M. LeSuer, *Org. Syn.*, **33,** 94 (1953); (b) see also K. J. Clark, G. I. Fray, R. N. Jaeger, and R. Robinson, *Tetrahedron*, **6,** 217 (1959).

(42) (a) J. E. Coleman, C. Ricciuti, and D. Swern, *J. Am. Chem. Soc.*, **78,** 5342 (1956); (b) K. B. Wiberg and K. A. Saegebarth, *ibid.*, **79,** 2822 (1957).

$KMnO_4$, NaOH; H_2O, t-C_4H_9OH, 0° → (40%) (Ref. 42b)

$KMnO_4$, $MgSO_4$; H_2O, CH_3COCH_3, −15° → CHO, CHO (54–66%)

[23], which undergoes the further changes indicated.[42b] Although

R—CH=CH—R + $MnO_4^{\ominus}$ → [23]

H_2O; $MnO_4^{\ominus}$; $OH^{\ominus}$

$MnO_3^{\ominus}$ + R—CH(HO)—C(=O)—R ← R—CH(HO)—CH(O—$MnO_3^{\ominus}$)—R ← R—CH(HO)—CH(O—MnO_2)—R

2 R—CHO + $MnO_3^{\ominus}$ R—CH(HO)—CH(OH)—R + $MnO_3^{\ominus}$

oxidation with potassium permanganate is almost always inferior to oxidation with osmium tetroxide[43] for selective conversion of olefins (e.g., [24]) to *cis*-1,2-diols in high yield, the permanganate oxidation is less hazardous (osmium tetroxide is very toxic) and

[24] —OsO_4, pyridine; $(C_2H_5)_2O$→ —KOH; mannitol, H_2O→ (70%) (Ref. 32)

(43) (a) F. D. Gunstone in R. A. Raphael, E. C. Taylor, and H. Winberg (eds.), *Advances in Organic Chemistry: Methods and Results*, Vol. 1, Wiley-Interscience, New York, 1960, pp. 103–147; (b) for an alternative isolation procedure in which the intermediate cyclic osmium ester is reduced with hydrogen sulfide, see D. H. R. Barton and D. Elad, *J. Chem. Soc.*, **1956,** 2085.

decidedly less expensive for reactions that are to be run on a relatively large scale.

An interesting modification of the permanganate hydroxylation procedure utilizes a mixture of potassium permanganate and potassium periodate in aqueous solution at pH 7.7 for the oxidation of olefins.[44] Under these conditions, the α-hydroxyketone and 1,2-diol resulting from reaction of the olefin (e.g., **[25]**) with permanganate are cleaved by the periodate to form carbonyl compounds; any aldehydes produced by this cleavage are oxidized to carboxylic acids. Only a catalytic amount of the permanganate is required because the lower-valent derivatives of manganese are reoxidized to permanganate ion by the periodate in the reaction mixture.

$$CH_3(CH_2)_7CH{=}CH(CH_2)_7CO_2H \xrightarrow[K_2CO_3,\ H_2O]{NaIO_4,\ KMnO_4} \xrightarrow{H_3O^{\oplus}} CH_3(CH_2)_7CO_2H + HO_2C(CH_2)_7CO_2H$$

[25] *(Ref. 44)*

The oxidation of carbon-carbon double bonds with chromic acid is often complicated by a competing oxidation that occurs at allylic C—H bonds, (e.g., oxidation of **[26]**), leading to mixtures of products, particularly when cyclic olefins are involved. As an

$$\text{cyclohexene} \xrightarrow[H_2O,\ CH_3CO_2H,\ 25\text{–}35°]{CrO_3} \text{cyclohex-2-enone} + HO_2C(CH_2)_4CO_2H$$

[26] (33–38%) (25%) *(Ref. 45)*

increasing number of phenyl groups is attached to the double bond (e.g., **[27]** and **[28]**), oxidation at the double bond rather than attack at an allylic position becomes the predominant reaction. The oxidative degradation of the ester **[29]** via the olefin **[28]**, known as the Barbier-Wieland degradation, illustrates the utility of this oxidation when two phenyl substituents are present. Even in cases such as **[30]** where no allylic C—H bonds are present,

(44) R. U. Lemieux and E. von Rudloff, *Can. J. Chem.*, **33**, 1701, 1710 (1955); E. von Rudloff, *ibid.*, **33**, 1714 (1955).

(45) F. C. Whitmore and G. W. Pedlow, Jr., *J. Am. Chem. Soc.*, **63**, 758 (1941).

[27] (1-phenylcyclohexene, C_6H_5) $\xrightarrow[CH_3CO_2H,\ 30°]{CrO_3}$ $C_6H_5CO(CH_2)_4CO_2H$ (major product) + (C_6H_5, O) (*Ref. 46*)

[29]: HO, CH_3, CH_3, CH_3, $CHCH_2CH_2CO_2CH_3$ $\xrightarrow[(C_2H_5)_2O,\ C_6H_6]{C_6H_5MgBr}$ $\xrightarrow[CH_3CO_2H,\ reflux]{(CH_3CO)_2O}$ [28]: CH_3CO_2, CH_3, CH_3, CH_3, $CHCH_2CH{=}C(C_6H_5)_2$, CH_3CO_2 (*Ref. 47*)

$\xrightarrow[H_2O,\ CH_3CO_2H,\ 50°]{CrO_3}$ CH_3CO_2, CH_3, CH_3, CH_3, $CH—CH_2CO_2H$, CH_3CO_2

(57–68% as the diol)

different oxidation products can be made to predominate by varying the reaction conditions. A thorough study of the oxidation of

$(C_6H_5)_2C{=}C(C_6H_5)_2$ [30] $\xrightarrow[90–95°]{CrO_3,\ H_2O,\ CH_3CO_2H}$ $(C_6H_5)_2C{=}O$ + $(C_6H_5)_2C—C(C_6H_5)_2$ (O) + $(C_6H_5)_3C—CO—C_6H_5$

(26–44%) (36–56%) (5–16%)

(*Ref. 48*)

[30] $\xrightarrow[CH_3CO_2H,\ 90–95°]{CrO_3,\ (CH_3CO)_2O}$ $(C_6H_5)_2C{=}O$ + $(C_6H_5)_2C—C(C_6H_5)_2$ (O) + $(C_6H_5)_2C—C(C_6H_5)_2$ (O, O, C, O)

(10–20%) (51–69%) (13–27%)

(46) L. F. Fieser and J. Szmuskovicz, *J. Am. Chem. Soc.*, **70,** 3352 (1948).

(47) B. Riegel, R. B. Moffett, and A. V. McIntosh, *Org. Syn.*, **Coll. Vol. 3,** 234, 237 (1955).

(48) W. A. Mosher, F. W. Steffgen, and P. T. Lansbury, *J. Org. Chem.*, **26,** 670 (1961).

cholesterol (partial structure **[31]**)[14d] has revealed that, although the major course of the reaction is the one indicated in the accompanying equations, a variety of minor by-products are also formed.

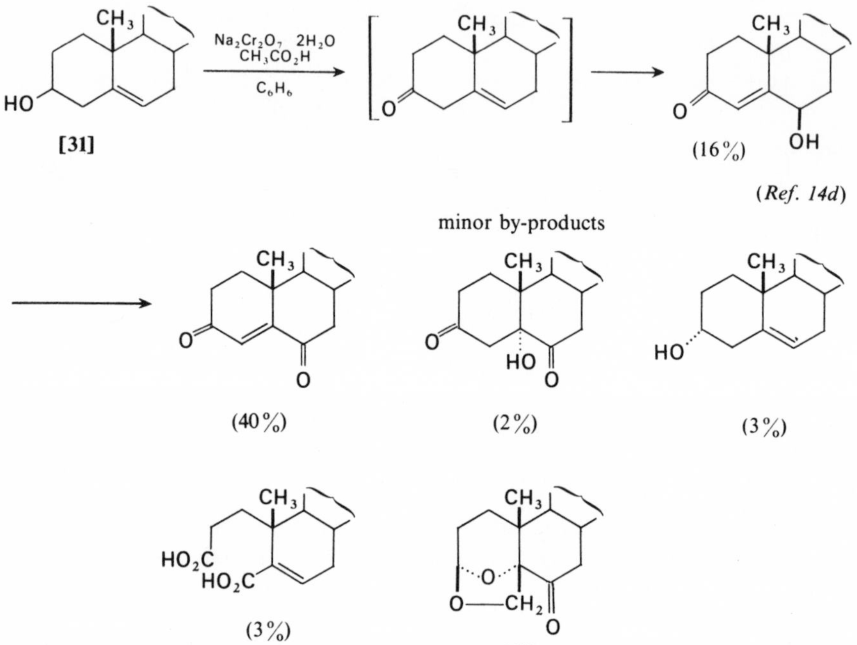

$Na_2Cr_2O_7 \cdot 2H_2O$, CH_3CO_2H, C_6H_6

[31] (16%)

(*Ref. 14d*)

minor by-products

(40%) (2%) (3%)

(3%) (1%)

In general, the use of chromic acid in a partially aqueous medium favors oxidative cleavage of carbon-carbon double bonds, whereas anhydrous conditions (chromium trioxide in glacial acetic acid or acetic anhydride,[49a] sodium dichromate dihydrate in glacial acetic acid, *t*-butyl chromate in carbon tetrachloride–acetic acid,[49b] or chromyl chloride in carbon tetrachloride[50]) favor either attack at allylic positions or partial oxidation of the double bond to form epoxides, diol derivatives, or ketols; rearrangements of the intermediate oxidation products may also be observed.[51] Since studies

(49) (a) H. Schildknecht and W. Fättinger, *Ann. Chem.*, **659,** 20 (1962); (b) D. Ginsburg and R. Pappo, *J. Chem. Soc.*, **1951,** 516.

(50) S. J. Cristol and K. R. Eilar, *J. Am. Chem. Soc.*, **72,** 4353 (1950).

(51) (a) W. J. Hickinbottom, D. Peters, and D. G. M. Wood, *J. Chem. Soc.*, **1955,** 1360; (b) M. A. Davis and W. J. Hickinbottom, *ibid.*, **1958,** 2205; (c) H. H. Zeiss and F. R. Zwanzig, *J. Am. Chem. Soc.*, **79,** 1733 (1957).

of olefin oxidations with chromic acid[7,51] have dealt primarily with the composition of the product mixtures, a good deal of uncertainty exists about the mechanism of these reactions. The identity of the reacting Cr^{VI} species has not been established and probably differs for reactions run in the various media that have been employed. The formations of epoxides and diol carbonates are known not to be stereospecific processes (e.g., the oxidation of [**32**]), indicating that a cyclic chromate ester, analogous to intermediate [**23**] in permanganate oxidations, is not formed directly from the olefin and the Cr^{VI} reactant (cf. Ref. 51c). The reaction has been suggested to proceed by an electrophilic attack

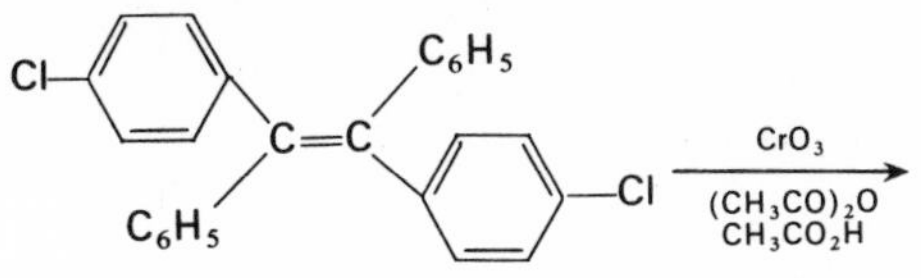

CrO_3, $(CH_3CO)_2O$, CH_3CO_2H

[**32**]

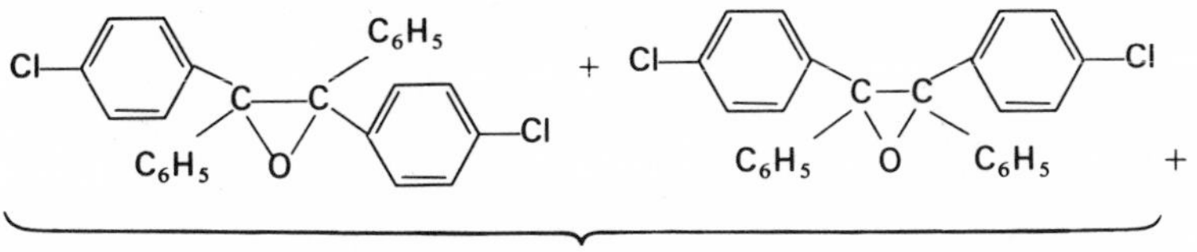

(*Ref. 48*)

(22% of a 1:1 mixture)

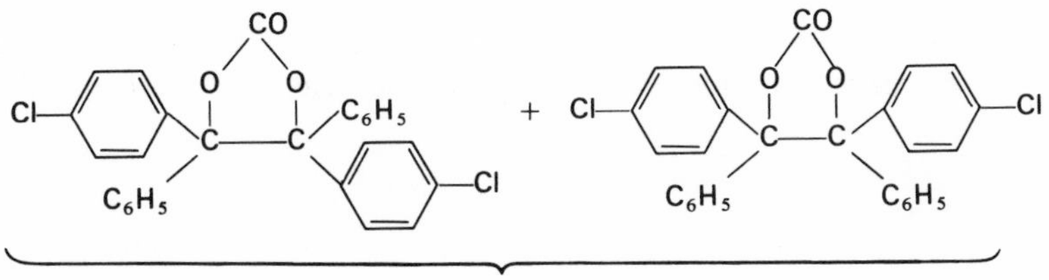

(53% of a 1:1 mixture)

of the Cr^{VI} species (represented as chromic acid in the accompanying equations) on the olefin to form a transient carbonium ion such as [**33**].[7,51a,51b] (An initial one-electron transfer to form the analogous radical has not been excluded.) The intermediate [**33**] may then either lose a proton (as in the conversion of cholesterol [**31**] to 6-hydroxy-4-cholesten-3-one) or react with a nucleophile (e.g., water, acetate ion, or acetic acid) in the reaction mixture to form intermediates such as [**34**] and [**35**]. It is not clear whether the various products with rearranged carbon skeletons that have been isolated from chromic acid oxidations[48,51] result from rearrangement of initially formed oxidation products or from rearrangement of the ion [**33**]. In support of the above mechanistic scheme, olefins (e.g., [**39**]) have reacted with chromyl chloride[50] to form chromium esters of chlorohydrins that could be reduced and hydrolyzed with aqueous sodium bisulfite to chlorohydrins. In the presence of water and excess chromic acid, the intermediates

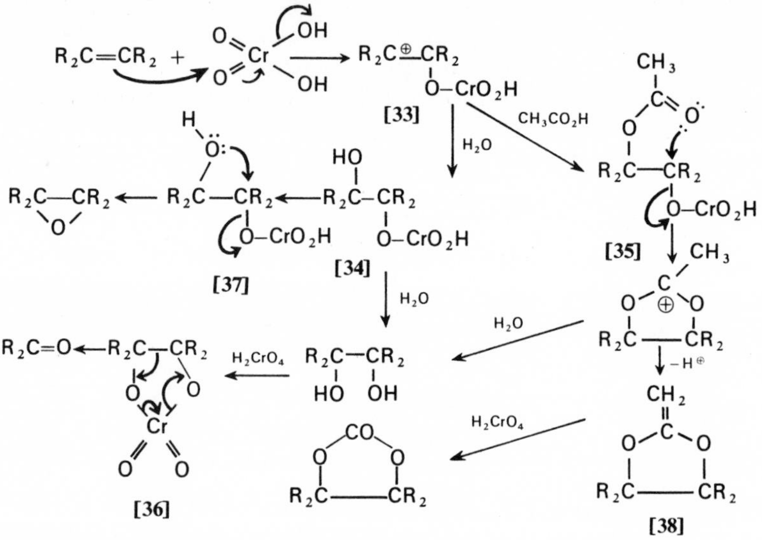

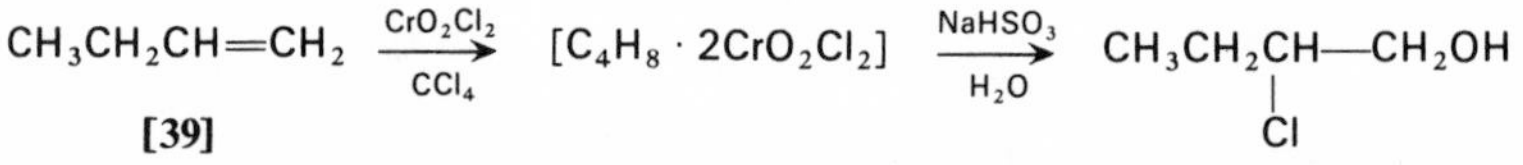

$$\underset{[39]}{CH_3CH_2CH{=}CH_2} \xrightarrow[CCl_4]{CrO_2Cl_2} [C_4H_8 \cdot 2CrO_2Cl_2] \xrightarrow[H_2O]{NaHSO_3} \underset{(49\%)}{CH_3CH_2CH(Cl){-}CH_2OH} \quad (Ref.\ 50)$$

[**34**] and [**35**] could be converted to the cyclic chromate ester [**36**] (analogous to the intermediate [**16**] postulated for the cleavage of glycols) and then cleaved or converted to an α-hydroxyketone. Alternatively, the intramolecular displacements represented in structures [**35**] and [**37**] could lead to an epoxide or to a precursor [**38**] for a diol carbonate. This general scheme serves to account for the ready oxidative cleavage of 1,1-diphenylethylene derivatives such as [**28**] with aqueous chromic acid since the initially formed

ion (i.e., **[33]**) could be stabilized by the two adjacent phenyl rings.

Such a reaction scheme also accounts for the oxidative cleavage of ketones (e.g., **[40]**), which is believed to proceed by electrophilic

CH_3, OH, H $\xrightarrow[H_2O,\ 30°]{CrO_3,\ H_2SO_4}$ [CH_3, O] **[40]** $\longrightarrow$ $CH_3CO(CH_2)_4CO_2H$ (45–55%) (*Ref.* 52)

attack on the enol[53] as illustrated in the accompanying equations. The successful oxidation to diketones of certain diterpene derivatives having rings A and B *cis*-fused (e.g., **[41]**), under conditions

O $\underset{}{\overset{H^{\oplus}}{\rightleftharpoons}}$ OH $\xrightarrow{H_2CrO_4}$ $\overset{\oplus}{O}H$, $O—CrO_2H$, H $\xrightarrow[H_2CrO_4]{H_2O}$

O–H, OH, $O—CrO_3H$, H $\longrightarrow$ CO_2H, CHO $\xrightarrow{H_2CrO_4}$ $HO_2C(CH_2)_4CO_2H$

where corresponding *trans*-fused compounds (e.g., **[42]**) form only monoketones, has been attributed to steric hindrance to attack of the enol in the latter case.

[41] (CH_3, CH_3, H, CN) $\xrightarrow[H_2O,\ CH_3CO_2H,\ 25°]{CrO_3}$ (CH_3, CH_3, H, CN, O, O) + (CH_3, CH_3, H, CN, O) (*Ref.* 53*b*)

(52) J. R. Schaeffer and A. O. Snoddy, *Org. Syn.*, **31,** 3 (1951).

(53) (a) P. A. Best, J. S. Littler, and W. A. Waters, *J. Chem. Soc.*, **1962,** 822; (b) E. Wenkert and B. G. Jackson, *J. Am. Chem. Soc.*, **80,** 211 (1958).

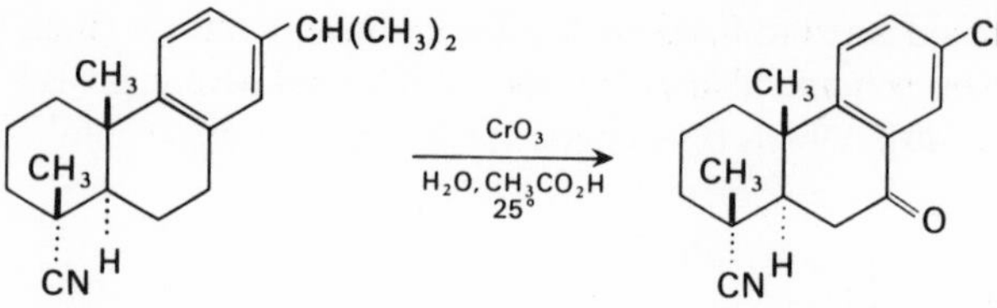
CH(CH3)2
CH3
CH3
CN
H
CrO3
H2O, CH3CO2H
25°
O

(*Ref.* 53*b*)

[42]

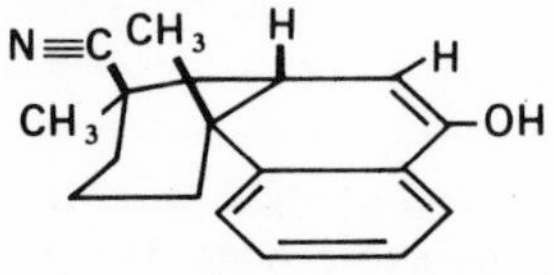
N≡C
CH3
H
OH

intermediate enol from **[41]**

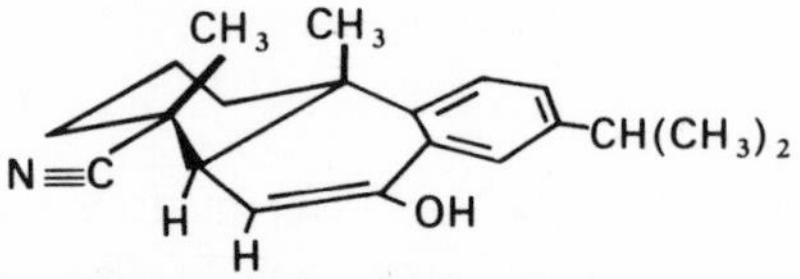
CH3
N≡C
CH(CH3)2
OH
H

intermediate enol from **[42]**

Oxidation of Carbon-Hydrogen Bonds in Hydrocarbons

Perhaps the most common application of this process is the oxidation of the side chain of benzene derivatives with aqueous potassium permanganate (e.g., **[43]**), with chromic acid (e.g., **[44]**) in aqueous solution or in acetic acid, or with aqueous sodium

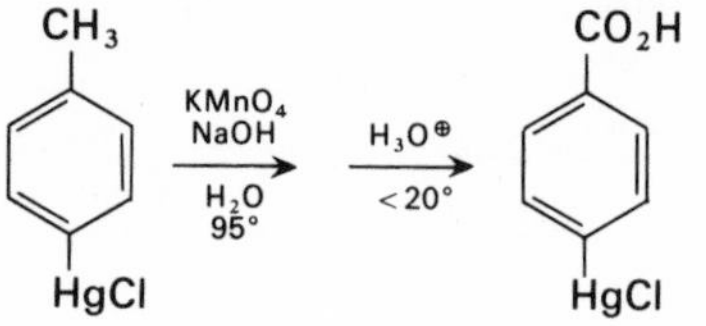
CH3
KMnO4
NaOH
H2O
95°
H3O⊕
<20°
CO2H
HgCl

(*Ref.* 54*a*)

[43] (61–74%)

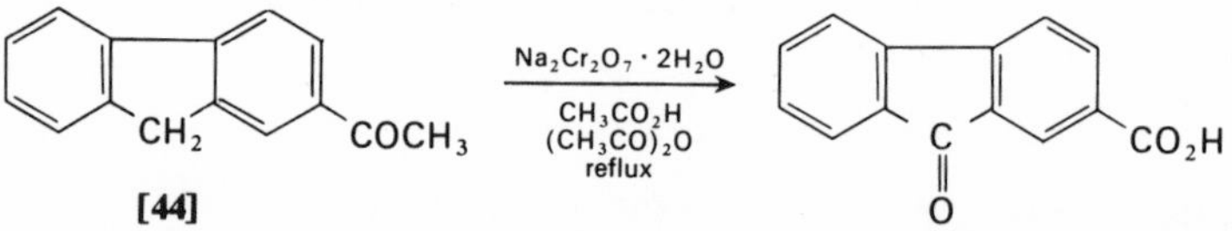
CH2
COCH3
Na2Cr2O7 · 2H2O
CH3CO2H
(CH3CO)2O
reflux
C
O
CO2H

[44] (67–74%)

(*Ref.* 54*b*)

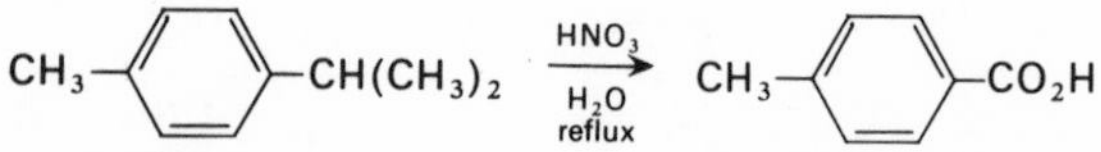
CH3
CH(CH3)2
HNO3
H2O
reflux
CO2H

(*Ref.* 55*a*)

[45] (56–59%)

(54) (a) F. C. Whitmore and G. E. Woodward, *Org. Syn.*, **Coll. Vol. 1,** 159 (1944); (b) G. Rieveschl, Jr. and F. E. Ray, *ibid.*, **Coll. Vol. 3,** 420 (1955).

(55) (a) W. F. Tuley and C. S. Marvel, *ibid.*, **Coll. Vol. 3,** 822 (1955); (b) L. Friedman, *ibid.*, **43,** 80 (1963); (c) L. Friedman, D. L. Fishel, and H. Shechter, *J. Org. Chem.*, **30,** 1453 (1965).

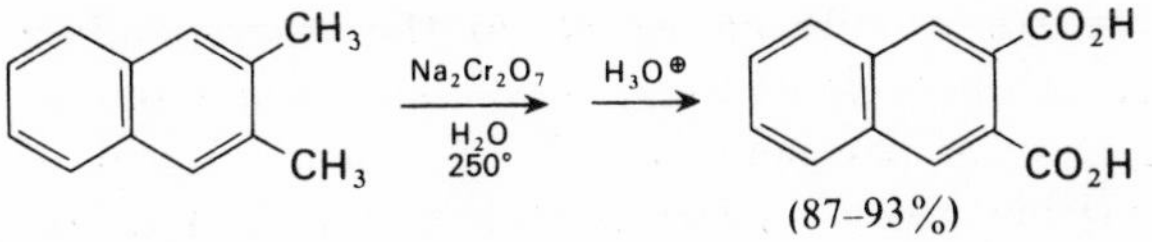

CH_3 CH_3 $\xrightarrow[H_2O, 250°]{Na_2Cr_2O_7}$ $\xrightarrow{H_3O^{\oplus}}$ CO_2H CO_2H (87–93%) (*Ref.* 55*b*)

dichromate at elevated temperatures. This type of oxidation has also been effected with nitric acid (e.g., **[45]**). The previously mentioned chromic acid oxidation of olefins (e.g., **[46]**) at the allylic position, although probably mechanistically related to the side-chain oxidation, is complicated by the concurrent oxidation that occurs at the double bond and by the fact that the intermediate allylic radical (e.g., **[47]** or the corresponding cation) can often lead to structurally isomeric products. For the successful oxidation of side chains attached to benzene rings, it is necessary that the

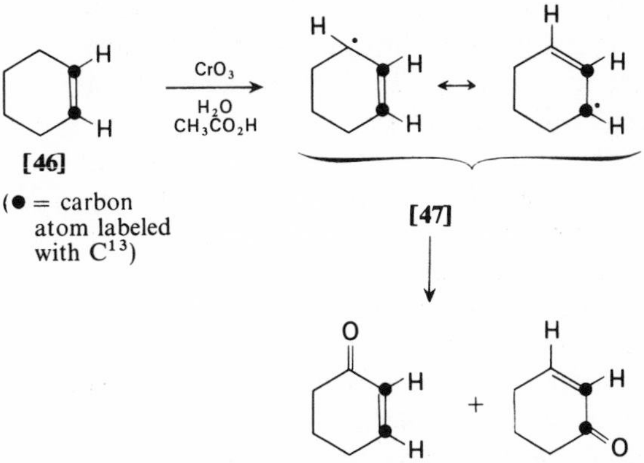

$\xrightarrow[H_2O, CH_3CO_2H]{CrO_3}$ (*Ref.* 56)

[46]

(● = carbon atom labeled with C^{13})

[47]

ring contain no hydroxyl or amino substituent since aromatic compounds of these types (e.g., **[48]**) are readily oxidized to quinones and, with excess oxidant, to carbon dioxide and water. Phenolic hydroxyl groups may be protected as their methyl ethers;

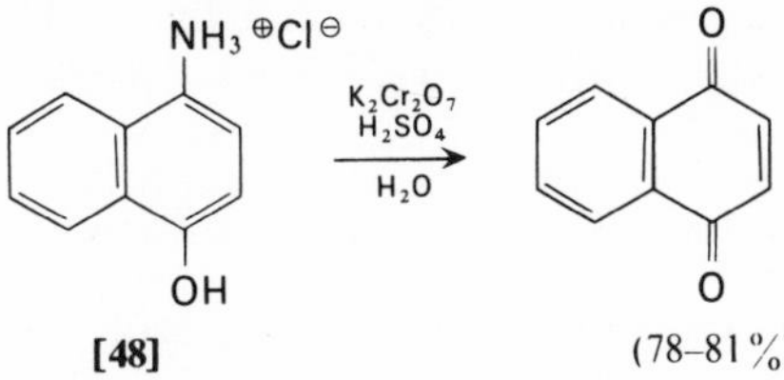

$NH_3{}^{\oplus}Cl^{\ominus}$ OH $\xrightarrow[H_2O]{K_2Cr_2O_7, H_2SO_4}$ O O (*Ref.* 57)

[48] (78–81%)

(56) K. B. Wiberg and S. D. Nielsen, *J. Org. Chem.*, **29**, 3353 (1964).

(57) L. F. Fieser, *Org. Syn.*, **Coll. Vol. 1,** 383 (1944).

aniline derivatives are usually converted to the corresponding acetanilide or benzanilide derivatives, which are then oxidized with aqueous potassium permanganate.[18] For the oxidation of acetanilides, magnesium sulfate is sometimes added to the reaction mixture to prevent it from becoming strongly basic and, consequently, to avoid hydrolysis of the amide. The selective oxidation of the side chains on polycyclic aromatic compounds with chromic acid is usually an unsatisfactory synthetic procedure because of competing oxidation of the aromatic system.[2,58] However, as indicated in an earlier equation, successful side-chain oxidation of such systems have been accomplished using aqueous sodium dichromate at 250°.[55b]

Since the side chain of *t*-butylbenzene is not oxidized by chromic acid, oxidation of aromatic side chains is believed to be initiated by attack at a benzylic C—H bond. However, occasionally products in which the oxygen has been introduced at the carbon atom beta or gamma to the aromatic ring are formed; such products are presumably the result of initial attack at the benzylic position followed by rearrangement.[59] The chromic acid oxidation of aromatic side chains is accelerated by electron-donating substituents, and the rate of reaction in aqueous acetic acid is increased by increasing the concentration of mineral acid or by decreasing the concentration of water.[60] The accompanying equations illustrate the reaction path that is believed to be operative. Whether the initial hydrogen transfer involves a hydride ion (two-electron transfer) or a hydrogen atom (one-electron transfer, as illustrated) has been suggested to depend upon the substituents present.[60] One solution to this ambiguity was offered in the proposal[61] that the transition state for hydrogen transfer is a resonance hybrid (e.g., [**49**]), in which the carbon atom has both radical and carbonium ion character. From studies of the oxidation of the tertiary C—H bond of certain alkanes (e.g., [**50**] and [**51**]) by either chromic acid or potassium permanganate, the initial conversion of the C—H bond to a C—O bond is known to proceed with at least partial retention of configuration.

(58) For example, see L. F. Fieser, W. P. Campbell, E. M. Fry, and M. D. Gates, Jr., *J. Am. Chem. Soc.*, **61,** 3216 (1939).

(59) (a) K. B. Wiberg, B. Marshall, and G. Foster, *Tetrahedron Letters,* **No. 8,** 345 (1962); (b) R. H. Reitsema and N. L. Allphin, *J. Org. Chem.*, **27,** 27 (1962).

(60) K. B. Wiberg and R. J. Evans, *Tetrahedron,* **8,** 313 (1960).

(61) J. Rocek, *Tetrahedron Letters,* **No. 4,** 135 (1962).

$$(C_6H_5)_2CH_2 + H_2CrO_4 \xrightarrow[CH_3CO_2H,\ 30°]{H_2O} (C_6H_5)_2CH\cdot \quad O{=}Cr(OH)_3 \longrightarrow (C_6H_5)_2CH{-}O{-}Cr(OH)_3$$

C—O bond cleavage: $(C_6H_5)_2CH{-}O{-}Cr(OH)_3 \rightarrow (C_6H_5)_2CH^{\oplus} \xrightarrow{H_2O} (C_6H_5)_2CH{-}OH$

H_2O, O—Cr bond cleavage: $(C_6H_5)_2CH{-}O{-}Cr(OH)_3 \rightarrow (C_6H_5)_2CH{-}OH \xrightarrow{H_2CrO_4} (C_6H_5)_2C{=}O$ (90%)

$(C_6H_5)_2CH{-}O{-}Cr(OH)_3 \xrightarrow{H_2Cr_2O_4} (C_6H_5)_2C(H){-}O{-}CrO_3H \longrightarrow (C_6H_5)_2C{=}O$

(*Refs. 60, 62*)

$$\rangle C{-}H + O{=}Cr(=O)(OH)_2 \longrightarrow \left[{-}\dot{C}{-} \quad H{-}O{-}Cr^{5}(=O)(OH){-}OH \longleftrightarrow {-}C^{\oplus} \quad H{-}O{-}Cr^{4}(O^{\ominus})(OH){-}OH \right]$$

[49]

$$n\text{-}C_4H_9(CH_3)(C_2H_5)C{-}H \ \textbf{[50]} \xrightarrow[H_2O,\ CH_3CO_2H]{Na_2Cr_2O_7,\ HClO_4} n\text{-}C_4H_9(CH_3)(C_2H_5)C{-}OH$$

(*Ref. 62*)

$$\textbf{[51]}\ (CH_3)_2C(OH){-}C_6H_{10}{-}CH(CH_3)H \xrightarrow[H_2O,\ 25°]{KMnO_4} (CH_3)_2C(OH){-}C_6H_{10}{-}C(CH_3)OH \ (39\%)$$

(*Ref. 63*)

The conversion of methyl groups bonded to aromatic rings (e.g., **[52]**) to the corresponding aldehydes has been accomplished in moderate yield by oxidation with chromium trioxide in acetic anhydride. The success of this procedure has been attributed[7] to the formation of the diacetate **[53]**, which is relatively stable to the

(62) (a) K. B. Wiberg and G. Foster, *J. Am. Chem. Soc.*, **83,** 423 (1961); (b) see also P. von R. Schleyer and R. D. Nicholas, 140th meeting of the ACS, Chicago, Ill., Sept. 3–8, 1961, Abstracts of Papers, p. 75*Q*.

(63) R. H. Eastman and R. A. Quinn, *J. Am. Chem. Soc.*, **82,** 4249 (1960); (b) see also K. B. Wiberg and A. S. Fox, *ibid.*, **85,** 3487 (1963).

reaction conditions. The same type of conversion has been achieved

CH_3 / NO_2 **[52]** $\xrightarrow[(CH_3CO)_2O,\ 5\text{–}10^\circ]{CrO_3,\ H_2SO_4}$ $CH(OCOCH_3)_2$ / NO_2 **[53]** (66–67%) $\xrightarrow[H_2O,\ C_2H_5OH]{H_2SO_4}$ CHO / NO_2 (89–94%) (*Ref. 64*)

by treating toluene derivatives (e.g., **[54]**) with chromyl chloride in either carbon tetrachloride or carbon disulfide. This reaction, known as the Etard reaction,[2,4,65] produces an initial precipitate

CH_3 / NO_2 / OCH_3 **[54]** $\xrightarrow[CS_2,\ 25^\circ]{CrO_2Cl_2}$ precipitate $\xrightarrow{H_2O}$ CHO / NO_2 / OCH_3 (50%) (*Ref. 66*)

(containing two atoms of chromium for each hydrocarbon molecule), which yields an aldehyde or ketone upon treatment with water. The mechanism of the transformation is uncertain at the present time.[65]

(64) (a) T. Nishimura, *Org. Syn.*, **36,** 58 (1956); (b) S. V. Lieberman and R. Connor, *ibid.*, **Coll. Vol. 2,** 441 (1943).

(65) I. Necsoiu, A. T. Balaban, I. Pascaru, E. Sliam, M. Elian, and C. D. Nenitzescu, *Tetrahedron*, **19,** 1133 (1963); (b) O. H. Wheeler, *Can. J. Chem.*, **42,** 706 (1964); (c) R. A. Stairs, *ibid.*, **42,** 550 (1964); (d) K. B. Wiberg and R. Eisenthal, *Tetrahedron*, **20,** 1151 (1964).

(66) W. R. Boon, *J. Chem. Soc.*, **1940,** S230.

5

· OXIDATIONS WITH PERACIDS AND PERESTERS

PERACIDS HAVE BEEN USED MOST EXTENSIVELY for the selective oxidation of carbon-carbon double bonds; they also slowly convert ketones to esters. The only perester oxidations to be considered here are the copper-catalyzed reactions that allow selective oxidation of allylic and other activated C—H bonds. In general, the peroxide reagents accomplish the oxidation of functions that are frequently difficult to oxidize selectively with chromium and manganese compounds.

Below are listed formulas for the peracids commonly used in the organic laboratory.[1] Performic acid [**1**] is prepared by the addition of hydrogen peroxide to excess formic acid; the resulting solution, which loses oxygen on standing must be used immediately.

(1) (a) D. Swern, *Chem. Rev.*, **45**, 1 (1949); (b) D. Swern, *Org. Reactions*, **7**, 378 (1953); (c) R. Criegee in E. Müller (ed.), *Methoden der organischen Chemie (Houben–Weyl)*, Vol. 8, Georg Thieme Verlag, Stuttgart, Germany, 1952, pp. 1–74; (d) other peracids that have been used include *p*-nitroperbenzoic acid and *m*-chloroperbenzoic acid; the latter offers the advantage of being commercially available from the FMC Corp. (Ref. 4).

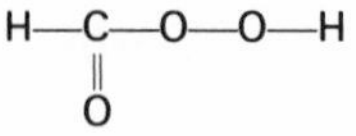

$$H-\underset{\underset{O}{\|}}{C}-O-O-H$$
[1]

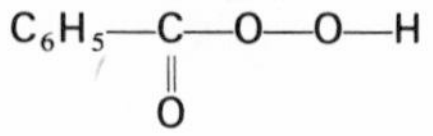

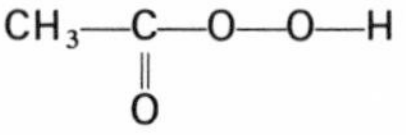

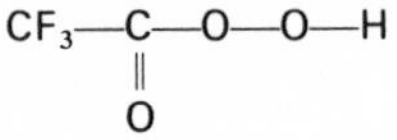

$$CH_3-\underset{\underset{O}{\|}}{C}-O-O-H$$
[2]

$$CF_3-\underset{\underset{O}{\|}}{C}-O-O-H$$
[3]

$$C_6H_5-\underset{\underset{O}{\|}}{C}-O-O-H$$
[4]

$$C_6H_4(CO_3H)(CO_2H) \quad \text{(o-)}$$
[5]

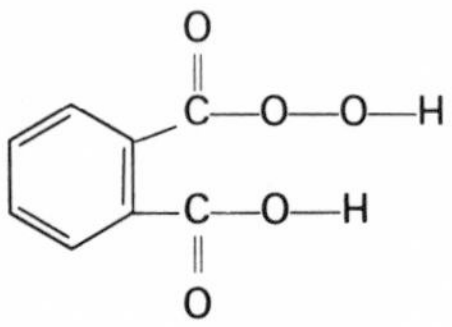

Equilibria comparable to that illustrated for performic acid occur

$$H-CO_2H + \underset{\text{(30\% aqueous solution)}}{H_2O_2} \rightleftharpoons H-CO_3H + H_2O \qquad (\textit{Ref. 2})$$

with all the peracids. However, with most higher-molecular-weight acids it is necessary to add a mineral acid such as sulfuric acid as a catalyst to establish equilibrium rapidly.[1,3] Peracetic acid **[2]** is commercially available as a 40 per cent solution in acetic acid containing a small amount of sulfuric acid.[4] Similar solutions may be prepared by reaction of hydrogen peroxide with acetic acid in the presence of sulfuric acid or by reaction of hydrogen peroxide with acetic anhydride.[1] The concentrations of peracetic acid and hydrogen peroxide in such solutions may be determined by a double titration procedure.[5] The hydrogen peroxide content is measured by titrating a weighed sample of the peracid in cold aqueous sulfuric acid with a standard solution of ceric sulfate until the salmon color of Ferroin indicator is just discharged. The resulting solution is then treated with excess potassium iodide, and the iodine liberated by reaction of the peracid with iodide ion is titrated with standard sodium thiosulfate. Since solutions of peracetic acid slowly lose oxygen on standing, this standardization prior to use is always desirable.

(2) (a) A. Roebuck and H. Adkins, *Org. Syn.*, **Coll. Vol. 3,** 217 (1955); (b) J. E. Horan and R. W. Schiessler, *ibid.*, **41,** 53 (1961).

(3) (a) L. S. Silbert, E. Siegel, and D. Swern, *J. Org. Chem.*, **27,** 1336 (1962); (b) L. S. Silbert, E. Siegel, and D. Swern, *Org. Syn.*, **43,** 93 (1963).

(4) The FMC Corp., Inorganic Chemical Div., New York, N.Y.

(5) F. P. Greenspan and D. G. MacKellar, *Anal. Chem.*, **20,** 1061 (1948).

Solutions of peracetic acid that do not contain acetic acid and a mineral acid have been obtained in relatively inert solvents such as ethyl acetate by air oxidation of acetaldehyde and subsequent thermal decomposition of the intermediate oxidation product **[6]**.[6] Since this procedure is not readily adapted to laboratory preparations, however, an alternative method has been described in which

$$CH_3CHO \xrightarrow[CH_3CO_2C_2H_5,\ 0^\circ]{O_2} CH_3{-}CH(OH){-}O{-}O{-}C(=O){-}CH_3\ \textbf{[6]} \xrightarrow[\text{distil}]{100^\circ} CH_3CO_3H \text{ (as a solution in } CH_3CO_2C_2H_5) \qquad (Ref.\ 6)$$

water is distilled as its azeotrope with ethyl acetate to displace to the right the equilibrium illustrated in the accompanying equations. The residual liquid is then distilled under reduced pressure to separate a solution of peracetic acid in ethyl acetate. Care must

$$CH_3CO_2H + H_2O_2 \underset{CH_3CO_2C_2H_5,\ 50^\circ}{\overset{H_2SO_4}{\rightleftharpoons}} H_2O + CH_3CO_3H \xrightarrow{\text{distil}} CH_3CO_3H \text{ (87\% as a solution in } CH_3CO_2C_2H_5) \qquad (Ref.\ 7)$$

be exercised in this preparation to avoid very concentrated solutions of peracetic acid, which will detonate on impact.

Peroxytrifluoroacetic acid **[3]**, the most powerful oxidizing agent of the peracids previously listed, is prepared by the illustrated reaction of trifluoroacetic anhydride with hydrogen peroxide in methylene chloride. Perbenzoic acid **[4]** has been prepared by the

$$(CF_3CO)_2O + H_2O_2 \text{ (90\% aqueous solution)} \xrightarrow{CH_2Cl_2} CF_3CO_2H + CF_3CO_3H \qquad (Ref.\ 8)$$

reaction of benzoyl peroxide **[7]** with methanolic sodium methoxide.[1,9] Although these procedures specify the use of chloroform

(6) (a) B. Phillips, F. C. Frostick, Jr., and P. S. Starcher, *J. Am. Chem. Soc.*, **79,** 5982 (1957); (b) P. S. Starcher, B. Phillips, and F. C. Frostick, Jr., *J. Org. Chem.*, **26,** 3568 (1961).

(7) B. Phillips, P. S. Starcher, and B. D. Ash, *ibid.*, **23,** 1823 (1958).

(8) (a) W. D. Emmons, *J. Am. Chem. Soc.*, **76,** 3468, 3470 (1954); (b) the reagent obtained from peroxytrifluoroacetic acid and boron trifluoride has been found to oxidize certain reactive aromatic compounds to phenols, quinones, or cyclohexadienone derivatives; C. A. Buehler and H. Hart, *ibid.*, **85,** 2178 (1963); A. J. Waring and H. Hart, *ibid.*, **86,** 1454 (1964).

(9) G. Braun, *Org. Syn.*, **Coll. Vol. 1,** 431 (1944).

as a co-solvent, the rapid rate at which chloroform reacts with

$$(C_6H_5{-}CO{-}O{-})_2 + NaOCH_3 \xrightarrow[CHCl_3,\ 0^\circ]{CH_3OH} C_6H_5CO_2CH_3 + C_6H_5CO_3Na$$

[7]

$$C_6H_5CO_3Na \xrightarrow{H_3O^\oplus} C_6H_5CO_3H$$

(83–86% as a $CHCl_3$ solution) (*Ref.* 9)

alkoxide ions[10] makes preferable a modification employing methylene chloride rather than chloroform.[11] Perhaps the most convenient method of preparation for perbenzoic acid (and other higher-molecular-weight peracids) is the reaction of benzoic acid with hydrogen peroxide in methanesulfonic acid; the sulfonic acid

$$C_6H_5{-}CO_2H + H_2O_2 \underset{25\text{–}30^\circ}{\overset{CH_3SO_3H}{\rightleftharpoons}} H_2O + C_6H_5{-}CO_3H$$

(70% aqueous solution) (85–90%) (*Ref.* 3b)

serves as both the solvent and the acid catalyst. The reaction mixture is diluted with ice and water and the peracid is isolated by extraction (or filtration if the peracid is a solid).

Monoperphthalic acid **[5]** is most conveniently prepared by the reaction of phthalic anhydride with hydrogen peroxide in ether

$$C_6H_4(CO)_2O + H_2O_2 \xrightarrow{(C_2H_5)_2O} C_6H_4(CO_3H)(CO_2H)$$

(30% aqueous solution) (65% as an ether solution) (*Ref.* 12)

solution. A comparable method has been used to prepare monopermaleic acid **[8]**. This peracid appears to be a more powerful oxidant than most common peracids—with the exception of peroxytrifluoroacetic acid—and is useful for the oxidation of ketones and amines.[13]

(10) J. Hine, *Physical Organic Chemistry*, 2d ed., McGraw-Hill, New York, 1962, p. 484.

(11) (a) R. F. Kleinschmidt and A. C. Cope, *J. Am. Chem. Soc.*, **66**, 1929 (1944); (b) for an alternative preparation of perbenzoic acid, see J. R. Moyer and N. C. Manley, *J. Org. Chem.*, **29**, 2099 (1964).

(12) E. E. Royals and L. L. Harrell, Jr., *J. Am. Chem. Soc.*, **77**, 3405 (1955): this procedure is superior to the reaction of phthalic anhydride with sodium hydroperoxide described by H. Böhme, *Org. Syn.*, **Coll. Vol. 3**, 619 (1955); see also G. B. Payne, *ibid.*, **42**, 77 (1962).

(13) R. H. White and W. D. Emmons, *Tetrahedron*, **17**, 31 (1962).

$$\begin{array}{c} CH{-}CO \\ \| \qquad\quad O \\ CH{-}CO \end{array} + H_2O_2 \text{ (90\% aqueous solution)} \xrightarrow{CH_2Cl_2} \underset{\textbf{[8]}}{\begin{array}{c} H \quad CO{-}OOH \\ C \\ \| \\ C \\ H \quad COOH \end{array}} \qquad (Ref.\ 13)$$

That the peracids are substantially weaker than the corresponding carboxylic acids is illustrated by the pK_a values for formic acid (3.6), performic acid (7.1), acetic acid (4.8), and peracetic acid (8.2).[14] This fact permits the use of various inorganic buffers that do not react with the weakly acidic peracids but do react with the corresponding carboxylic acids, a technique which will be illustrated in the subsequent discussion. Although carboxylic acids exist in solution as hydrogen-bonded dimers (e.g., **[9]**), the corresponding peracids appear to be hydrogen-bonded intramolecularly (e.g., **[10]**) and exist as monomers,[1,3,15] As a result, the peracids are more volatile than the corresponding carboxylic acids.

$$\underset{\textbf{[9]}}{CH_3{-}C{\overset{O\cdots H{-}O}{\underset{O{-}H\cdots O}{\lessgtr}}}C{-}CH_3} \qquad \underset{\textbf{[10]}}{CH_3{-}C\overset{O\cdots H}{\underset{O{-}O}{\lessgtr}}}$$

Oxidation of Carbon-Carbon Double Bonds

The reaction of olefins (e.g., **[11]**) with peracids to form epoxides (called epoxidation)[1] provides a convenient and selective method for the oxidation of carbon-carbon double bonds in the presence

$$\underset{\textbf{[11]}}{C_6H_5{-}CH{=}CH_2} + C_6H_5{-}CO_3H \xrightarrow[0^\circ]{CHCl_3} \underset{(69\text{–}75\%)}{C_6H_5{-}\overset{}{CH{-}CH_2}\ (\text{epoxide, }O)} \qquad (Ref.\ 16)$$

of hydroxyl (e.g., **[12]**) and carbonyl functions. Although amines are readily attacked by peracids, unsaturated amides (e.g., **[13]**) may be epoxidized without difficulty.

(14) A. J. Everett and G. S. Minkoff, *Trans. Faraday Soc.*, **49**, 410 (1953).

(15) B. M. Lynch and K. H. Pausacker, *J. Chem. Soc.*, **1955**, 1525.

(16) (a) H. Hibbert and P. Burt, *Org. Syn.*, **Coll. Vol. 1**, 494 (1944); (b) for epoxidations with the commercially available *m*-chloroperbenzoic acid, see N. N. Schwartz and J. H. Blumbergs, *J. Org. Chem.*, **29**, 1976 (1964); these authors report that the rate of epoxidation is retarded by the use of solvents that can form hydrogen bonds with the peracid.

[12]

$p\text{-}Cl\text{—}C_6H_4(H)C\text{=}C(H)\text{—}CH(OH)\text{—}C_6H_4\text{—}Cl\text{-}p \xrightarrow[CHCl_3]{CH_3CO_3H,\ CH_3CO_2Na} p\text{-}Cl\text{—}C_6H_4(H)C\text{—}C(H)\text{—}CH(OH)\text{—}C_6H_4\text{—}Cl\text{-}p$ (epoxide, O bridging the two carbons) (55%) (*Ref. 17*)

[13]

$CH_3(CH_2)_7(H)C\text{=}C(H)(CH_2)_7CONH\text{—}C_6H_{13}\text{-}n \xrightarrow[CH_3CO_2H,\ 20\text{–}25°]{CH_3CO_3H} CH_3(CH_2)_7(H)C\text{—}C(H)(CH_2)_7CONH\text{—}C_6H_{13}\text{-}n$ (epoxide, O bridging the two carbons) (53%) (*Ref. 18*)

The epoxides are susceptible to attack by carboxylic acids to form the monoesters of 1,2-diols, a reaction catalyzed by mineral acids.[1,19] Consequently, epoxidation reactions (e.g., [**14**]) run with

[14]

Cyclohexene $\xrightarrow[HCO_2H,\ 40\text{–}45°]{H_2O_2}$ 2-(formyloxy)cyclohexanol (OH, O—CHO) $\xrightarrow[H_2O,\ 45°]{NaOH}$ 1,2-cyclohexanediol (OH, OH) (65–73%) (*Ref. 2a*)

a peracid in the presence of an excess of the corresponding carboxylic acid frequently yield the hydroxy esters derived from the initially formed epoxide. This is especially true for reactions run in formic acid and for reaction mixtures that contain a strongly acidic mineral acid. Reactions run either with monopermaleic acid in methylene chloride[13] or with mixtures of peroxytrifluoroacetic acid and the strongly acidic trifluoroacetic acid (pK_a 0.3) in methylene chloride[20] (e.g., [**15**]) also usually produce 1,2-diol

[15]

$n\text{-}C_{10}H_{21}\text{—}CH\text{=}CH_2 \xrightarrow[(C_2H_5)_3NH^{\oplus}CF_3CO_2^{\ominus},\ CF_3CO_2H,\ CH_2Cl_2]{CF_3CO_3H} n\text{-}C_{10}H_{21}\text{—}CH\text{—}CH_2$ (OH, O—COCF$_3$) (mixture) $\xrightarrow[CH_3OH,\ reflux]{HCl} n\text{-}C_{10}H_{21}\text{—}CH\text{—}C$ (OH, O) (95%) (*Ref. 2*

(17) H. O. House, *J. Am. Chem. Soc.*, **78,** 2298 (1956).

(18) E. T. Roe, J. T. Scanlan, and D. Swern, *ibid.*, **71,** 2219 (1949).

(19) (a) R. E. Parker and N. S. Isaac, *Chem. Rev.*, **59,** 737 (1959); (b) S. Winstein and R. B. Henderson in R. C. Elderfield, (ed.), *Heterocyclic Compounds*, Vol. 1, Wiley, New York, 1950, pp. 1–60.

(20) (a) W. D. Emmons, A. S. Pagano, and J. P. Freeman, *J. Am. Chem. Soc.*, **76,** 3472 (1954); (b) W. D. Emmons and A. S. Pagano, *ibid.*, **77,** 89 (1955).

derivatives. However, the use of perbenzoic acid in chloroform or methylene chloride, of monoperphthalic acid in ether, or of peracetic acid in ethyl acetate[21] (e.g., **[16]**) permits the isolation of the initially formed epoxide. Reaction of the olefin (e.g., **[17]**) with a

$$\text{[16]: cyclohexenyl}-CH_2-O-COCH\overset{O}{-}CH-CH_3 \xrightarrow[CH_3CO_2C_2H_5,\ 40^\circ]{CH_3CO_3H} \text{epoxycyclohexyl}-CH_2-O-CO-CH\overset{O}{-}CH-CH_3\ (77\%)$$

(*Ref. 21b*)

mixture of the commercial 40 per cent peracetic acid–acetic acid reagent plus sodium acetate (to neutralize the sulfuric acid present) in methylene chloride solution also permits isolation of epoxides. Although the latter procedure is less satisfactory than that utilizing

$$\text{[17]: } C_6H_5(H)C{=}C(H)C_6H_5 \xrightarrow[CH_3CO_2H,\ CH_2Cl_2,\ 30\text{–}35^\circ]{CH_3CO_3H,\ CH_3CO_2Na} C_6H_5(H)C\overset{O}{-}C(H)C_6H_5\ (78\text{–}83\%)$$

(*Ref. 22*)

a pure peracid in an inert solvent, it is none the less frequently used because of the ready commercial availability of the peracetic acid–acetic acid mixture. In certain cases peracetic acid has decided advantages over perbenzoic acid or monoperphthalic acid because both the peracid and the corresponding carboxylic acid are volatile and can readily be removed.

By the addition of anhydrous sodium carbonate to a reaction mixture containing peroxytrifluoroacetic acid and trifluoroacetic acid in methylene chloride, the concentration of the trifluoroacetic acid (which reacts immediately with the sodium carbonate) may be lowered, permitting the successful conversion of olefins (e.g., **[18]**) to epoxides.[20b] However, the peroxytrifluoroacetic acid also reacts slowly with the sodium carbonate to form a salt (which decomposes); with olefins that react slowly with the peroxytrifluoroacetic acid, disodium hydrogen phosphate is therefore a more satisfactory buffer.

(21) (a) D. L. MacPeek, P. S. Starcher, and B. Phillips, *ibid.*, **81,** 680 (1959); (b) P. S. Starcher, F. C. Frostick, Jr., and B. Phillips, *J. Org. Chem.*, **25,** 1420 (1960).

(22) D. J. Reif and H. O. House, *Org. Syn.*, **Coll. Vol. 4,** 860 (1963).

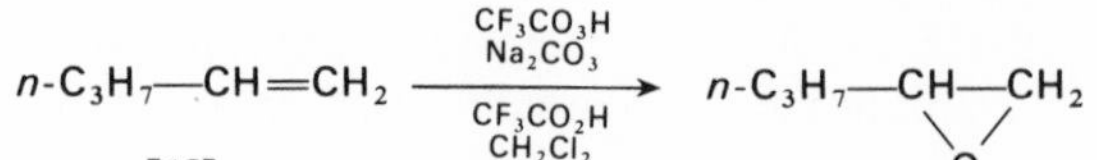

[18] (81%) (*Ref. 20b*)

From several of the previously cited examples it will be noted that the epoxidation reaction is stereospecific, leading to a *cis* addition of the oxygen atom to the double bond. The subsequent opening of the epoxide (e.g., **[19]**) by reaction with some nucleophilic reagent usually proceeds with inversion of configuration

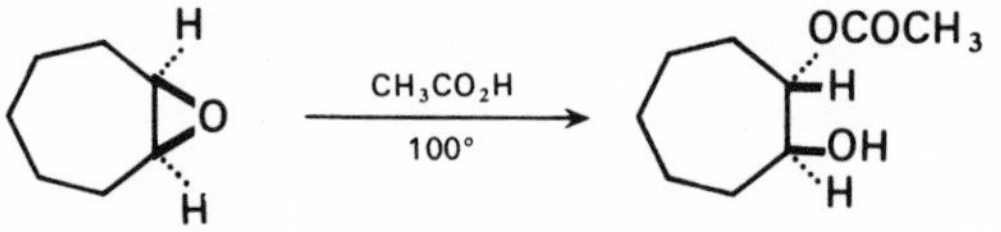

[19] (65%) (*Ref. 23*)

at the carbon atom attacked,[19] resulting in an over-all *trans* addition to the double bond. Thus, the preparation of *trans*-1,2-diols by this sequence complements the previously discussed oxidations with alkaline potassium permanganate and with osmium tetroxide, both of which result in *cis* hydroxylation. The epoxide ring may be opened by a variety of nucleophilic reagents,[19] among them metal hydrides (see Chapter 2), hydrogen halides, enolate anions (e.g., **[20]**), and aqueous acids (e.g., **[21]**). The presence, in the molecule being epoxidized, of a hydroxyl or carboxyl function may lead to the intramolecular displacement of the epoxide C—O bond to form a hydroxy ether or a hydroxy lactone.[24] The opening of the three-membered ring in compound **[21]** is of particular

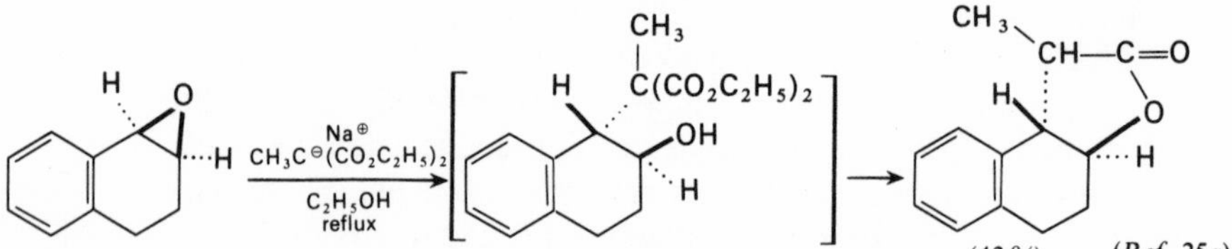

[20] (43%) (*Ref. 25a*)

(23) L. N. Owen and G. S. Saharia, *J. Chem. Soc.*, **1953,** 2582.

(24) For example, see G. Berti, *J. Org. Chem.*, **24,** 934 (1959).

(25) (a) E. E. van Tamelen, G. Van Zyl, and G. D. Zuidema, *J. Am. Chem. Soc.*, **72,** 488 (1950); (b) H. B. Henbest, M. Smith, and A. Thomas, *J. Chem. Soc.*, **1958,** 3293.

H_2SO_4, H_2O, CH_3COCH_3, 20°

[21] → **[22]** (71%) + **[23]** (23%) (*Ref. 25b*)

interest since it illustrates the general rule[26] that a cyclohexene epoxide ring is opened predominantly in such a way as to produce two new substituents, which are *trans* and diaxial (as in **[22]**) rather than *trans* and diequatorial (as in **[23]**). The same phenomenon is seen in the reaction of the epoxide **[24]** with hydrogen bromide.

HBr, H_2O, $CHCl_3$

[24] (*Ref. 27*)

In certain cases (e.g., **[25]**) where at least one aryl substituent is bonded to the epoxide ring, opening of the heterocyclic ring with

$C_6H_5CO_2H$, $CHCl_3$, 25°

[25] (70%) (*Ref. 28*)

retention of configuration has been observed. In other similar systems (e.g., **[26]**), ring opening with either retention or inversion of configuration may be obtained by the appropriate choice of

(26) (a) D. H. R. Barton and R. C. Cookson, *Quart. Rev.* (*London*), **10,** 44 (1956); (b) E. L. Eliel in M. S. Newman (ed.), *Steric Effects in Organic Chemistry*, Wiley, New York, 1956, pp. 130–134; (c) E. L. Eliel, *Stereochemistry of Carbon Compounds*, McGraw-Hill, 1962, pp. 229–231.

(27) G. H. Alt and D. H. R. Barton, *J. Chem. Soc.*, **1954,** 4284.

(28) (a) D. Y. Curtin, A. Bradley, and Y. G. Hendrickson, *J. Am. Chem. Soc.*, **78,** 4064 (1956); (b) J. H. Brewster, *ibid.*, **78,** 4061 (1956); (c) G. Berti, F. Bottari, and B. Macchia, *Tetrahedron*, **20,** 545 (1964); (d) W. E. Rosen, L. Dorfman, and M. P. Linfield [*J. Org. Chem.*, **29,** 1723 (1964)] have reported that indene reacts with performic acid to form *cis*-2-formyloxy-1-hydroxyindane and suggest a concerted addition of the elements of performic acid to the olefin.

C_6H_5—CO, H, H, C_6H_5 epoxide **[26]**

→ HCl, $(C_2H_5)_2O$ → C_6H_5—CO, H / C—C / H, C_6H_5, OH Cl (43%)

→ HCl, C_2H_5OH → C_6H_5—CO, Cl / C—C / H, OH, H, C_6H_5 (44%)

(*Ref.* 29)

reaction conditions. The direction of ring opening when an unsymmetrical epoxide is allowed to react with a nucleophile is also determined, at least in part, by the reaction conditions. In general, nucleophiles attack at the less highly substituted carbon atom of the epoxide ring in neutral or basic media, as would be anticipated for a normal S_N2 process; in acidic media, the proportion of attack at the more highly substituted carbon is increased[19] and may become the predominant reaction.

CH_3—CH—CH_2 (epoxide, O) ⟶ CH_3—CH(OH)—CH_2Br + CH_3—CH(Br)—CH_2OH

(*Ref.* 30)

reaction conditions	product composition	
HBr, H_2O, 15°	76%	24%
NaBr, H_2O, 22°	95%	5%

The epoxidation of olefins is believed to proceed by an electrophilic attack, as indicated in the accompanying equations.[15] In accord with this mechanism, the peracid usually attacks the olefin

C=C + H—O—O—C(=O)—C_6H_5 ⟶ epoxide (C—O—C) + H—O—C(=O)—C_6H_5

(e.g., **[27]**) from its less hindered side to produce the less hindered epoxide as the major product. However, the epoxidations of olefins **[28]** and **[29]** illustrate the fact that the direction of attack by the

(29) H. O. House, *J. Org. Chem.*, **21,** 1306 (1956); (b) C. C. Tung and A. J. Speziale, *ibid.*, **28,** 2009 (1963); (c) see also H. H. Wasserman and N. E. Aubrey, *J. Am. Chem. Soc.*, **78,** 1726 (1956).

(30) C. A. Stewart and C. A. VanderWerf, *J. Am. Chem. Soc.*, **76,** 1259 (1954).

CH_3 $C_{16}H_{30}$; o-$C_6H_4(CO_3H)(CO_2H)$, $(C_2H_5)_2O$, 20° → (72%) (*Ref. 31*)

[27]

peracid may be influenced by nearby polar substituents. The directive effect of the hydroxyl group in **[28]** has been suggested to arise because of hydrogen bonding between the hydroxyl group and the attacking peracid; the reason for observed directive effects with other polar substituents is not clear.[32]

[28] $\xrightarrow[C_6H_6,\ 0°]{C_6H_5CO_3H}$ (80%) (*Ref. 32b*)

[29] $\xrightarrow[C_6H_6,\ 0°]{C_6H_5CO_3H}$ (major product) +

The epoxidation reaction is not catalyzed by acids[15,16b] and, as noted previously, the presence of strong acids in the reaction mixture is usually undesirable. However, the rate of epoxidation is enhanced by the presence either of electron-withdrawing groups in the peracid (e.g., CF_3CO_3H is more reactive than CH_3CO_3H) or of electron-donating groups in the olefin.[1,15] Thus, olefins with three or four alkyl substituents are rapidly epoxidized by peracids whereas terminal, monosubstituted olefins react very slowly[1] unless a highly reactive peracid such as peroxytrifluoroacetic acid is used.[20] Conjugation of the olefin with aromatic rings or with other multiple bonds also reduces the rate of epoxidation, since the delocalization of pi electrons possible in the conjugated systems reduces the electron density at the double bond undergoing

(31) H. B. Henbest and R. A. L. Wilson, *J. Chem. Soc.*, **1956,** 3289.

(32) (a) H. B. Henbest and R. A. L. Wilson, *ibid.*, **1957,** 1958; (b) H. B. Henbest, *Proc. Chem. Soc.*, **1963,** 159.

electrophilic attack.[15] Although the rate of reaction of α,β-unsaturated esters with peracids is relatively slow, it is possible to epoxidize the double bond in these compounds either with peroxytrifluoroacetic acid (e.g., [**30**]) or with peracetic acid in ethyl acetate (e.g., [**31**]). On the other hand, the reaction of α,β-unsaturated ketones with peracids usually does not lead to epoxidation of

$$CH_2{=}C(CH_3){-}CO_2CH_3 \ \textbf{[30]} \xrightarrow[\substack{CF_3CO_2H \\ CH_2Cl_2 \\ \text{reflux}}]{\substack{CF_3CO_3H \\ Na_2HPO_4}} \underset{\text{(84\%)}}{CH_2{-}C(CH_3)(O){-}CO_2CH_3 \ \text{(epoxide)}} \qquad (\textit{Ref. 20b})$$

$$C_6H_5CH{=}CH{-}CO_2C_2H_5 \ \textbf{[31]} \xrightarrow[\substack{CH_3CO_2C_2H_5 \\ 80^\circ}]{CH_3CO_3H} \underset{\text{(70\%)}}{C_6H_5{-}CH{-}CH{-}CO_2C_2H_5 \ \text{(epoxide, O bridging)}} \qquad (\textit{Ref. 21a})$$

the double bond; as illustrated in the accompanying equations, reaction with the double bond is retarded sufficiently that reaction with the ketone becomes the predominant process.

$$\text{2-benzylidenecyclopentanone } (C_6H_5{-}CH{=}) \xrightarrow[\substack{CH_3CO_2K \\ CH_3CO_2H \\ 30^\circ}]{CH_3CO_3H} \underset{\text{(50\%)}}{C_6H_5{-}CH{=}\text{(six-membered lactone, ring O, C=O)}} \qquad (\textit{Ref. 33})$$

$$(CH_3)_2C{=}CH{-}CO{-}CH_3 \xrightarrow[\substack{CH_3CO_2H \\ CHCl_3 \\ 20\text{–}25^\circ}]{\substack{CH_3CO_3H \\ CH_3CO_2Na}}$$

$$\underset{\substack{\text{(ca. 20\% of} \\ \text{product)}}}{(CH_3)_2\overset{O}{C{-}CH}{-}CO{-}CH_3} + \underset{\substack{\text{(ca. 80\% of product)} \\ \text{[from } (CH_3)_2C{=}CHOCOCH_3]}}{(CH_3)_2\overset{O}{C{-}CH}{-}OCOCH_3} \qquad (\textit{Ref. 34})$$

However, α,β-unsaturated ketones (e.g., [**32**]) can be epoxidized, using nucleophilic reagents such as the sodium salt of hydrogen

(33) H. M. Walton, *J. Org. Chem.*, **22,** 1161 (1957).

(34) G. B. Payne and P. H. Williams, *ibid.*, **24,** 284 (1959).

peroxide (NaOOH) or the sodium salt of *t*-butyl hydroperoxide[35] rather than a peracid. The reaction is believed to proceed by

$$\text{[32]} \xrightarrow[\text{CH}_3\text{OH, } 15\text{–}20^\circ]{\text{H}_2\text{O}_2,\ \text{NaOH}} \text{epoxyketone } (70\text{–}72\%) \qquad (\textit{Ref. 36})$$

nucleophilic addition of the hydroperoxide anion at the beta carbon of the unsaturated ketone followed by intramolecular displacement of hydroxide ion, as illustrated.[37]

$$R{-}CH{=}CH{-}\underset{\underset{O}{\|}}{C}{-}R + H{-}O{-}O^{\ominus} \rightleftharpoons R{-}\underset{\underset{HO-O}{|}}{CH}{-}CH{=}\underset{\underset{O^{\ominus}}{|}}{C}{-}R \rightarrow R{-}CH{-}CH{-}\underset{\underset{O}{\|}}{C}{-}R \text{ (epoxide)}$$

Similar reaction conditions have been used for the epoxidation of alkylidenemalonic esters[38] and α,β-unsaturated aldehydes (e.g., **[33]**).

$$\underset{\textbf{[33]}}{C_6H_5{-}CH{=}CH{-}CHO} \xrightarrow[\text{pH 8.5, CH}_3\text{OH, } 35\text{–}40^\circ]{(CH_3)_3C{-}OOH,\ \text{NaOH}} C_6H_5{-}CH{-}CH{-}CHO \text{ (epoxide, O bridging)}\ (73\%) \qquad (\textit{Ref. 39})$$

Epoxidation with alkaline hydrogen peroxide differs from peracid epoxidation in that the former is not stereospecific (i.e., the stereochemistry of the reactant and the product do not bear a definite relationship to one another) but is stereoselective (i.e., a single stereoisomer of the product is formed, which bears no definite relationship to the stereochemistry of the reactant). Thus, epoxidation of either isomer **[34]** or **[35]** of the unsaturated ketone yields a single epoxyketone in which the ketone function and the larger group on the beta carbon atom are *trans* to one another. This stereoselectivity has been justified on the basis that the intermediate

(35) N. C. Yang and R. A. Finnegan, *J. Am. Chem. Soc.*, **80**, 5845 (1958).
(36) R. L. Wasson and H. O. House, *Org. Syn.*, **Coll. Vol. 4,** 552 (1963).
(37) C. A. Bunton and G. J. Minkoff, *J. Chem. Soc.*, **1949,** 665.
(38) G. B. Payne, *J. Org. Chem.*, **24,** 2048 (1959).
(39) (a) G. B. Payne, *ibid.*, **25,** 275 (1960); (b) G. B. Payne, *J. Am. Chem. Soc.*, **81,** 4901 (1959).

(*Ref. 40*)

[34] [35] [36]

enolate anion **[36]** will be more stable if it is not eclipsed with a large beta substituent in the transition state, leading to formation of the three-membered ring.[40b] It should also be noted that, at least for the example cited, the *cis* starting material **[35]** is isomerized to the more stable *trans* isomer **[34]** in the reaction mixture at approximately the same rate as it is epoxidized; consequently, stereospecific epoxidation would not be expected in any case.

The reaction of α,β-unsaturated nitriles (e.g., **[37]**) with alkaline hydrogen peroxide yields epoxyamides. Although this product

(*Ref. 41*)

[37] (60%)

would appear to result from the previously discussed base-catalyzed epoxidation and a subsequent known (e.g., **[38]**) rapid conversion of the epoxynitrile to the epoxyamide by further reaction with the

$C_6H_5—C{\equiv}N$ + $\xrightarrow[H_2O,\ CH_3COCH_3]{H_2O_2,\ NaOH}$ $C_6H_5—C(=NH)—O—O—H$ $\xrightarrow[OH^{\ominus}]{H_2O_2}$ $C_6H_5—CO—NH_2$ + H_2O + O_2

[38] (*Ref. 42*)

(40) (a) H. O. House and R. S. Ro, *J. Am. Chem. Soc.*, **80,** 2428 (1958); (b) H. E. Zimmerman, L. Singer, and B. S. Thyagarajan, *ibid.*, **81,** 108 (1959).

(41) (a) G. B. Payne and P. H. Williams, *J. Org. Chem.*, **26,** 651 (1961); (b) G. B. Payne, P. H. Deming, and P. H. Williams, *ibid.*, **26,** 659 (1961); (c) G. B. Payne, *ibid.*, **26,** 663, 668 (1961); (d) G. B. Payne, *Tetrahedron*, **18,** 763 (1962); (e) Y. Ogata and Y. Sawaki, *ibid.*, **20,** 2065 (1964).

(42) K. B. Wiberg, *J. Am. Chem. Soc.*, **75,** 3961 (1953); **77,** 2519 (1955).

salt of hydrogen peroxide, detailed examination revealed a very different reaction course.[41] The probable path, illustrated in the accompanying equations, involves a peroxyimidic acid intermediate **[39]**, which acts as an electrophilic reagent. This intermediate either may be intercepted by a more reactive olefin such as cyclohexene to produce cyclohexene epoxide and the unsaturated amide, or may react with more of the hydroperoxide anion to form the unsaturated amide plus oxygen. Although the origin of

$$CH_2{=}CH{-}C{\equiv}N \xrightarrow[NaOH,\ H_2O]{H_2O_2} CH_2{=}CH{-}C({=}NH){-}O{-}O{-}H \ \textbf{[39]} \longrightarrow \text{(cyclic transition state)} \longrightarrow CH_2{-}CH{-}C({=}O){-}NH_2 \text{ (epoxide)}$$

(this step may be bimolecular) *(Ref. 41)*

$$\textbf{[39]} \xrightarrow{H_2O_2} CH_2{=}CH{-}CONH_2 + O_2$$

$$\textbf{[39]} \xrightarrow{\text{cyclohexene}} CH_2{=}CH{-}CONH_2 + \text{cyclohexene oxide}$$

the oxygen formed in the latter process is not known, it could result from an attack of the hydroperoxide anion at the terminal oxygen atom of the intermediate **[39]** to displace the amide and form the species H—O—O—O—H, which decomposes to water and oxygen. The intermediate peroxyimidic acid derived from benzonitrile has been used to epoxidize olefins (e.g., **[40]**) under neutral conditions. This procedure would appear to be useful for the preparation of epoxides that are very unstable to acid, in spite of the difficulty of separating the product from benzamide.

$$\text{methylenecyclohexane } \textbf{[40]} + C_6H_5{-}C{\equiv}N \xrightarrow[CH_3OH,\ 45^\circ]{H_2O_2,\ K_2CO_3} \text{1-oxaspiro epoxide } (73\%) + C_6H_5CONH_2$$

(Ref. 41d)

Olefins with chlorine substituents, alkoxy substituents (i.e., enol ethers), or acyloxy substituents (i.e., enol esters) are readily epoxidized with peracids. However, the products of these reactions are unstable to acid and heat and frequently undergo further change in the reaction mixture. For example, reaction of the chloroölefin **[41]** with peracid produced the chloroketone **[42]**,

$$p\text{-}CH_3\text{—}C_6H_4\text{—}\underset{\displaystyle Cl}{\underset{|}{C}}\text{=}CH\text{—}C_6H_5 \xrightarrow[CH_2Cl_2]{CH_3CO_3H} p\text{-}CH_3\text{—}C_6H_4\text{—}CO\text{—}\underset{\displaystyle Cl}{\underset{|}{CH}}\text{—}C_6H_5$$

[41] **[42]** (71%) (*Ref. 43*)

presumably by initial formation of a chloroepoxide and subsequent rearrangement with the migration of chlorine. Although certain enol ethers (e.g., **[43]**) have been successfully converted to epoxy ethers by the use of low temperatures and short reaction times, other enol ethers (e.g., **[44]**) give intermediates which appear to react with the carboxylic acid in the reaction mixture too rapidly to permit isolation.

$$C_6H_5\text{—}\underset{\displaystyle OC_2H_5}{\underset{|}{C}}\text{=}C(CH_3)_2 \xrightarrow[\substack{(C_2H_5)_2O \\ 0°,\ 30\ sec}]{C_6H_5CO_3H} C_6H_5\text{—}\underset{\displaystyle OC_2H_5}{\underset{|}{C}}\overset{O}{\text{—}}C(CH_3)_2$$

[43] (70%)

$$\text{[44] (1-ethoxycyclohexene)} \xrightarrow[\substack{(C_2H_5)_2O \\ 0°,\ 30\ sec}]{C_6H_5CO_3H} \left[\text{1-ethoxycyclohexene oxide} + C_6H_5CO_2H \rightarrow \text{1-(}O\text{—}CO\text{—}C_6H_5\text{)-1-}OC_2H_5\text{-2-}OH\text{-cyclohexane}\right] \rightarrow \text{2-(}O\text{—}CO\text{—}C_6H_5\text{)cyclohexanone}$$

[44] (61%) (*Ref. 44*)

The epoxidation of aliphatic enol acetates (e.g., **[45]**) leads to the formation of epoxyacetates, which undergo an intramolecular isomerization to α-acetoxyketones when heated or chromatographed on silica gel. Enol acetates with aryl substituents (e.g.,

(43) (a) R. N. McDonald and P. A. Schwab, *J. Am. Chem. Soc.*, **85**, 820, 4004 (1963); (b) aliphatic chloroepoxides have been isolated from the free-radical chlorination of epoxides: see C. Walling and P. S. Fredricks, *ibid.*, **84**, 3326 (1962).

(44) C. L. Stevens and J. Tazuma, *J. Am. Chem. Soc.*, **76**, 715 (1954); for a discussion of the epoxy ether–carboxylic acid reaction, see C. L. Stevens and S. J. Dykstra, *ibid.*, **75**, 5975 (1953).

[45] $\xrightarrow[\text{CHCl}_3,\ -5°]{C_6H_5CO_3H}$ (80%) $\xrightarrow[160°]{\text{no solvent}}$ (*Ref. 45a*)

(85%)

[46] $\xrightarrow[\text{CHCl}_3,\ C_6H_6,\ 30°]{C_6H_5CO_3H}$ [ ] → (49%) (*Ref. 45b*)

[**46**]) appear to undergo rearrangement more readily since acetoxy-ketones have been isolated directly from the epoxidation mixture. By an appropriate choice of reaction conditions, it is possible to convert an unsymmetrical ketone (e.g., [**47**]) predominantly to either the more highly substituted or the less highly substituted enol acetate. Consequently, by preparation of the appropriate enol acetate and subsequent epoxidation and rearrangement it is possible to introduce an α-acetoxyl substituent on either side of the carbonyl function in an unsymmetrical ketone.

(45) (a) K. L. Williamson and W. S. Johnson, *J. Org. Chem.*, **26,** 4563 (1961); (b) P. D. Gardner, *J. Am. Chem. Soc.*, **78,** 3421 (1956); (c) A. H. Soloway, W. J. Considine, D. K. Fukushima, and T. F. Gallagher, *ibid.*, **76,** 2941 (1954); (d) N. S. Leeds, D. K. Fukushima, and T. F. Gallagher, *ibid.*, **76,** 2943 (1954); (e) H. J. Shine and G. E. Hunt, *ibid.*, **80,** 2434 (1958); (f) A. L. Draper, W. J. Heilman, W. E. Schaefer, H. J. Shine, and J. N. Shoolery, *J. Org. Chem.*, **27,** 2727 (1962).

$$[47] \xrightarrow[\text{reflux}]{(CH_3CO)_2O,\ p\text{-}CH_3C_6H_4SO_3H} \text{enol acetates (90\%)} + (5\%) + (3\%)$$

$$[47] \xrightarrow[CH_3OCH_2CH_2OCH_3]{(C_6H_5)_3CLi} \text{Li enolates} \xrightarrow{(CH_3CO)_2O} \text{enol acetates (10\%)} + (68\%) + (22\%)$$

(*Ref. 46*)

Among the synthetic uses of epoxidation products, the acid-catalyzed rearrangements of epoxides[19] (e.g., **[48]**) or of their corresponding 1,2-diol monoesters (e.g., **[49]**) are of special interest

$$\underset{[48]}{C_6H_5\text{—}CH\text{—}CH\text{—}C_6H_5 \ (\text{epoxide})} \xrightarrow[C_6H_6,\ 25°]{BF_3\text{—}(C_2H_5)_2O} \underset{(73\text{–}83\%)}{(C_6H_5)_2CHCHO}$$

(*Ref. 47*)

$$\text{indene} \xrightarrow[HCO_2H,\ 35\text{–}40°]{H_2O_2} \underset{[49]}{\text{1-hydroxy-2-indanyl formate}} \xrightarrow[H_2O,\ \text{reflux}]{H_2SO_4} \underset{(69\text{–}81\%)}{\text{2-indanone}}$$

(*Refs. 2b, 28d*)

since the over-all reaction scheme provides a method for the conversion of an olefin to a carbonyl compound. The acid catalysts commonly employed are aqueous mineral acid, boron trifluoride etherate in benzene, or anhydrous magnesium bromide in benzene or ether.[48] Either the mineral acid or the boron trifluoride catalyst gives satisfactory results with 1,1-dialkylepoxides, with trisubstituted epoxides, and with epoxides that have at least one aryl

(46) (a) H. O. House and H. W. Thompson, *J. Org. Chem.*, **26**, 3729 (1961); (b) H. O. House and V. Kramar, *ibid.*, **28**, 3362 (1963); (c) H. O. House and B. M. Trost, *ibid.*, **30**, 1341 (1965).

(47) D. J. Reif and H. O. House, *Org. Syn.*, **Coll. Vol. 4,** 375 (1963).

(48) (a) H. O. House, *J. Am. Chem. Soc.*, **77,** 3070, 5083 (1955); (b) S. M. Naqvi, J. P. Horwitz, and R. Filler, *ibid.*, **79,** 6283 (1957).

or vinyl substituent. The procedure has proved useful for the conversion of substituted cyclohexene derivatives (e.g., **[50]**) to corresponding cyclohexanones. 1,2-Dialkylepoxides usually give satisfactory yields of rearrangement products with magnesium bromide, a reagent that converts the epoxides to bromohydrin derivatives prior to rearrangement.[48]

[50] $\xrightarrow[C_6H_6,\ 25°]{BF_3 \cdot (C_2H_5)_2O}$ (99%) (*Ref. 49*)

Oxidation of Carbonyl Compounds

Although the reaction of peracids with ketones is normally much slower than the epoxidation of olefins, relatively long reaction times, strong acids as catalysts, or very reactive peracids permit the conversion of ketones to esters in good yield. This conversion, known as the Baeyer-Villiger reaction,[50] is usually accomplished either by the use of a solution of peracetic acid in acetic acid containing sulfuric acid (e.g., **[51]**) or *p*-toluenesulfonic acid as a

$$p\text{-}O_2N{-}C_6H_4{-}CO{-}C_6H_5 \xrightarrow[H_2SO_4,\ CH_3CO_2H,\ 25°]{CH_3CO_3H} p\text{-}O_2N{-}C_6H_4{-}CO{-}O{-}C_6H_5$$

[51] (95%) (*Ref. 51*)

$$c\text{-}C_3H_5{-}COCH_3 \xrightarrow[CF_3CO_2H,\ Na_2HPO_4,\ CH_2Cl_2,\ \text{reflux}]{CF_3CO_3H} c\text{-}C_3H_5{-}O{-}COCH_3$$

[52] (53%) (*Ref. 52*)

$$(CH_3)_2CH{-}CH_2{-}COCH_3 \xrightarrow[CH_2Cl_2,\ \text{reflux}]{CH{-}CO_3H \,\|\, CH{-}CO_2H} (CH_3)_2CH{-}CH_2{-}O{-}COCH_3$$

[53] (72%) (*Ref. 13*)

(49) H. B. Henbest and T. I. Wrigley, *J. Chem. Soc.*, **1957,** 4596, 4765.

(50) (a) C. H. Hassall, *Org. Reactions*, **9,** 73 (1957); (b) P. A. S. Smith in P. deMayo (ed.), *Molecular Rearrangements*, Vol. 1, Wiley-Interscience, New York, 1963, pp. 568–591.

(51) W. von E. Doering and L. Speers, *J. Am. Chem. Soc.*, **72,** 5515 (1950).

(52) W. D. Emmons and G. B. Lucas, *ibid.*, **77,** 2287 (1955).

catalyst, or by the use of one of the more reactive peracids—peroxytrifluoroacetic acid (e.g., **[52]**) or monopermaleic acid (e.g., **[53]**)—in methylene chloride solution. Persulfuric acid (Caro's acid, $H_2S_2O_8$) or a mixture of hydrogen peroxide and an acid or a base have also been utilized, as have such other peracids as perbenzoic and monoperphthalic.

Peroxytrifluoroacetic acid is generally the reagent of choice because of the speed with which the oxidation occurs. However, use of this peracid is complicated by transesterification, which occurs between the initial ester product and trifluoroacetic acid as illustrated in the accompanying equation.[52,53] Although this transesterification is of no concern if the crude ester product is to be hydrolyzed prior to the isolation of products, a buffer such as

$$CH_3CO_2C_2H_5 + CF_3CO_2H \rightleftharpoons CH_3CO_2H + CF_3CO_2C_2H_5$$

solid disodium hydrogen phosphate must be added to the reaction mixture if isolation of the ester is desired; the buffer reacts with the trifluoroacetic acid to form a salt and hence minimize transesterification.

The oxidation of cyclic ketones (e.g., **[54]** and **[55]**), with peracids serves as a useful preparative route to lactones. Since the six-membered- and larger-ring lactones are equilibrated with the

[54] $\xrightarrow[\text{CHCl}_3,\ 25°]{C_6H_5CO_3H}$ (71%) (*Ref. 54*)

[55] $\xrightarrow[\text{CF}_3\text{CO}_2\text{H},\ 10\text{–}15°]{CF_3CO_3H}$ (81%) (*Ref. 55*)

(53) (a) M. F. Hawthorne, W. D. Emmons, and K. S. McCallum, *ibid.*, **80,** 6393 (1958); (b) M. F. Hawthorne and W. D. Emmons, *ibid.*, **80,** 6398 (1958).

(54) (a) S. L. Friess, *J. Am. Chem. Soc.*, **71,** 2571 (1949); see also S. L. Friess and P. E. Frankenburg, *ibid.*, **74,** 2679 (1952); (b) see also J. L. Mateos and H. Menchaca, *J. Org. Chem.*, **29,** 2026 (1964).

(55) W. F. Sager and A. Duckworth, *J. Am. Chem. Soc.*, **77,** 188 (1955).

corresponding dimers, trimers, and linear polymeric esters in the presence of strong acids, the use of distilled solutions of peracetic acid in ethyl acetate has been recommended for this type of oxidation (e.g., **[56]**). Under these conditions, however, elevated temperatures were required for reasonably rapid reactions with the less

CH_3CO_3H / $CH_3CO_2C_2H_5$, 70° → (29%) + $HO_2C(CH_2)_5CO_2H$ (33%) (*Ref. 56*)

[56]

reactive[54] seven- and eight-membered-ring ketones, and a substantial amount of further oxidation to form dicarboxylic acids was observed.

A variety of studies[51,53,54,57] of the Baeyer-Villiger reaction indicate that the mechanism is that shown in the accompanying equations. The reaction is catalyzed by acid and the rate of oxidation is accelerated by electron-donating groups in the ketone and by electron-withdrawing groups in the peracid. Furthermore, the

$$R_2C{=}O + CH_3CO_3H \underset{}{\overset{H^\oplus}{\rightleftharpoons}} R\text{-}\underset{R}{\overset{OH}{C}}\text{-}O\text{-}O\text{-}\underset{O}{\overset{}{C}}\text{-}CH_3 \xrightarrow[\text{(slow)}]{H^\oplus} R{-}\overset{\oplus OH}{\overset{\|}{C}}{-}OR \xrightarrow{-H^\oplus} R{-}CO{-}O{-}R$$

reaction has been demonstrated to occur with retention of configuration,[58] as is illustrated by the oxidation of ketone **[57]**. It

—COCH$_3$ (H) $\xrightarrow[\text{CHCl}_3,\ 25^\circ]{C_6H_5CO_3H}$ —OCOCH$_3$ (H) (*Ref. 59*)

(optically active) **[57]** (81%) (optically active)

(56) P. S. Starcher and B. Phillips, *ibid.*, **80,** 4079 (1958).

(57) (a) W. von E. Doering and E. Dorfman, *J. Am. Chem. Soc.*, **75,** 5595 (1953); (b) S. L. Friess and N. Franham, *ibid.*, **72,** 5518 (1950); (c) S. L. Friess and A. H. Soloway, *ibid.*, **73,** 3968 (1951); (d) S. L. Friess and R. Pinson, Jr., *ibid.*, **74,** 1302 (1952).

(58) (a) R. B. Turner, *J. Am. Chem. Soc.*, **72,** 878 (1950); (b) T. F. Gallagher and T. H. Kritchevsky, *ibid.*, **72,** 882 (1950); (c) K. Mislow and J. Brenner, *ibid.*, **75,** 2318 (1953).

(59) J. A. Berson and S. Suzuki, *ibid.*, **81,** 4088 (1959).

will be noted from this example that the oxidation not only provides a useful method for the conversion of a methyl ketone to an alcohol but also offers a method for relating the stereochemistry of a ketone and an alcohol.

It is apparent that the oxidation of an unsymmetrical ketone (e.g., **[58]**) can lead to two isomeric esters. From a study of a series of alkyl phenyl ketones[53] as well as from earlier studies,[51] the

$$\text{C}_6\text{H}_{11}\text{–CO–C}_6\text{H}_5 \xrightarrow[\text{CHCl}_3,\ 25^\circ]{\text{C}_6\text{H}_5\text{CO}_3\text{H}} \text{C}_6\text{H}_{11}\text{–O–CO–C}_6\text{H}_5 + \text{C}_6\text{H}_{11}\text{–CO–O–C}_6\text{H}_5$$

[58] (71%, isolated as alcohol) (14%, isolated as phenol) (*Ref. 57b*)

relative ease of migration (i.e., the migratory aptitude) of various groups in the Baeyer-Villiger reaction has been found to be *t*-alkyl > cyclohexyl ~ *sec*-alkyl ~ benzyl ~ phenyl > primary alkyl > methyl. Interestingly, even a bridgehead *t*-alkyl group (e.g., **[59]**) migrates readily, providing a useful synthetic route to bridgehead alcohols. The migration of a phenyl ring is facilitated by the presence of

[59] (bridgehead CO–C_6H_5, CH_3, CH_3) $\xrightarrow[\substack{CF_3CO_2H \\ CH_2Cl_2 \\ 25^\circ}]{CF_3CO_3H}$ [bridgehead O–COC_6H_5] $\xrightarrow[\text{diethylene glycol}]{\text{NaOH}}$ bridgehead OH (90%) (*Ref. 53*)

electron-donating substituents and retarded by the presence of electron-withdrawing substituents. The relative ease of migration of the various groups in the Baeyer-Villiger reaction has been suggested to reflect the ability of the migrating group to accept a partial positive charge in the transition state. However, this property, arising from the electronic distribution in the migrating group, cannot be the only factor determining migratory aptitude. In rearrangements involving the migration of groups to electron-deficient carbon atoms, different reactions and different reaction conditions result in different orders of migratory aptitude.

The reactions of peracids with several cyclic ketones ([**60**]–[**62**]) have been studied[60] to examine the suggestion[61] that a chairlike transition state (e.g., [**63**]) should be favored over a boatlike transition state (e.g., [**64**]) in the Baeyer-Villiger migration step. Although the mechanistic interpretation of the results obtained is

[60] CH_3CO_3H, CH_3CO_2Na, CH_3CO_2H, 27° → (75% of product) + (25% of product) (*Refs. 60a, b*)

[60] CH_3CO_3H, H_2SO_4, CH_3CO_2H, 27° → (30%)

[61] CH_3CO_3H, CH_3CO_2Na, CH_3CO_2H, 25° → (88%) (*Ref. 60c*)

[62] CH_3CO_3H, CH_3CO_2Na, CH_3CO_2H, 25° → (94%) (*Ref. 60b*)

O–OCOCH$_3$, OH → **[63]** (HO, O····OCOCH$_3$) →

→ **[64]** (O····OCOCH$_3$, OH) →

not clear, it is apparent that factors other than the electronic distribution in the migrating group may influence the relative ease of

(60) (a) R. R. Sauers, *J. Am. Chem. Soc.*, **81,** 925 (1959); (b) R. R. Sauers and G. P. Ahearn, *ibid.*, **83,** 2759 (1961); (c) J. Meinwald and E. Frauenglass, *ibid.*, **82,** 5235 (1960); A. Rassat and G. Ourisson, *Bull. Soc. Chim. France*, **1959,** 1133; (d) R. R. Sauers and J. A. Beisler, *J. Org. Chem.*, **29,** 210 (1964).

(61) M. F. Murray, B. A. Johnson, R. L. Pederson, and A. C. Ott, *J. Am. Chem. Soc.*, **78,** 981 (1956).

migration. Furthermore, the different results obtained by oxidizing camphor **[60]** on the one hand in neutral and on the other in strongly acidic media illustrate the fact that reaction conditions may influence the reaction course.

Aldehydes react with peracids to form either carboxylic acids or formate esters; 1,2-dicarbonyl compounds are oxidized to acid anhydrides (or acids after hydrolysis) with peracids.[50] These two classes of compounds are also frequently oxidized with hydrogen peroxide in alkaline solution, as illustrated by the oxidations of **[65]** and **[66]**. The reaction of a carbonyl group with alkaline

CHO, OH, OCH_3 **[65]** $\xrightarrow[H_2O,\ 40\text{–}50°]{H_2O_2,\ NaOH}$ OH, OH, OCH_3 (68–80%) (*Ref.* 62)

CH_3O, CH_3O –CH_2—CO—CO_2H **[66]** $\xrightarrow[H_2O,\ 25°]{H_2O_2,\ NaOH}$ CH_3O, CH_3O –CH_2CO_2H (*Ref.* 63)

hydrogen peroxide is believed to proceed as indicated in the accompanying equations; in the oxidation of α-keto acids, the intermediate **[67]** presumably undergoes protonation followed by loss of carbon dioxide and hydroxide ion rather than rearrangement. Monoketones are also cleaved by reaction with hydrogen

$$R'(R)C{=}O + HOO^{\ominus} \rightleftharpoons R'\text{–}C(O^{\ominus})(R)\text{–}O\text{–}OH \longrightarrow R'\text{–}C(=O)\text{–}O\text{–}R \xrightarrow[OH^{\ominus}]{H_2O} R'\text{—}CO_2^{\ominus} + ROH$$

[67]

peroxide or an alkyl hydroperoxide in alkaline solution.[64] Although this oxidation is of interest because the direction of cleavage

(62) A. R. Surrey, *Org. Syn.*, **Coll. Vol. 3,** 759 (1955).

(63) H. R. Snyder, J. S. Buck, and W. S. Ide, *Org. Syn.*, **Coll. Vol. 2,** 333 (1943).

(64) (a) H. O. House and R. L. Wasson, *J. Org. Chem.*, **22,** 1157 (1957); (b) K. Maruyama, *Bull. Chem. Soc. Japan*, **33,** 1516 (1960); **34,** 102, 105 (1961).

sometimes differs from that observed in a Baeyer-Villiger reaction (e.g., **[68]**), it is currently of little preparative value because of the poor yields obtained.

$$C_6H_5{-}CO{-}CH_2CH_2CH_3 \xrightarrow[CH_3OH,\ reflux]{H_2O_2,\ NaOH} C_6H_5CO_2H + CH_3CH_2CH_2OH + CH_3CH_2CO_2H$$

[68] $C_6H_5CO_2H$ (11%); + starting ketone (81% recovered)

(*Ref.* 64*a*)

Oxidation of Amines

Tertiary amines (e.g., **[69]** and **[70]**) are oxidized by either hydrogen peroxide or peracids to produce amine oxides that serve

$$C_6H_{11}{-}CH_2{-}N(CH_3)_2 \xrightarrow[CH_3OH,\ 25^\circ]{H_2O_2} C_6H_{11}{-}CH_2{-}\overset{\oplus}{N}(CH_3)_2{-}O^{\ominus}$$

[69] (*Ref.* 65)

$$C_5H_5N \xrightarrow[CH_3CO_2H,\ 85^\circ]{CH_3CO_3H} C_5H_5\overset{\oplus}{N}{-}O^{\ominus}$$

[70] (76–83% as the hydrochloride) (*Ref.* 66)

as useful synthetic intermediates.[67,68] The mechanism of this oxidation is presumably analogous to the epoxidation of olefins, involving an electrophilic attack by the peracid to transfer an oxygen atom to the amine. Although the same initial step may be involved in the reaction of peracids with primary and secondary amines, the initial product, a hydroxylamine derivative after transfer of a proton, is susceptible to further oxidation. Nitrones are formed by the oxidation of secondary aliphatic amines with peracids, and nitroso compounds result from the oxidation of primary amines (e.g., **[71]**); the nitroso compounds may be oxidized further to nitro compounds.[69] Peroxytrifluoroacetic acid has been

(65) A. C. Cope and E. Ciganek, *Org. Syn.*, **Coll. Vol. 4,** 612 (1963).

(66) H. S. Mosher, L. Turner, and A. Carlsmith, *ibid.*, **Coll. Vol. 4,** 828 (1963).

(67) A. R. Katritzky, *Quart. Rev.* (*London*), **10,** 395 (1956).

(68) A. C. Cope and E. R. Trumbull, *Org. Reactions*, **11,** 317 (1960).

(69) W. D. Langley, *Org. Syn.*, **Coll. Vol. 3,** 334 (1955).

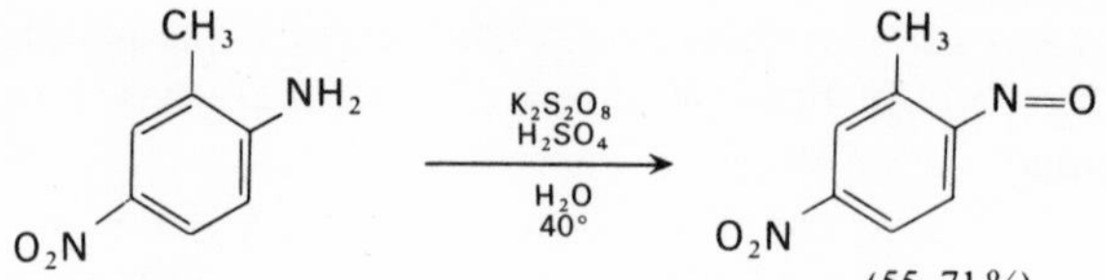

[71] $\xrightarrow[H_2O,\ 40°]{K_2S_2O_8,\ H_2SO_4}$ (55–71%) (*Ref. 69*)

found a useful reagent for the direct oxidation of primary aromatic amines (e.g., **[72]**) to nitro compounds[70] as well as for the oxidation of other nitrogen-containing compounds.[71] Although peroxytrifluoroacetic acid has proved unsuitable for the oxidation of primary aromatic amines that contain electron-donating groups (e.g., **[73]**), amines of this type have been oxidized to nitro compounds with anhydrous peracetic acid.

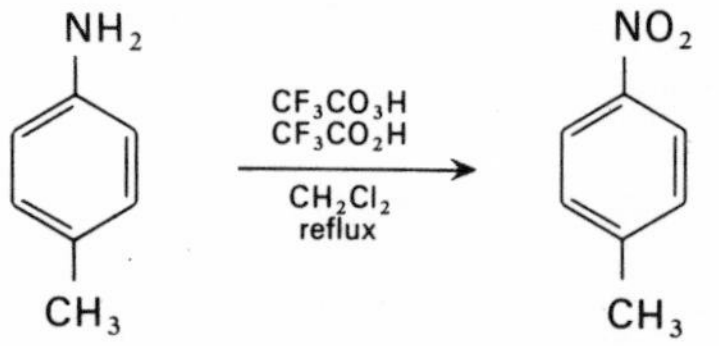

[72] $\xrightarrow[CH_2Cl_2,\ reflux]{CF_3CO_3H,\ CF_3CO_2H}$ (78%) (*Ref. 70*)

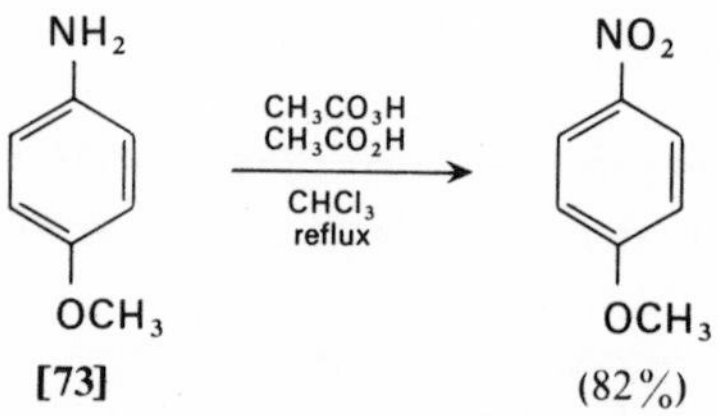

[73] $\xrightarrow[CHCl_3,\ reflux]{CH_3CO_3H,\ CH_3CO_2H}$ (82%) (*Ref. 70*)

Oxidation at Allylic Carbon-Hydrogen Bonds

Although allylic C—H bonds are susceptible to attack by a wide variety of free radicals to form allylic radicals and, subsequently, allyl derivatives, perhaps the most convenient route to

(70) W. D. Emmons, *J. Am. Chem. Soc.*, **76,** 3470 (1954); **79,** 5528 (1957).

(71) (a) W. D. Emmons, *J. Am. Chem. Soc.*, **76,** 3468 (1954); (b) W. D. Emmons and A. S. Pagano, *ibid.*, **77,** 4557 (1955): for a discussion of the oxidation of primary amines to nitro compounds with peracids and with potassium permanganate, see N. Kornblum, *Org. Reactions*, **12,** 101 (1962); for an example of the use of potassium permanganate to oxidize a primary amine to a nitro compound, see N. Kornblum and W. J. Jones, *Org. Syn.*, **43,** 87 (1963).

allyl alcohol derivatives involves the reaction of the hydrocarbon (e.g., **[74]**) with a perester in the presence of cuprous ion. The

$$\text{cyclohexene [74]} + C_6H_5{-}CO{-}OOC(CH_3)_3 \xrightarrow[\substack{\text{excess cyclohexene}\\ \text{(as solvent)}\\ \text{reflux}}]{CuBr} \text{3-(}O{-}CO{-}C_6H_5\text{)cyclohexene (73\%)} + (CH_3)_3COH$$

(Ref. 72)

commonly employed peresters are the commercially available[73] *t*-butyl esters of perbenzoic and peracetic acid. Mechanism studies point to the operation of a chain reaction following the path indicated in the accompanying equations.[74] As would be anticipated in

$$CH_3CO{-}O{-}OC(CH_3)_3 + Cu^{\oplus} \longrightarrow CH_3CO_2^{\ominus}Cu^{\oplus} + (CH_3)_3C{-}O\cdot$$

$$(CH_3)_3C{-}O\cdot + \text{cyclohexene} \longrightarrow (CH_3)_3COH + \text{cyclohexenyl radical} \longleftrightarrow \text{cyclohexenyl radical}$$

$$\text{cyclohexenyl radical} + CH_3CO_2^{\ominus}Cu^{\oplus} \longrightarrow Cu^{\oplus} + \text{cyclohexenyl cation} + CH_3CO_2^{\ominus} \longrightarrow \text{3-(}O{-}COCH_3\text{)cyclohexene}$$

the case of an intermediate allylic free radical, reaction with an unsymmetrical olefin (e.g., **[75]**) leads to a mixture of isomeric products. It is of interest that the major product formed from a

$$\underset{[75]}{n\text{-}C_5H_{11}{-}CH_2{-}CH{=}CH_2} \xrightarrow[\substack{C_6H_5Cl\\ 70^\circ}]{\substack{CH_3CO_3C(CH_3)_3\\ CuCl}} \underset{(87\%\text{ of product})}{n\text{-}C_5H_{11}{-}\underset{OCOCH_3}{CH}{-}CH{=}CH_2} + \underset{(13\%\text{ of product})}{n\text{-}C_5H_{11}{-}CH{=}CH{-}CH_2{-}OCOCH_3}$$

(Ref. 74c)

(72) (a) M. S. Kharasch, G. Sosnovsky, and N. C. Yang, *J. Am. Chem. Soc.*, **81,** 5819 (1959); (b) G. Sosnovsky and N. C. Yang, *J. Org. Chem.*, **25,** 899 (1960); (c) for an example of the reaction of a Grignard reagent with *t*-butyl perbenzoate to form a *t*-butyl ether, see C. Frisell and S. O. Lawesson, *Org. Syn.*, **43,** 55 (1963).

(73) Lucidol Div., Wallace and Tiernan Corp., Buffalo, N.Y.

(74) (a) J. K. Kochi, *Tetrahedron*, **18,** 483 (1962); (b) J. K. Kochi, *J. Am. Chem. Soc.*, **84,** 774 (1962); (c) C. Walling and A. A. Zavitsas, *ibid.*, **85,** 2084 (1963).

terminal olefin such as **[75]** is the allylic ester with a terminal double bond. The reason for this product distribution is not yet clear. From the oxidation of the cyclohexyl system **[76]** the major product isolated was the ester of an axial alcohol. Both the initial abstraction of a hydrogen atom and the final attack of the benzoate anion on the allylic carbonium ion **[77]** would be expected to occur from an axial direction in order that continuous pi-orbital overlap be maintained (i.e., stereoelectronic control).

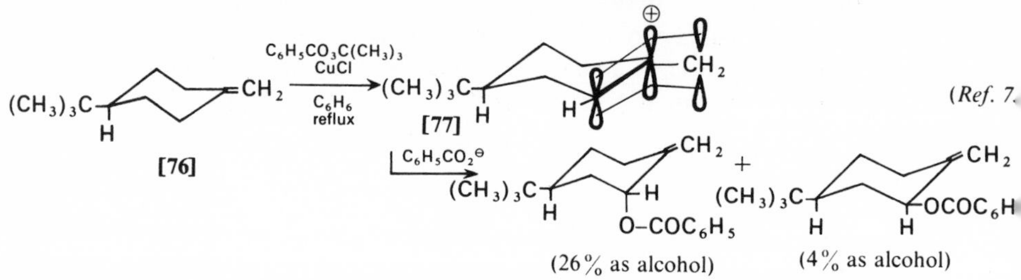

$(CH_3)_3C$ ... $=CH_2$ **[76]** $\xrightarrow[C_6H_6,\ \text{reflux}]{C_6H_5CO_3C(CH_3)_3,\ CuCl}$ **[77]** $\xrightarrow{C_6H_5CO_2^{\ominus}}$ $O\text{–}COC_6H_5$ (26% as alcohol) + $OCOC_6H_5$ (4% as alcohol)

(*Ref. 75*)

Reaction of the diene **[78]** with *t*-butyl perbenzoate was found to yield an ether that appeared to arise from attack at a nonallylic position. However, subsequent investigation demonstrated that the reaction occurred by initial addition of the *t*-butoxy radical to the olefin followed by oxidation of the carbon radical with cupric

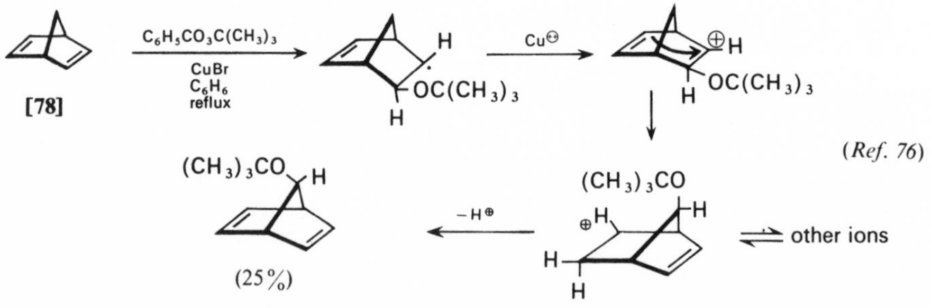

[78] $\xrightarrow[CuBr,\ C_6H_6,\ \text{reflux}]{C_6H_5CO_3C(CH_3)_3}$ $OC(CH_3)_3$ $\xrightarrow{Cu^{\ominus}}$ $OC(CH_3)_3$ → $(CH_3)_3CO$ ⇌ other ions

$\xrightarrow{-H^{\oplus}}$ $(CH_3)_3CO$ (25%)

(*Ref. 76*)

ion and rearrangement, as illustrated. The copper-catalyzed reaction of peresters has also proved useful for the oxidation of benzylic

(75) B. Cross and G. H. Whitham, *J. Chem. Soc.*, **1961,** 1650.

(76) (a) P. R. Story, *J. Org. Chem.*, **26,** 287 (1961); (b) P. R. Story, *Tetrahedron Letters,* **No. 9,** 401 (1962).

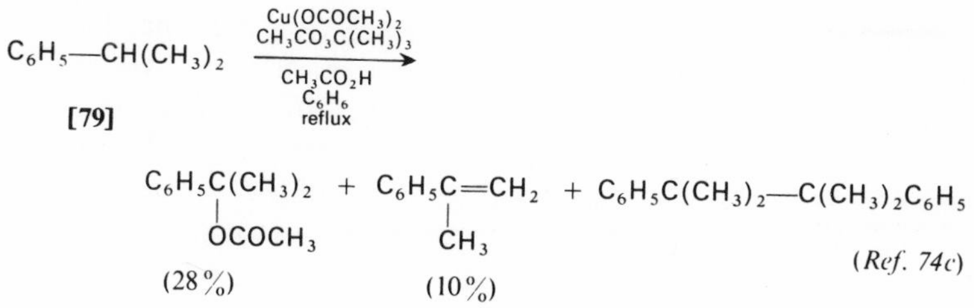

$$C_6H_5{-}CH(CH_3)_2 \xrightarrow[\substack{CH_3CO_2H \\ C_6H_6 \\ \text{reflux}}]{\substack{Cu(OCOCH_3)_2 \\ CH_3CO_3C(CH_3)_3}}$$

[79]

$$\underset{(28\%)}{\underset{\substack{| \\ OCOCH_3}}{C_6H_5C(CH_3)_2}} + \underset{(10\%)}{\underset{\substack{| \\ CH_3}}{C_6H_5C{=}CH_2}} + C_6H_5C(CH_3)_2{-}C(CH_3)_2C_6H_5$$

(*Ref.* 74*c*)

C—H bonds (e.g., **[79]**), of alpha C—H bonds in ethers[77] and thioethers,[78] as well as of other activated C—H bonds.[72b]

(77) (a) S. O. Lawesson and C. Berglund, *Tetrahedron Letters*, **No. 2,** 4 (1960); (b) G. Sosnovsky, *Tetrahedron*, **13,** 241 (1961).

(78) (a) G. Sosnovsky, *ibid.*, **18,** 15 (1962); G. Sosnovsky and H. J. O'Neill, *J. Org. Chem.*, **27,** 3469 (1962); (c) S. O. Lawesson and C. Berglund, *Acta Chem. Scand.*, **15,** 36 (1961).

6

HALOGENATION

ALTHOUGH A VARIETY OF METHODS have been used to introduce halogen atoms into organic molecules, the discussion here will cover only reactions between halogens or halogen derivatives and carbon-carbon double bonds, introduction of halogen atoms alpha to a carbonyl function, and substitution of halogen atoms for hydrogen atoms at allylic or benzylic C—H bonds; the preparation of fluorine-containing compounds will not be considered. Both the substitution of halogen for hydrogen and the addition of halogen to a multiple bond bear a formal resemblance to previously discussed oxidation reactions. In fact, many of the intermediates formed in halogenation reactions may be converted to products (e.g., 1,2-diols, epoxides, carbonyl compounds) also available from oxidation procedures.

Reactions with Carbon-Carbon Double Bonds

Solutions of bromine in carbon tetrachloride, chloroform, carbon disulfide, acetic acid, ether, or ethyl acetate are usually employed for reaction with olefins (e.g., [**1**] and [**2**]) to form 1,2-dibromides. The corresponding reactions with iodine to form thermally unstable

$$C_6H_5CH{=}CHCOC_6H_5 \; [1] \xrightarrow[\text{CCl}_4 \text{ or } CS_2,\ \text{ice bath}]{Br_2} C_6H_5CHBr{-}CHBrCOC_6H_5 \; (84\%)$$ (*Ref. 1*)

$$\text{cyclohexene} \; [2] \xrightarrow[\text{CCl}_4,\ -5 \text{ to } -1^\circ]{Br_2} \textit{trans}\text{-1,2-dibromocyclohexane} \; (95\%)$$ (*Ref. 2*)

1,2-diiodides and with chlorine to form 1,2-dichlorides also occur but are less often used in the laboratory. The crystalline complex from pyridine hydrobromide and bromine (pyridinium bromide perbromide)[3] has also found limited use[4] for the bromination of both olefins and ketones. The addition of bromine to an unhindered carbon-carbon double bond is often so rapid that the reaction may be performed as a titration, the bromine reacting with the olefin as quickly as it is introduced into the reaction mixture. Consequently, bromine will add to olefinic double bonds in the presence of aldehyde (e.g., **[3]**), ketone (e.g., **[4]**), ester (e.g., **[5]**), alcohol (e.g., **[6]**), carboxylic acid, or amide functions without serious competing reactions.

$$C_6H_5CH{=}CH{-}CHO \; [3] \xrightarrow[CH_3CO_2H]{Br_2} C_6H_5CHBr{-}CHBr{-}CHO$$ (*Ref. 5*)

(75–85%, isolated after dehydrobromination)

$$C_6H_5CH{=}CHCOCH_3 \; [4] \xrightarrow[\text{CCl}_4,\ 10\text{–}20^\circ]{Br_2} C_6H_5CHBr{-}CHBrCOCH_3$$ (*Ref. 6*)

(52–57%)

(1) C. F. H. Allen, R. D. Abell, and J. B. Normington, *Org. Syn.*, **Coll. Vol. 1,** 205 (1944).

(2) H. R. Snyder and L. A. Brooks, *Org. Syn.*, **Coll. Vol. 2,** 171 (1943).

(3) Commercially available from Arapahoe Chemicals, Inc., Boulder, Colorado.

(4) (a) C. Djerassi and C. R. Scholz, *J. Am. Chem. Soc.*, **70**, 417 (1948); (b) L. F. Fieser, *Experiments in Organic Chemistry*, Heath, Boston, 1955, pp. 65, 180.

(5) C. F. H. Allen and C. O. Edens, Jr., *Org. Syn.*, **Coll. Vol. 3,** 731 (1955).

(6) N. H. Cromwell and R. Benson, *ibid.*, **Coll. Vol. 3,** 105 (1955).

[5] $\xrightarrow[\text{CCl}_4,\ 0°]{\text{Br}_2}$ (83–85%) (*Ref. 7*)

[6] $\xrightarrow[\text{NaOCOCH}_3,\ \text{CH}_3\text{CO}_2\text{H},\ (\text{C}_2\text{H}_5)_2\text{O}]{\text{Br}_2}$ (84–85%) (*Ref. 8*)

The reaction of bromine with an olefin is thought to proceed by electrophilic attack of the bromine on the double bond to form an intermediate pi complex or bromonium ion [**7**]. This intermediate may also be represented as the resonance hybrid [**8**]; in some cases at least, carbonium ion structures [**8a**] or [**8c**] possibly serve as better representations than does the bromonium ion [**7**]. However represented, the intermediate is susceptible to further attack by a nucleophile such as bromide ion, the result being the over-all *trans* addition of two bromine atoms to the double bond. The

[**7**] (contains 1% of *meso* isomer) (*Ref. 9*)

[**8a**] ⟷ [**8b**] ⟷ [**8c**]

[**9**]

(7) T. W. Abbott and D. Althousen, *Org. Syn.*, **Coll. Vol. 2**, 270 (1943).

(8) (a) L. F. Fieser, *Org. Syn.*, **Coll. Vol. 4**, 195 (1963); (b) L. F. Fieser and M. Fieser, *Steroids*, Reinhold, New York, 1959, pp. 37–41.

(9) (a) W. G. Young, R. T. Dillon, and H. J. Lucas, *J. Am. Chem. Soc.*, **51**, 2528 (1929); (b) S. Winstein and H. J. Lucas, *ibid.*, **61**, 1576 (1939); (c) H. O. House and R. S. Ro, *ibid.*, **80**, 182 (1958).

reaction of the intermediate bromonium ion with a nucleophile is similar in many respects to the previously discussed (Chapter 5) acid-catalyzed ring opening of epoxides, which is believed to proceed by attack of the nucleophile on the conjugate acid [**9**] of the epoxide. Not only is the reaction of bromine with olefins a *trans* addition, as several of the foregoing examples illustrate, but the predominant product from the addition of bromine to a conformationally rigid cyclohexane is a *trans* diaxial dibromide.[10] This stereochemical result is illustrated, both by the aforementioned[8] bromination of cholesterol [**6**] to form the dibromide [**10**] via the bromonium ion [**11**], and by the bromination of 2-cholestene [**12**]. In each case the initial bromonium ion was produced by attack of the halogen from the less hindered side

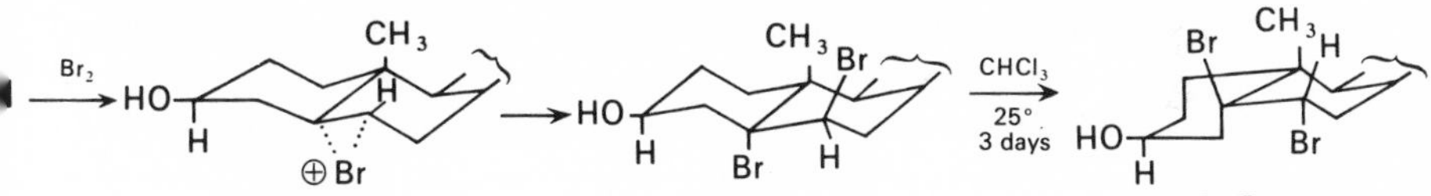

Br_2 → [**11**] → [**10**] $\xrightarrow[\text{25°, 3 days}]{CHCl_3}$ [**14**]

(*Refs. 8, 11*)

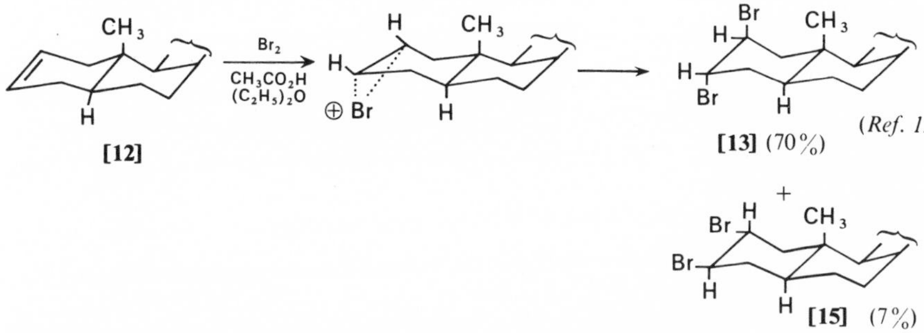

[**12**] $\xrightarrow[CH_3CO_2H, (C_2H_5)_2O]{Br_2}$ → [**13**] (70%) + [**15**] (7%)

(*Ref. 12*)

of the double bond. The initially formed *trans* diaxial dibromides [**10**] and [**13**] were found to rearrange on standing or heating to become the more stable *trans* diequatorial dibromides [**14**] and [**15**], respectively. This diaxial-to-diequatorial rearrangement, which presumably occurs[12,13] by formation and collapse of the ion pair

(10) D. H. R. Barton and R. C. Cookson, *Quart. Rev.* (*London*), **10,** 44 (1956).

(11) (a) D. H. R. Barton and E. Miller, *J. Am. Chem. Soc.*, **72**, 1066 (1950); (b) D. H. R. Barton, E. Miller, and H. T. Young, *J. Chem. Soc.*, **1951**, 2598.

(12) G. H. Alt and D. H. R. Barton, *ibid.*, **1954,** 4284.

(13) C. A. Grob and S. Winstein, *Helv. Chim. Acta*, **35**, 782 (1952).

[16], has been suggested to be general for compounds containing *trans* diaxial substituents.[14]

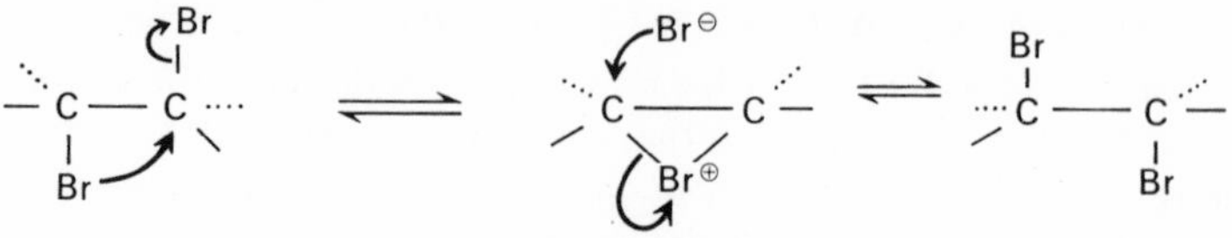

[16]

Although the addition of chlorine to many olefins appears to follow the same mechanistic path as that of bromine,[12] examples of the *cis* addition of chlorine to certain olefins (e.g., **[17]**) have been reported,[15] leading to the suggestion[16] that at least in some cases, intermediate chlorocarbonium ions (analogs of **[8a]** and **[8c]**) rather than chloronium ions (analogs of **[7]**) are involved.

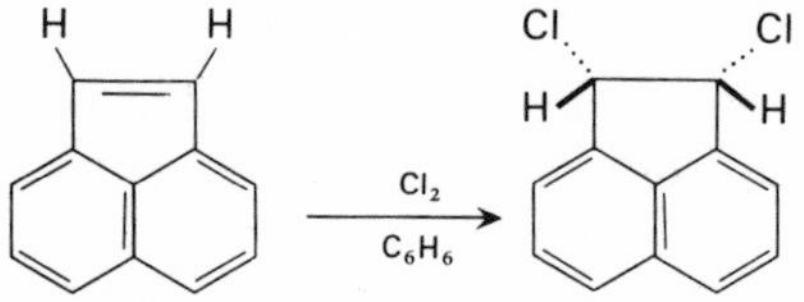

Cl_2, C_6H_6

[17] (27%) (*Ref. 15*)

The reaction of bromine with an olefin to form a 1,2-dibromide does not differ fundamentally from its reaction with an aromatic compound (e.g., **[18]**) to substitute a bromine atom for an aromatic

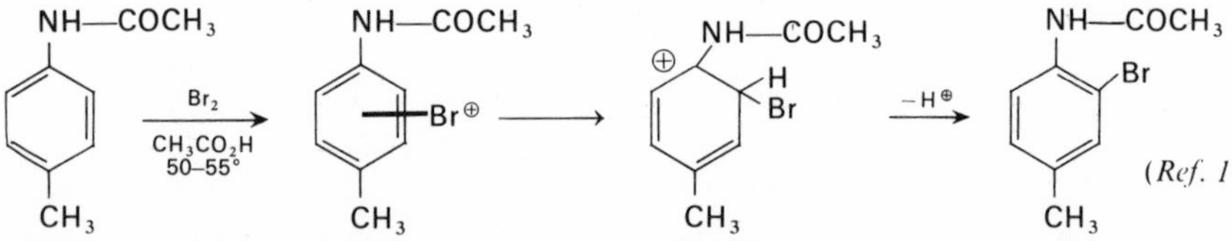

Br_2, CH_3CO_2H, 50–55°; $-H^{\oplus}$

[18] **[19]** **[20]** (79%) (*Ref. 17*)

hydrogen atom. Aromatic bromination is usually regarded as an electrophilic attack of bromine (or a complex of bromine with a Lewis acid) on the aromatic ring to produce successively a pi

(14) D. H. R. Barton and J. F. King, *J. Chem. Soc.*, **1958**, 4398.

(15) S. J. Cristol, F. R. Stermitz, and P. S. Ramey, *J. Am. Chem. Soc.*, **78**, 4939 (1956).

(16) M. J. S. Dewar and R. C. Fahey, *ibid.*, **85**, 2245, 2248, 3645 (1963).

(17) J. R. Johnson and L. T. Sandborn, *Org. Syn.*, **Coll. Vol. 1,** 111 (1944).

complex [**19**], a sigma complex [**20**], and, after loss of a proton, the bromo derivative. Thus, this substitution reaction differs from the conversion of an olefin to a dibromide only in the sense that loss of a proton from the intermediate bromine-containing cation is energetically favored over addition of a bromide ion to form another carbon-bromine bond. A similar situation exists in the reaction of bromine with enols, which will be considered subsequently.

As would be anticipated from the above discussion, the intermediate bromonium ion formed from bromine and an olefin may react with any nucleophile in the reaction medium. For example, the olefin [**21**] will react with bromine in methanol solution to produce both a dibromide and a methoxybromide. Reactions of this type have greater preparative value when an

$C_6H_5(H)C{=}C(H)C_6H_5$ [**21**] $\xrightarrow[CH_3OH,\ 0°]{Br_2}$ $C_6H_5CH(Br)-CH(OCH_3)C_6H_5$ + $C_6H_5CH(Br)-CH(Br)C_6H_5$ (*Ref. 18*)

N-bromoamide (such as N-bromosuccinimide[3] or N-bromoacetamide[3,19]) is used as the source of the positive bromine, allowing the concentration of bromide ion to be kept low and minimizing dibromide formation. The preparation of bromohydrin derivatives by this method, illustrated in the accompanying equations, is believed to involve an electrophilic attack on the olefin

$CH_3(H)C{=}C(H)CH_3$ $\xrightarrow[H_2SO_4,\ CH_3OH,\ 0–25°]{CH_3CONH—Br}$ $CH_3CH(Br)-CH(OCH_3)CH_3$ (50%) (*Ref. 20*)

$C_6H_5—CH{=}CH_2$ [**22**] $\xrightarrow[H_2O,\ 25°]{\text{N-bromosuccinimide } (CH_2—CO)_2N—Br}$ $C_6H_5—CH(HO)—CH_2—Br$ (82%) (*Ref. 21*)

(18) P. D. Bartlett and D. S. Tarbell, *J. Am. Chem. Soc.*, **58**, 466 (1936).

(19) Directions for the preparation of this amide have been provided by E. P. Oliveto and C. Gerold, *Org. Syn.*, **Coll. Vol. 4,** 104 (1963).

(20) (a) S. Winstein and R. B. Henderson, *J. Am. Chem. Soc.*, **65**, 2196 (1943); (b) for the analogous preparation of bromohydrins, see Ref. 9b.

(21) C. O. Guss and R. Rosenthal, *J. Am. Chem. Soc.*, **77**, 2549 (1955).

by the protonated bromoamide to form a bromonium ion. In the absence of the previously discussed conformational factors (favoring opening of the intermediate to give a *trans* diaxial

$$CH_3-C(=\overset{\oplus}{O}H)-NH-Br + >C{=}C< \longrightarrow >C-C< \text{ (bridged by } \overset{\oplus}{Br}\text{, attacked by } OH_2) \xrightarrow{-H^{\oplus}} >C(Br)-C(OH)<$$

product), the predominant product from subsequent reaction of the bromonium ion with the nucleophile is the isomer in which bromine is bonded to the less highly substituted carbon atom. This orientation, illustrated by the reactions of olefins **[22]** and **[23]**, presumably reflects the fact that the more important contributor

$$\underset{\textbf{[23]}}{(CH_3)_2C{=}CH_2} \xrightarrow[KBr,\ H_2O]{Br_2} (CH_3)_2C(OH)-CH_2Br \qquad (\textit{Ref. 22})$$

to the bromonium ion is that structure (**[8a]** or **[8c]**) in which carbon is better able to tolerate a positive charge. Since secondary alcohols are readily oxidized to ketones by reaction with N-bromoacetamide or N-bromosuccinimide[23] in aqueous acetone or aqueous *t*-butyl alcohol, the preparation of bromohydrins utilizing these reagents may be complicated by the further oxidation of the bromohydrin to a bromoketone.

Although chlorohydrins may be similarly prepared by the reaction of olefins with N-chloroamides in aqueous acid[24] or with a preformed aqueous solution of hypochlorous acid,[25] perhaps the most convenient procedure utilizes hypochlorous acid generated

$$CH_3-CH{=}CH-CH_3 \xrightarrow[CH_3CO_2H,\ H_2O]{Ca(ClO)_2} \underset{(55\%)}{CH_3-CH(OH)-CH(Cl)-CH_3} + CH_3-CH(Cl)-CH(Cl)-CH_3 \qquad (\textit{Ref. 26})$$

(22) (a) C. M. Suter and H. D. Zook, *ibid.*, **66**, 738 (1944); (b) H. O. House, *ibid.*, **77**, 5083 (1955).

(23) (a) L. F. Fieser and S. Rajagopalan, *J. Am. Chem. Soc.*, **71**, 3935, 3938 (1949); **72**, 5530 (1950); **73**, 118 (1951); (b) H. L. Herzog, M. A. Jevnik, and E. B. Hershberg, *ibid.*, **75**, 269 (1953); (c) R. Filler, *Chem. Rev.*, **63**, 21 (1963).

(24) H. B. Donahoe and C. A. Vanderwerf, *Org. Syn.*, **Coll. Vol. 4**, 157 (1963).

(25) G. H. Coleman and H. F. Johnstone, *Org. Syn.*, **Coll. Vol. 1,** 158 (1944).

(26) C. E. Wilson and H. J. Lucas, *J. Am. Chem. Soc.*, **58**, 2396 (1936).

from calcium hypochlorite in the reaction mixture. The reaction of bromohydrins or chlorohydrins (e.g., **[24]**) with bases offers a useful route to epoxides and is often a more satisfactory method

[24] $\xrightarrow[H_2O]{NaOH}$ (70–73%) (*Ref. 27*)

for the preparation of low-molecular-weight epoxides than is the direct reaction of the olefin with a peracid.

The formation of bromohydrin or iodohydrin esters as a result of reaction between a bromonium or iodonium ion and a carboxylate anion is most readily accomplished using an olefin (e.g., **[25]**), equimolar amounts of silver acetate or benzoate, and iodine or bromine[28] in an inert solvent such as carbon tetrachloride, chloroform, or ether. Under these circumstances the halogen and the silver carboxylate react to produce an acyl

[25] $\xrightarrow[\text{1 equiv. } I_2,\ (C_2H_5)_2O,\ \text{reflux}]{\text{1 equiv. } CH_3CO_2Ag}$ (O—$COCH_3$, I) (80%) (*Ref. 28a*)

hypohalite (e.g., CH_3CO—O—I), which either can undergo thermal decomposition (presumably via free-radical chain mechanism) to form an alkyl or aryl halide (the Hunsdiecker reaction[28a]) or can add to an olefin. The latter process is thought to be an ionic

CH_3CO–O–I ⟶ ($\ominus$ O-$COCH_3$, I $\oplus$) ⟶ (O—$COCH_3$, I)

(27) A. E. Osterberg, *Org. Syn.*, **Coll. Vol. 1,** 185 (1944).

(28) (a) C. V. Wilson, *Org. Reactions*, **9**, 332 (1957); an improved procedure for the Hunsdiecker reaction utilizing bromine and mercuric oxide with the carboxylic acid has been described: S. J. Cristol and W. C. Firth, *J. Org. Chem.*, **26**, 280 (1961); J. S. Meek and D. T. Osaga, *Org. Syn.*, **43**, 9 (1963); (b) F. D. Gunstone in R. A. Raphael, E. C. Taylor, and H. Wynberg (eds.), *Advances in Organic*

reaction in which the acyl hypoiodite attacks the olefin to form an iodonium ion that is in turn attacked by the carboxylate ion, resulting in over-all *trans* addition. Two molar equivalents of the silver salt treated with one equivalent of iodine will produce a complex ($C_6H_5CO_2Ag \cdot C_6H_5CO_2I$, called a Simonini complex) which also adds the elements of the acyl hypoiodite to an olefin. If the resulting mixture is subsequently heated in an inert solvent

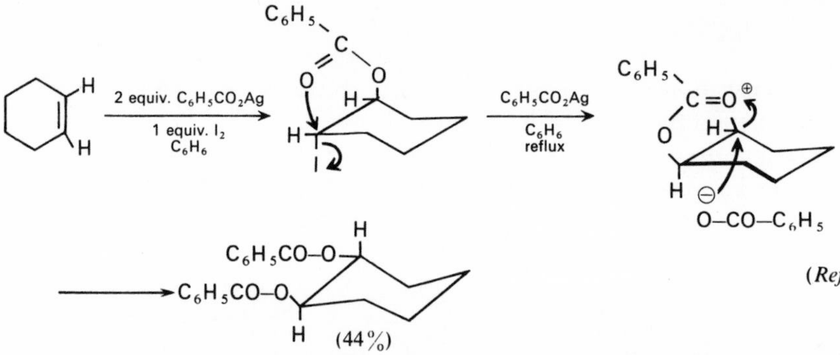

(*Ref. 29*)

(usually anhydrous benzene), the further changes indicated in the accompanying equations occur to form a *trans*-diol diester which may be saponified to form a *trans*-diol. This reaction sequence, called the Prevost reaction, involves two nucleophilic displacements with inversion of configuration and results in the over-all *trans* addition of two oxygen functions to the double bond. A useful modification of the process utilizes an olefin with silver acetate and iodine in acetic acid. In the second stage of this reaction, the oxonium ion intermediate **[26]** is produced in the presence of at least one equivalent of water and under these conditions undergoes hydrolysis (rather than a second nucleophilic displacement) to form a hydroxy acetate. Subsequent saponification leads to a diol **[27]** whose stereochemistry corresponds to *cis* addition of the two hydroxyl groups from the more hindered side of the double bond. The direction of this *cis* hydroxylation is of particular interest since it is opposite to that from the less hindered side (to form diol **[28]**) which is observed with osmium tetroxide or potassium permanganate.

Chemistry: Methods and Results, Vol. 1, Wiley-Interscience, New York, 1960, pp. 117–124.

(29) G. E. McCasland and E. C. Horswill, *J. Am. Chem. Soc.*, **76**, 1654 (1954).

2 equiv. CH_3CO_2Ag, 1 equiv. I_2, CH_3CO_2H → H_2O, CH_3CO_2H, 90–95° → [26] (*Ref. 30*)

H_2O → (mixture of hydroxy acetate) → KOH, CH_3OH → [27] (71%) + [28] (3%)

The reaction of an iodonium or bromonium ion intermediate with a carboxylate ion in the absence of silver ion occurs readily if an intramolecular reaction is sterically favorable. The process, called halolactonization, is illustrated in the accompanying examples. This reaction, which is believed to proceed by intramolecular attack of the carboxylate anion on the iodonium ion

I_2, KI, $NaHCO_3$, H_2O → [29] → (88%) (*Ref. 31*)

Br_2, $CHCl_3$ → (69%) + (*Ref. 32*)

(30) R. B. Woodward and F. V. Brutcher, Jr., *ibid.*, **80**, 209 (1958); see also (b) C. B. Anderson, E. C. Friedrick, and S. Winstein, *Tetrahedron Letters*, **No. 29**, 2037 (1963); (c) C. A. Bunton and M. D. Carr, *J. Chem. Soc.*, **1963**, 770.

(31) (a) E. E. van Tamelen and M. Shamma, *J. Am. Chem. Soc.*, **76**, 2315 (1954); (b) J. Klein, *ibid.*, **81**, 3611 (1959).

(32) G. Berti, *Tetrahedron*, **4**, 393 (1958).

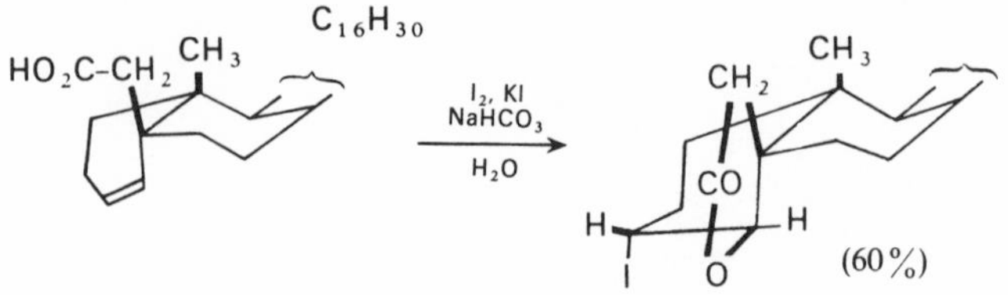

$C_{16}H_{30}$ $HO_2C\text{-}CH_2$ CH_3 $\xrightarrow[H_2O]{I_2,\ KI,\ NaHCO_3}$ (60%) (*Ref. 33*)

as in structure [**29**], provides a useful method for the conversion of unsaturated acids (e.g., [**30**]) to halolactones and, after hydrogenolysis,[34] to saturated lactones. It has also been useful for separating and assigning stereochemistry to unsaturated acids

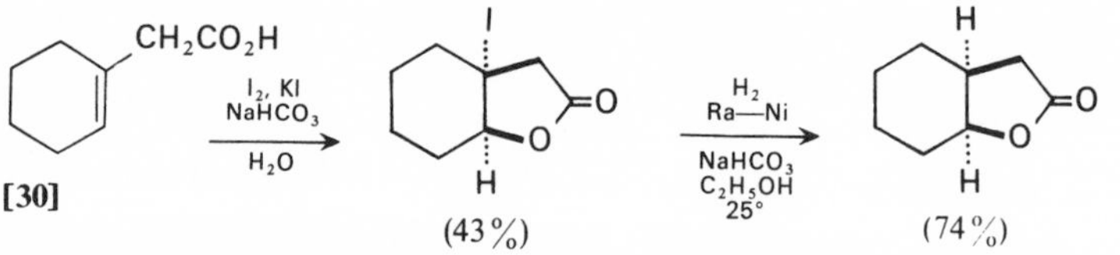

[**30**] CH_2CO_2H $\xrightarrow[H_2O]{I_2,\ KI,\ NaHCO_3}$ (43%) $\xrightarrow[NaHCO_3,\ C_2H_5OH,\ 25°]{H_2,\ Ra\text{—}Ni}$ (74%) (*Ref. 31b*)

(e.g., [**31**]) in cases where only one epimeric acid is capable of forming an iodolactone.

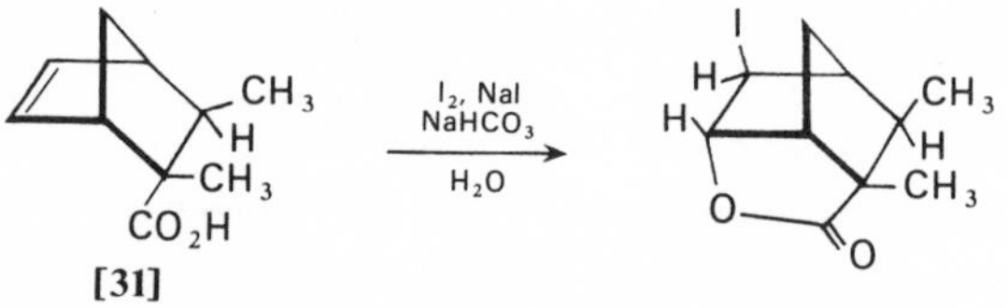

[**31**] $\xrightarrow[H_2O]{I_2,\ NaI,\ NaHCO_3}$ (*Ref. 35*)

Halogenation of Carbonyl Compounds

As the accompanying equations illustrate, the reaction conditions employed for the bromination or chlorination of ketones are often similar to those used for the addition of a halogen to olefins. Common solvents employed include carbon tetrachloride, chloroform, ether, and acetic acid. The reaction is catalyzed by acid and, if no acid is present initially (as when carbon tetrachloride or chloroform is used as solvent), often exhibits an induction period

(33) A. W. Burgstahler and I. C. Nordin, *J. Am. Chem. Soc.*, **83**, 198 (1961).

(34) For other hydrogenolysis procedures, see (a) R. Grewe, A. Heinke, and C. Sommer, *Chem. Ber.*, **89**, 1978 (1956); (b) H. W. Whitlock, Jr., *J. Am. Chem. Soc.*, **84**, 3412 (1962); (c) Ref. 35a.

(35) (a) S. Beckmann and H. Geiger, *Chem. Ber.*, **92**, 2411 (1959); see also (b) J. Meinwald, S. S. Labana, and M. S. Chadha, *J. Am. Chem. Soc.*, **85**, 582 (1963) and (c) J. A. Berson and A. Remanick, *ibid.*, **83**, 4947 (1961).

$$Br-C_6H_4-CO-CH_3 \xrightarrow[CH_3CO_2H,\ 20°]{Br_2} Br-C_6H_4-CO-CH_2Br$$ (*Ref. 36*)

(69–72%)

$$\text{cycloheptanone} \xrightarrow[\text{CCl}_4,\ \text{reflux}]{(CH_2CO)_2N-Br,\ [(CH_3)_2C(C\equiv N)-N=]_2} \text{2-bromocycloheptanone}$$ (*Ref. 37a*)

$$\text{2-methylcyclohexanone} \xrightarrow[CCl_4,\ 25°]{SO_2Cl_2} \text{2-chloro-2-methylcyclohexanone}$$ (*Ref. 38*)

(83–85%)

until some hydrogen bromide has been generated in the reaction mixture. Apart from adding acid, the bromination or chlorination of ketones may be initiated by holding a light bulb next to the reaction flask.

The reaction of a ketone with bromine proceeds by the acid-catalyzed enolization of the ketone and subsequent electrophilic attack on the enol by bromine; loss of a proton from the intermediate oxonium ion [32] leads to the bromoketone. For the

$$CH_3-CO-CH_3 \underset{}{\overset{H^{\oplus}}{\rightleftharpoons}} CH_2(H)-C(=\overset{\oplus}{O}H)-CH_3 \rightleftharpoons CH_2=C(OH)-CH_3 \xrightarrow{Br_2} Br-CH_2-C(=\overset{\oplus}{O}H)-CH_3 \xrightarrow{-H^{\oplus}}$$

base; [32]

$$Br-CH_2-CO-CH_3$$

(36) W. D. Langley, *Org. Syn.*, **Coll. Vol. 1,** 127 (1944).

(37) (a) E. J. Corey, *J. Am. Chem. Soc.*, **75**, 2301, 3297, 4832 (1953); **76**, 175 (1954); (b) E. J. Corey, T. H. Topie, and W. A. Wozniak, *ibid.*, **77**, 5415 (1956); (c) E. J. Corey and H. J. Burke, *ibid.*, **77**, 5418 (1955); (d) E. J. Corey and R. A. Sneen, *ibid.*, **78**, 6269 (1956).

(38) (a) E. W. Warnhoff, D. G. Martin, and W. S. Johnson, *Org. Syn.*, **Coll. Vol. 4,** 162 (1963); (b) for further studies of the chlorination of ketones with sulfuryl chloride, see D. P. Wyman and P. R. Kaufman, *J. Org. Chem.*, **29**, 1956 (1964); D. P. Wyman, P. R. Kaufman, and W. R. Freeman, *ibid.*, **29**, 2706 (1964).

majority of ketones, which exist largely in the keto rather than the enol form, enolization is the rate-limiting step and the over-all rate of halogenation is independent of the nature or concentration of the halogen. It will be noted that the formation of the enol requires the presence of both an acid and a base. In inert solvents such as carbon tetrachloride or chloroform, the only base present is the unprotonated ketone; a large excess of a Lewis acid such as aluminum chloride serves to convert all the ketone to its conjugate acid and to prevent enolization. The following equations illustrate the use of this technique to prevent bromination alpha to a carbonyl function; the technique has also found utility in other types of

$$C_6H_5{-}CO{-}CH_3 \xrightarrow[\text{cat. amt. } AlCl_3,\ (C_2H_5)_2O,\ 0^\circ]{Br_2} C_6H_5{-}CO{-}CH_2{-}Br \quad (88\text{–}96\%) \quad (\textit{Ref. 39})$$

$$C_6H_5{-}CO{-}CH_3 \xrightarrow[\text{2.5 equiv. } AlCl_3,\ 80\text{–}85^\circ]{Br_2} m\text{-}BrC_6H_4{-}CO{-}CH_3 \quad (70\text{–}75\%) \quad (\textit{Ref. 40})$$

reactions.[41] Although halogenations of ketones with N-bromosuccinimide or with sulfuryl chloride (SO_2Cl_2) are frequently initiated by light, a peroxide, or some other free-radical initiator, it appears likely that once an appreciable concentration of halogen acid has accumulated in the reaction mixture these halogenations, too, proceed by an ionic mechanism involving electrophilic attack on the enol. The use of N-bromosuccinimide for ketone bromination offers the advantage that little hydrogen bromide, which may catalyze aldol condensation of the ketone, is produced in the reaction mixture. Alternatively, as illustrated below, aqueous potassium chlorate may be used to remove hydrogen bromide during direct bromination of ketones.

In the bromination of unsymmetrical ketones, the position taken by the entering bromine is determined by the relative ease of formation of the structurally isomeric enols. In general, this ease of

(39) R. M. Cowper and L. H. Davidson, *Org. Syn.*, **Coll. Vol. 2,** 480 (1943).

(40) (a) D. E. Pearson, H. W. Pope, and W. W. Hargrove, *Org. Syn.*, **40**, 7 (1960); (b) D. E. Pearson, H. W. Pope, W. W. Hargrove, and W. E. Stamper, *J. Org. Chem.*, **23**, 1412 (1958); (c) D. E. Pearson, W. E. Stamper, and B. R. Suthers, *ibid.*, **28**, 3147 (1963).

(41) (a) H. O. House, V. Paragamian, R. S. Ro, and D. J. Wluka, *J. Am. Chem. Soc.*, **82**, 1457 (1960); (b) C. G. Swain and A. S. Rosenberg, *ibid.*, **83**, 2154 (1961).

formation is enhanced by the presence of alpha alkyl substituents or other unsaturated alpha substituents, which stabilize the enol by forming a conjugated system. Consequently, the predominant isomer produced on bromination of a ketone is normally that in which the bromine atom has entered the more highly substituted alpha position, as illustrated in the accompanying equations. However, the presence of an alpha halogen substituent retards

$$CH_3{-}CO{-}CH_2CH_2CH_3 \xrightarrow[\substack{H_2O\\40\text{–}45^\circ\\\text{light}}]{Br_2,\ KClO_3} \underset{(53\%)}{CH_3{-}CO{-}\underset{Br}{\underset{|}{CH}}{-}CH_2CH_3} + \underset{(32\%)}{BrCH_2{-}CO{-}CH_2CH_2CH_3}$$

(*Ref. 42*)

$$CH_3{-}CO{-}CH(CH_3)_2 \xrightarrow[\substack{H_2O\\40\text{–}45^\circ\\\text{light}}]{\substack{Br_2\\KClO_3}} \underset{(35\%)}{CH_3{-}CO{-}\underset{Br}{\underset{|}{C}}(CH_3)_2}$$

the rate of enol formation. As a result, the substitution of each successive halogen atom becomes more difficult, making it possible to introduce one, two, three, or more halogen atoms into a ketone in controlled fashion simply by limiting the amount of halogen added. A quite different order of reactivity is found for the base-catalyzed halogenations of ketones, where the halogen reacts with the enolate anion **[33]** rather than with the enol. In these reactions,

$$CH_3{-}\underset{O}{\underset{\|}{C}}{-}CH_3 \underset{}{\overset{\text{base}}{\rightleftharpoons}} \underset{[33]}{CH_3{-}\underset{O^{\ominus}}{\underset{|}{C}}{=}CH_2} \xrightarrow{Br_2} CH_3{-}\underset{O}{\underset{\|}{C}}{-}CH_2{-}Br$$

the rate of enolate formation is retarded by alpha alkyl substituents and enhanced by alpha halogen substituents. As a result, base-catalyzed halogenation is usually of no value for the preparation of monohaloketones; however, it is used for the conversion of methyl ketones (e.g., **[34]** and **[35]**) to trihalomethyl ketones, which are usually cleaved in the basic reaction mixture to form acids and trihalomethanes (the haloform reaction[43]). The successful degradation of the unsaturated ketone **[35]** is interesting because halogenation of the enolate is more rapid than reaction at the carbon-carbon double bond of the ketone.

(42) J. R. Catch, D. H. Hey, E. R. H. Jones, and W. Wilson, *J. Chem. Soc.*, **1948**, 276.
(43) R. C. Fuson and B. A. Bull, *Chem. Rev.*, **15**, 275 (1934).

$$(CH_3)_3C{-}CO{-}CH_3 \xrightarrow[\substack{NaOH\\H_2O\\0^\circ}]{Br_2} (CH_3)_3C{-}\overset{\overset{}{}}{C}(=O){-}CBr_3 \xrightarrow{OH^\ominus} (CH_3)_3C{-}C(OH)(O^\ominus){-}CBr_3 \xrightarrow{H_3O^\oplus}$$

[34]

$$HCBr_3 + (CH_3)_3C{-}CO_2H$$

(71–74%) (*Ref.* 44)

$$(CH_3)_2C{=}CH{-}CO{-}CH_3 \xrightarrow[\substack{H_2O\\dioxane}]{KOCl} \xrightarrow{H_3O^\oplus} (CH_3)_2C{=}CH{-}CO_2H + CHCl_3$$

[35] (49–53%) (*Ref.* 45)

The position of bromination of 3-ketosteroids (e.g., **[36]** and **[37]**) is determined not only by the presence of alpha substituents but also by the stereochemistry of the A-B ring junction. The tendency

[36] $\xrightarrow[CH_3CO_2H]{C_5H_5N^\oplus H\ Br_3^\ominus}$ 2-bromo product (81%) (*Refs.* 4a, 37a)

[37] $\xrightarrow[CH_3CO_2H]{C_5H_5N^\oplus H\ Br_3^\ominus}$ 4-bromo product (61%) (*Refs.* 4a, 46)

of the *trans*-fused system to brominate selectively at position 2 has been attributed to the instability of a $\Delta^{3,4}$ double bond,[47] which results, at least in part, from repulsion between axial substituents at C-6 and C-10.[47b,48] The position and stereochemistry of a bromine atom in an α-bromoketone produced by ketone

(44) L. T. Sandborn and E. W. Bousquet, *Org. Syn.*, **Coll. Vol. 1,** 526 (1944).

(45) L. I. Smith, W. W. Pritchard, and L. J. Spillane, *Org. Syn.*, **Coll. Vol. 3,** 302 (1955).

(46) (a) L. F. Fieser and R. Ettorre, *J. Am. Chem. Soc.*, **75**, 1700 (1953); (b) L. F. Fieser and X. A. Dominguez, *ibid.*, **75**, 1704 (1953).

(47) (a) See Ref. 8b, pp. 276–279; (b) E. J. Corey and R. A. Sneen, *J. Am. Chem. Soc.*, **77**, 2505 (1955).

(48) (a) C. Djerassi, N. Finch, R. C. Cookson, and C. W. Bird, *ibid.*, **82**, 5488 (1960); (b) R. Mauli, H. J. Ringold, and C. Djerassi, *ibid.*, **82**, 5494 (1960); (c) R. Villotti, H. J. Ringold, and C. Djerassi, *ibid.*, **82**, 5693 (1960).

bromination may further depend on the reaction conditions employed, since the most rapidly formed bromoketone (kinetically controlled product) may be isomerized to a more stable bromoketone (thermodynamically controlled product) by the hydrogen bromide also formed in the reaction mixture. This acid-catalyzed isomerization, illustrated by the accompanying examples, may result either from enolization and reketonization of the bromoketone (as is probably the case for ketone **[38]**) or from reaction of

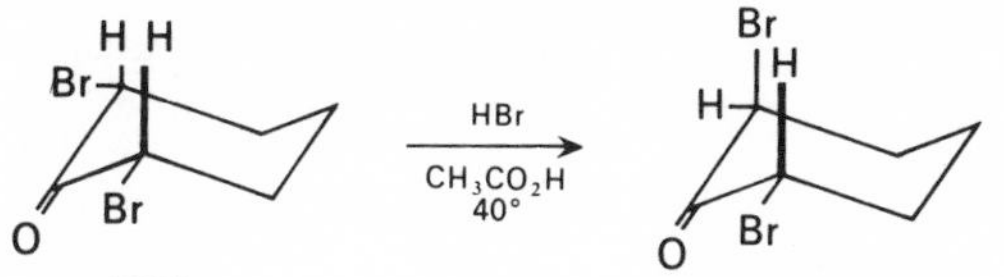

[38] $\xrightarrow[CH_3CO_2H,\ 40°]{HBr}$ (85% of mixture at equilibrium) (*Ref. 37a*)

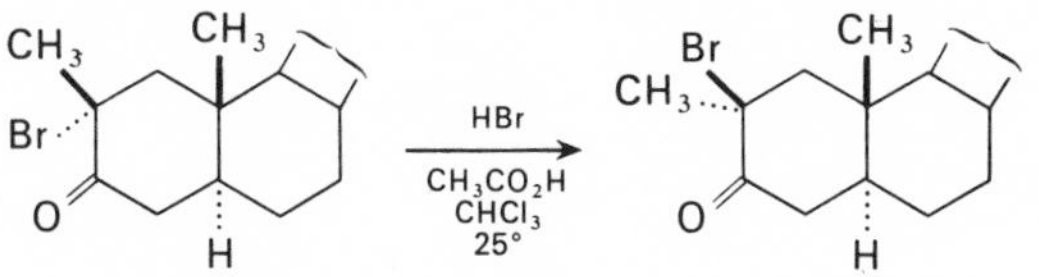

[39] $\xrightarrow[CH_3CO_2H,\ CHCl_3,\ 25°]{HBr}$ (*Ref. 48*)

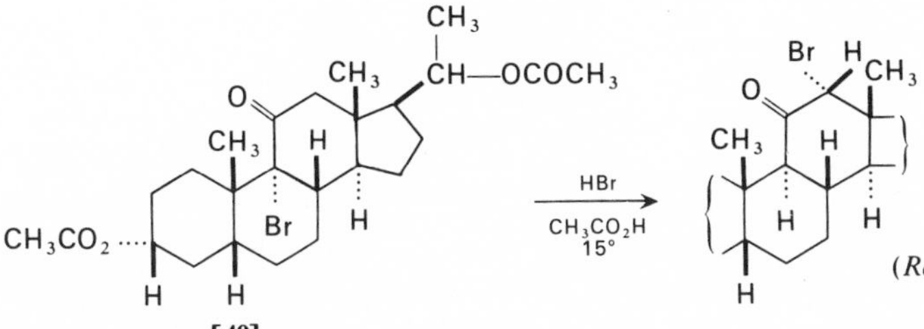

[40] $\xrightarrow[CH_3CO_2H,\ 15°]{HBr}$ (*Ref. 49*)

the protonated ketone with bromide ion (as in **[41]**) or some other nucleophile to produce an enol that undergoes isomerization and rebromination. This latter sequence is clearly necessary to explain the isomerization of ketones **[39]** and **[40]**. To obtain the kinetically controlled product from a ketone bromination, the reaction is

(49) (a) E. R. H. Jones and D. J. Wluka, *J. Chem. Soc.*, **1959**, 907, 911; (b) for an example of this isomerization in an acyclic system, see M. D. Mehta, D. Miller, and D. J. D. Tidy, *ibid.*, **1963**, 4614.

$$\text{[41]}\quad \text{CH-C-C-Br (protonated, } H\text{-}O^{\oplus}) + Br^{\ominus} \longrightarrow \text{CH—C=C(OH)} \rightleftharpoons \text{C=C(OH)—CH} \xrightarrow{Br_2} \text{Br—C—C(=O)—CH}$$

commonly run in acetic acid containing excess sodium acetate[48,50] or pyridine[48,49] to react with the hydrogen bromide as it is formed.

An alternative method for preparing a bromoketone of known structure consists of converting the ketone (e.g., **[42]**) to its enol acetate, which is then treated with bromine and sodium acetate or pyridine in acetic acid to form the desired product. Since the

$$\textbf{[42]} \xrightarrow[\substack{p\text{-}CH_3C_6H_4SO_3H \\ \text{reflux}}]{(CH_3CO)_2O} \text{enol acetates} \xrightarrow[\substack{CH_3CO_2H \\ 20^\circ \text{ or } 17^\circ}]{Br_2,\ C_5H_5N} \text{bromoketones } (62\%),\ (45\%)$$

(*Ref*

$$CH_3(CH_2)_4CH_2\text{—}CHO \xrightarrow[\substack{CH_3CO_2K \\ \text{reflux}}]{(CH_3CO)_2O} CH_3(CH_2)_4CH{=}CH\text{—}OCOCH_3 \xrightarrow[\substack{CCl_4 \\ 10^\circ}]{Br_2} [CH_3(CH_2)_4CHBr\text{—}CHBr\text{—}OCOCH_3]$$

$$\xrightarrow{CH_3OH} CH_3(CH_2)_4CHBr\text{—}CH(OCH_3)_2 \ (80\text{–}85\%) \xrightarrow[\substack{H_2O \\ \text{reflux}}]{HCl} CH_3(CH_2)_4CHBr\text{—}CHO \ (90\text{–}95\%) \quad (\textit{Ref. 51})$$

(50) (a) C. W. Shoppee, G. A. R. Johnston, and R. E. Lack, *J. Chem. Soc.*, **1962**, 3604; (b) C. W. Shoppee and T. E. Bellas, *ibid.*, **1963**, 3366.

(51) (a) P. Z. Bedoukian, *Org. Syn.*, **Coll. Vol. 3,** 127 (1955); (b) ketals of α-bromoketones have been prepared by reaction of the ketal with pyridinium bromide perbromide or with phenyltrimethylammonium tribromide: see P. E. Eaton,

direct bromination of aldehydes is often complicated by a competing reaction with the aldehyde C—H bond, a similar procedure involving bromination of an enol acetate is useful for the preparation of α-bromoaldehydes.

Stereochemical studies[37,46,48–50] of the bromination of cyclohexanone derivatives have been aided by physical measurements, which serve to define the conformation and configuration of the alpha bromine atom. Of special value have been infrared spectrometry,[37,52,53] ultraviolet spectrometry,[54] nuclear magnetic resonance spectrometry,[55] dipole moment data,[53] and optical rotatory dispersion data.[48,56] The stereochemistry of bromination of enols and enol acetates appears to be controlled by two factors that may either oppose or reinforce one another. The stereoelectronic factor,[37] which is applicable to cyclohexanone derivatives, may be illustrated by the accompanying equations. The energetically most favorable transition states for removal of an alpha proton (e.g., **[43]** and **[45]**) to form the enol **[47]** and for addition of a bromine atom (e.g., **[44]** and **[46]**) to form the product are those in which continuous overlap of the *p* orbitals involved is possible. If only the usually[57] more stable chair forms **[48]** and **[49]** of the starting material and product are considered, it is clear that there should be a preference for the removal of the axial proton H_a

---

J. Am. Chem. Soc., **84**, 2344 (1962); W. S. Johnson, J. D. Bass, and K. L. Williamson, *Tetrahedron*, **19**, 861 (1963).

(52) (a) R. N. Jones, D. A. Ramsay, F. Herling, and K. Dobriner, *J. Am. Chem. Soc.*, **74**, 2828 (1952); (b) R. N. Jones, *ibid.*, **75**, 4839 (1953); (c) J. Fishman, *J. Org. Chem.*, **27**, 1745 (1962).

(53) (a) J. Allinger and N. L. Allinger, *Tetrahedron*, **2**, 64 (1958); (b) N. L. Allinger, J. Allinger, and N. A. Lebel, *J. Am. Chem. Soc.*, **82**, 2926 (1960); for other α-haloketones, see N. L. Allinger and H. M. Blatter, *J. Org. Chem.*, **27**, 1523 (1962) and references therein.

(54) (a) R. C. Cookson, *J. Chem. Soc.*, **1954**, 282; (b) R. C. Cookson and S. H. Dandegaonker, *ibid.*, **1955**, 352; (c) C. Djerassi, H. Wolf, and E. Bunnenberg, *J. Am. Chem. Soc.*, **85**, 324 (1963).

(55) (a) A. Nickon, M. A. Castle, R. Harada, C. E. Berkoff, and R. O. Williams, *J. Am. Chem. Soc.*, **85**, 2185 (1963); (b) R. J. Abraham and J. S. E. Holker, *J. Chem. Soc.*, **1963**, 806; (c) see also K. L. Williamson and W. S. Johnson, *J. Am. Chem. Soc.*, **83**, 4623 (1961); (d) E. W. Garbisch, Jr., *ibid.*, **86**, 1780 (1964).

(56) C. Djerassi, *Optical Rotatory Dispersion*, McGraw-Hill, New York, 1960, pp. 115–131.

(57) For a review of instances where the boat form of a cyclohexane ring appears to be preferred, see M. Balasubramanian, *Chem. Rev.*, **62**, 591 (1962).

and for the addition of the bromine at an axial bond. However, the importance of this preference should diminish in proportion to the degree to which the transition states **[43]** and **[44]** resemble the planar enol **[47]** rather than the ketones **[48]** and **[49]**, and there is reason to believe that these transition states do resemble the enol rather than the ketones.[37d,58] The second factor of concern is the steric interference that exists in the transition states for proton removal (**[43]** and **[45]**) and for bromine addition (**[44]** and **[46]**). It is apparent that if serious steric interactions exist in the

base H R H_a R H_e O H-O H [48] [43] Br Br R H-O H [44] Br R H O [49] HO R H [47] R H_a O H_e H-O H H base [45] R H-O H Br Br [46] R H O Br R H O Br [50]

chairlike transition states **[43]** and **[44]**, the enolization and bromination may proceed via the boatlike transition states **[45]** and **[46]** and still allow continuous *p*-orbital overlap.

In general, the existence of one 1,3-diaxial interaction between bromine and a group larger than hydrogen in the chairlike transition state **[44]** appears to be sufficient cause for enols and

(58) (a) H. E. Zimmerman in P. deMayo (ed.), *Molecular Rearrangements*, Wiley-Interscience, New York, 1963, pp. 345–372; (b) H. Shechter, M. J. Collis, R. Dessy, Y. Okuzumi, and A. Chen, *J. Am. Chem. Soc.*, **84**, 2905 (1962).

enol acetates to react with bromine via the alternative transition state **[46]**, leading to an equatorial bromoketone **[50]** in conformationally fixed systems.[48,50,59] In the absence of such 1,3-diaxial interactions, the predominant product is usually the axial bromoketone anticipated on stereoelectronic grounds. The brominations of ketones **[51]** and **[52]** illustrate these generalities. The quite different behavior of ketones **[53]** and **[54]** on bromination illustrates

CH_3 — **[51]** $\xrightarrow[CH_3CO_2H,\ CCl_4,\ 25°]{Br—Cl,\ CH_3CO_2Na}$ Br, CH_3 (42%) *(Ref. 48)*

CH_3 — **[52]** $\xrightarrow[CH_3CO_2H]{Br_2}$ Br, CH_3 *(Ref. 50)*

the importance of steric factors in the reactions of ketones that are not cyclohexanone derivatives. The enol **[55]** from **[53]** is again brominated from the less hindered side. However, because of the substantial steric interference to the existence of the isomeric ketone **[54]** in a conformation that would permit removal of the tertiary alpha proton while maintaining continuous *p*-orbital overlap, this isomer enolizes in a different direction to form a structurally isomeric bromoketone.

CO—CH_3, C_6H_5 — **[53]** $\xrightarrow[CH_3CO_2H]{Br_2}$ C—OH, CH_3, C_6H_5 — **[55]** $\longrightarrow$ CO—CH_3, Br, C_6H_5 (67%) *(Ref. 60)*

CO—CH_3, C_6H_5 — **[54]** $\xrightarrow[CH_3CO_2H]{Br_2}$ CO—CH_2Br, C_6H_5 + CO—$CHBr_2$, C_6H_5 *(Ref. 60)*

(59) E. W. Warnhoff, *J. Org. Chem.*, **28**, 887 (1963).
(60) H. E. Zimmerman, *J. Am. Chem. Soc.*, **79**, 6554 (1957).

α-Haloketones serve as useful synthetic intermediates since they may be dehydrohalogenated[61] (e.g., **[55]**) or reduced with sodium borohydride to form halohydrins. The bromohydrins formed in this way are often different stereoisomers from those available by the direct addition of hypobromous acid to olefins or by the opening of epoxides with hydrogen bromide, and they have been used to form epoxides (e.g., **[56]**: cf. Chapter 5) that are stereoisomeric with those obtained by direct reaction of the corresponding olefin with a peracid. Also, the fact that halohydrins (e.g., **[57]**), regardless of their stereochemistry,[62] react readily with zinc to form olefins offers a convenient synthesis for olefins of known structure.

[55] — reflux (2,4,6-collidine); LiCl, $(CH_3)_2NCHO$, N_2 atmosphere, 100–110° — (43–49%) (*Ref. 38*)

$NaBH_4$, $(C_2H_5)_2O$, CH_3OH — (43%) — KOH, $(CH_3)_2CHOH$ — **[56]** (76%) (*Ref. 37a*)

$NaBH_4$, C_2H_5OH, 25° — **[57]** (both epimers) — Zn, CH_3CO_2H, reflux — (80–85%) (*Ref. 46*)

Although bromine may be introduced alpha to a nitrile function (e.g., **[58]**) by direct bromination, such a reaction is normally not

(61) Aside from the dehydrohalogenation methods illustrated for the chloroketone **[55]**, α-haloketones have also been dehydrohalogenated by reaction with 2,4-dinitrophenylhydrazine or with semicarbazide: see (a) Ref. 51b; (b) T. H. Kritchevsky, D. L. Garmaise, and T. F. Gallagher, *J. Am. Chem. Soc.*, **74**, 483 (1952); (c) W. F. McGuckin and E. C. Kendall, *ibid.*, **74**, 5811 (1952).

(62) S. J. Cristol and L. E. Rademacher, *J. Am. Chem. Soc.*, **81**, 1600 (1959).

$$C_6H_5{-}CH_2{-}CN \xrightarrow[105\text{–}110^\circ]{Br_2} C_6H_5{-}CH(Br){-}CN \qquad (Ref.\ 63)$$
[58]

a satisfactory procedure for monocarboxylic esters (which usually react at the carbon alpha to the ethereal oxygen) or for monocarboxylic acids (which usually do not react). However, malonic esters (e.g., **[59]**) and malonic acids (e.g., **[60]**) will react with

$$CH_2(CO_2C_2H_5)_2 \xrightarrow[\text{CCl}_4\ \text{(initiated with light)}]{Br_2} BrCH(CO_2C_2H_5)_2 \qquad (Ref.\ 64a)$$
[59] (73–75%)

$$(CH_3)_2CH{-}CH(CO_2C_2H_5)_2 \xrightarrow[\text{H}_2\text{O, reflux}]{KOH} \xrightarrow[\text{H}_2\text{O}]{HCl} (CH_3)_2CH{-}CH(CO_2H)_2 \xrightarrow[(C_2H_5)_2O,\ \text{reflux}]{Br_2}$$
[60]

$$(CH_3)_2CH{-}C(Br)(CO_2H)_2 \xrightarrow[125\text{–}130^\circ]{} (CH_3)_2CH{-}CH(Br){-}CO_2H \qquad (Ref.\ 64b)$$
(55–66%)

bromine. The latter reaction followed by decarboxylation serves as a convenient route to α-bromocarboxylic acids.

If carboxylic acids are first converted to their acid chloride, bromide, or anhydride derivatives, bromination alpha to the carbonyl group occurs readily. The reaction is frequently effected by adding bromine to the carboxylic acid in the presence of a catalytic amount of phosphorus trichloride, phosphorus tribromide, or phosphorus (which is converted to the tribromide in the reaction mixture). This method, the Hell-Volhard-Zelinsky reaction, relies upon an equilibrium between the small amount of brominated acid halide (or anhydride) present and the starting acid to permit complete bromination. Examples of the various procedures are provided in the following equations.

$$CH_3(CH_2)_3CH_2CO_2H \xrightarrow[\text{cat. amt. PCl}_3,\ 65\text{–}70^\circ]{Br_2} CH_3(CH_2)_3CH(Br)CO_2H \qquad (Ref.\ 65)$$
(83–89%)

(63) C. M. Robb and E. M. Schultz, *Org. Syn.*, **Coll. Vol. 3,** 347 (1955).

(64) (a) C. S. Palmer and P. W. McWherter, *Org. Syn.*, **Coll. Voll. 1,** 245 (1944); (b) C. S. Marvel and V. duVigneaud, *Org. Syn.*, **Coll. Vol. 2,** 93 (1943).

(65) H. T. Clarke and E. R. Taylor, *Org. Syn.*, **Coll. Vol. 1,** 115 (1944).

$$CH_3CO_2H + (CH_3CO)_2O \xrightarrow[C_5H_5N \text{ reflux}]{Br_2} \xrightarrow{H_2O} BrCH_2CO_2H \ (80\text{–}85\%) \qquad (Ref.\ 66)$$

$$HO_2C(CH_2)_4CO_2H \xrightarrow[\text{reflux}]{SOCl_2} Cl\text{—}CO(CH_2)_4CO\text{—}Cl \xrightarrow{Br_2} Cl\text{—}CO\text{—}CH(Br)(CH_2)_2CH(Br)\text{—}CO\text{—}Cl$$

$$\xrightarrow{C_2H_5OH} C_2H_5O_2C\text{—}CH(Br)(CH_2)_2CH(Br)\text{—}CO_2C_2H_5 \ (91\text{–}97\%) \qquad (Ref.\ 67)$$

$$(CH_3)_2CH\text{—}CO_2H \xrightarrow[P,\ 100^\circ]{Br_2} (CH_3)_2C(Br)\text{—}CO\text{—}Br \ (75\text{–}83\%) \qquad (Ref.\ 68)$$

$$CH_3(CH_2)_9CH(CH_3)\text{—}CO_2H \xrightarrow[PBr_3,\ 85\text{–}90^\circ]{Br_2} CH_3(CH_2)_9C(CH_3)(Br)\text{—}CO\text{—}Br \xrightarrow{(CH_3)_3COH}$$

$$CH_3(CH_2)_9C(CH_3)(Br)\text{—}CO_2C(CH_3)_3 \qquad (Ref.\ 69)$$

Substitution of Halogen at Benzylic and Allylic Carbon-Hydrogen Bonds

Unlike the previously discussed halogenations, the majority of reactions that substitute bromine or chlorine at an allylic or benzylic position are free-radical chain processes.[70] They are frequently run at elevated temperatures or make use of free-radical initiators such as light, a peroxide [usually dibenzoyl peroxide, $C_6H_5CO\text{—}OO\text{—}COC_6H_5$, or di-*t*-butyl peroxide, $(CH_3)_3C\text{—}OO\text{—}C(CH_3)_3$], or an azo compound [usually azobisisobutyronitrile, $(CH_3)_2C(CN)\text{—}N{=}N\text{—}C(CN)CH_3)_2$]. The commonly employed chlorinating agents are molecular chlorine, sulfuryl chloride

(66) S. Natelson and S. Gottfried, *Org. Syn.*, **Coll. Vol. 3,** 381 (1955).

(67) P. C. Guha and D. K. Sankaran, *ibid.*, **Coll. Vol. 3,** 623 (1955).

(68) C. W. Smith and D. G. Norton, *Org. Syn.*, **Coll. Vol. 4,** 348 (1963).

(69) C. F. Allen and M. J. Kalm, *ibid.*, **Coll. Vol. 4,** 608 (1963).

(70) (a) C. Walling, *Free Radicals in Solution,* Wiley, New York, 1957, pp. 347–396; (b) see, however, M. L. Poutsma, *J. Am. Chem. Soc.*, **85**, 3511 (1963).

(SO_2Cl_2), trichloromethanesulfonyl chloride, and *t*-butyl hypochlorite,[71,72] whereas either molecular bromine or N-bromosuccinimide[3,73] is normally used for bromination.

In the absence of other reactive functional groups, halogenation at a benzylic position is most readily effected with molecular bromine or chlorine as in the accompanying examples.

$O_2N-C_6H_4-CH_3 \xrightarrow[145\text{–}150°]{Br_2} O_2N-C_6H_4-CH_2Br$ (53–59%) (*Ref. 74*)

$Cl-C_6H_4-CH_3 \xrightarrow[160\text{–}170°,\ light]{Cl_2,\ PCl_5} Cl-C_6H_4-CHCl_2 \xrightarrow{H_2SO_4,\ H_2O} Cl-C_6H_4-CHO$ (54–60%) (*Ref. 75*)

$o\text{-}Cl-C_6H_4-CHO \xrightarrow[140\text{–}160°]{Cl_2} o\text{-}Cl-C_6H_4-CO-Cl$ (70–72%) (*Ref. 76*)

Phthalide $\xrightarrow[140\text{–}155°]{Br_2}$ 3-bromophthalide (CH–Br) (82–83%) (*Ref. 77*)

(71) The preparation of this reagent is described by H. M. Teeter and E. W. Bell, *Org. Syn.*, **Coll. Vol. 4,** 125 (1963).

(72) (a) C. Walling and B. B. Jacknow, *J. Am. Chem. Soc.*, **82**, 6108, 6113 (1960); (b) C. Walling and W. Thaler, *ibid.*, **83**, 3877 (1961); (c) C. Walling and P. S. Fredricks, *ibid.*, **84**, 3326 (1962).

(73) (a) C. Djerassi, *Chem. Rev.*, **43**, 271 (1948); (b) T. D. Waugh, *N-Bromosuccinimide: Its Reactions and Uses,* Arapahoe Chemicals, Inc., Boulder, Colorado, 1951; (c) H. J. Dauben and L. L. McCoy, *J. Am. Chem. Soc.*, **81**, 4863, 5404 (1959).

(74) G. H. Coleman and G. E. Honeywell, *Org. Syn.*, **Coll. Vol. 2,** 443 (1943).

(75) W. L. McEwen, *ibid.*, **Coll. Vol. 2,** 133 (1943).

(76) H. T. Clarke and E. R. Taylor, *Org. Syn.*, **Coll. Vol. 1,** 155 (1944).

(77) R. L. Shriner and F. J. Wolf, *Org. Syn.*, **Coll. Vol. 3,** 737 (1955).

The course of these reactions is illustrated in the scheme below. The hydrogen-abstraction step in the reactions constituting the propagation stage is retarded by the presence of electron-withdrawing

Invitation $R\cdot + Br_2 \longrightarrow R{-}Br + Br\cdot$

Propagation
$$Br\cdot + C_6H_5{-}CH_3 \longrightarrow HBr + C_6H_5{-}CH_2\cdot$$
$$C_6H_5{-}CH_2\cdot + Br_2 \longrightarrow C_6H_5{-}CH_2{-}Br + Br\cdot$$

Termination
$$C_6H_5CH_2\cdot + Br\cdot \longrightarrow C_6H_5{-}CH_2{-}Br$$
$$2\,C_6H_5{-}CH_2\cdot \longrightarrow C_6H_5{-}CH_2{-}CH_2{-}C_6H_5$$

substituents.[70] As a result, each successive halogen atom substituted at a benzylic position makes more difficult the abstraction of other hydrogen atoms at that position, a situation that facilitates the stepwise substitution of halogen (e.g., **[61]** and **[62]**). This

[61] o-xylene $\xrightarrow[\text{125°, light}]{Br_2}$ o-$C_6H_4(CH_2{-}Br)_2$ (48–53%) (*Ref.* 78)

[62] $CH_3{-}C_6H_4{-}CH_3$ $\xrightarrow[\text{140–160°, light}]{Br_2}$ $Br_2CH{-}C_6H_4{-}CHBr_2$ (51–55%) (*Ref.* 79)

same retarding effect by electron-withdrawing substituents is found in halogenations with sulfuryl chloride, *t*-butyl hypochlorite, or N-bromosuccinimide.

Benzylic bromination with N-bromosuccinimide is often a more convenient procedure (e.g., **[63]**) than bromination with molecular

[63] phthalide $\xrightarrow[\text{CCl}_4\text{, light, reflux}]{\text{N-bromosuccinimide}}$ 3-bromophthalide (75–81%) (*Ref.* 80)

(78) E. F. M. Stephenson, *Org. Syn.*, **Coll. Vol. 4,** 984 (1963).

(79) J. M. Snell and A. Weissberger, *Org. Syn.*, **Coll. Vol. 3,** 788 (1955).

(80) I. A. Koten and R. J. Sauer, *Org. Syn.*, **42,** 26 (1962).

$$\text{[64] 3-methylthiophene} + \underset{\text{CH}_2\text{—CO}}{\overset{\text{CH}_2\text{—CO}}{|}}\!\!>\text{N—Br} \xrightarrow[\text{C}_6\text{H}_6 \text{ reflux}]{(\text{C}_6\text{H}_5\text{CO—O—})_2} \text{3-(bromomethyl)thiophene } (70\text{–}80\%)$$

(*Ref. 81*)

$$\underset{[65]}{C_6H_5\text{—}CH_2CH_2CH_2CH_2CO\text{—}C_6H_5} \xrightarrow[\text{CCl}_4\text{ light, reflux}]{\text{N-bromosuccinimide}} C_6H_5\text{—}\underset{\text{Br}}{CH}\text{—}CH_2CH_2CH_2CO\text{—}C_6H_5 \quad (66\%)$$

(*Ref. 82*)

bromine and is definitely the method of choice when a reactive aromatic nucleus (e.g., **[64]**) or another functional group that can react with bromine (e.g., **[65]**) is present. Allylic and benzylic brominations with N-bromosuccinimide have been suggested[70,73] to proceed by a free-radical chain mechanism, with hydrogen abstraction by the succinimide radical. However, recent studies[83] indicate that a bromine radical is the hydrogen-abstracting agent in benzylic bromination and strongly suggest a similar mechanism for allylic bromination. According to this scheme, the bromine that is produced slowly by reaction of the N-bromosuccinimide with hydrogen bromide, as indicated below, enters into the previously illustrated free-radical chain reaction. It has been shown

$$\underset{\text{CH}_2\text{—CO}}{\overset{\text{CH}_2\text{—CO}}{|}}\!\!>\text{N—Br} + \text{HBr} \longrightarrow \underset{\text{CH}_2\text{—CO}}{\overset{\text{CH}_2\text{—CO}}{|}}\!\!>\text{N—H} + \text{Br}_2$$

that, at low concentration levels and in the absence of hydrogen bromide, bromine reacts with cyclohexene to form the allylic bromide **[66]** rather than the addition product, a 1,2-dibromide.[83b] Failure to observe addition of bromine to the double bond under

(81) E. Campaigne and B. F. Tullar, *Org. Syn.*, **Coll. Vol. 4**, 921 (1963).

(82) R. L. Huang and P. Williams, *J. Chem. Soc.*, **1958**, 2637.

(83) (a) R. E. Pearson and J. C. Martin, *J. Am. Chem. Soc.*, **85**, 354, 3142 (1963); (b) B. P. McGrath and J. M. Tedder, *Proc. Chem. Soc.*, **1961**, 80; (c) P. S. Skell, D. L. Tuleen, and P. D. Readio, *J. Am. Chem. Soc.*, **85**, 2850 (1963); (d) E. Hedaya, R. L. Hinman, and S. Theodoropulos, *ibid.*, **85**, 3052 (1963); (e) C. Walling, A. L. Rieger, and D. D. Tanner, *ibid.*, **85**, 3129 (1963); (f) G. A. Russell and K. M. Desmond, *ibid.*, **85**, 3139 (1963); (g) E. Hedaya, R. L. Hinman, L. M. Kibler, and S. Theodoropulos, *ibid.*, **86**, 2727 (1964); (h) T. Koenig and W. Brewer, *ibid.*, **86**, 2728 (1964).

these circumstances has been attributed to the reversibility of the

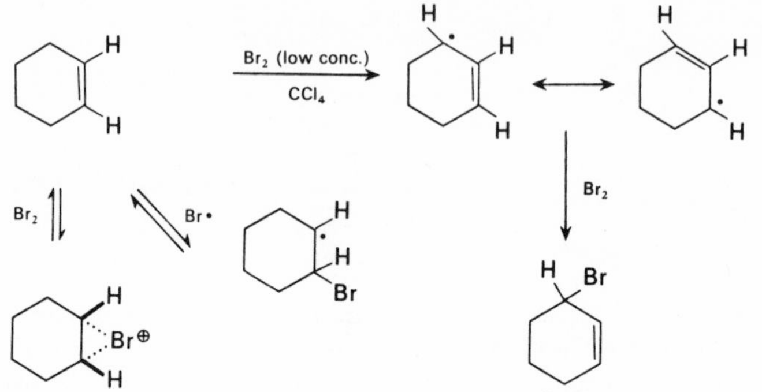

H H → Br_2 (low conc.), CCl_4 → H H H ↔ H H H

Br_2 ⇅ ⇅ $Br\cdot$ H H Br ↓ Br_2

H $Br^{\oplus}$ H H Br

[66]

first step in the addition reaction (by either a radical or an ionic mechanism). Since the concentrations of both bromine and hydrogen bromide (or bromide ion) are kept very low, little of the radical or ionic intermediate leading to addition is trapped to form the 1,2-dibromide.

The following equations illustrate the use of N-bromosuccinimide for allylic bromination. Since a free allylic carbon radical

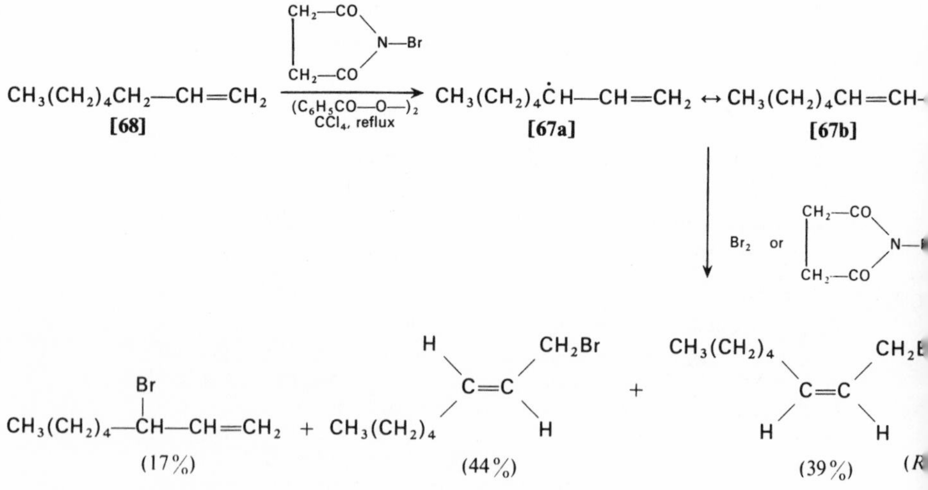

$CH_2—CO$, N—Br, $CH_2—CO$

$CH_3(CH_2)_4CH_2—CH=CH_2$ [68] → $(C_6H_5CO—O—)_2$, CCl_4, reflux → $CH_3(CH_2)_4\dot{C}H—CH=CH_2$ [67a] ↔ $CH_3(CH_2)_4CH=CH-$ [67b]

↓ Br_2 or $CH_2—CO$, N—, $CH_2—CO$

Br

$CH_3(CH_2)_4—CH—CH=CH_2$ (17%) + $CH_3(CH_2)_4$ C=C H, CH_2Br, H (44%) + $CH_3(CH_2)_4$ C=C CH_2, H, H (39%) (R

(84) L. Bateman and J. I. Cunneen, *J. Chem. Soc.*, **1950**, 941.

$$(CH_3)_2CH{-}CH{=}CH{-}CO_2C_2H_5 \xrightarrow[CCl_4,\ \text{reflux}]{N\text{-bromosuccinimide}} (CH_3)_2C(Br){-}CH{=}CH{-}CO_2C_2H_5$$

(81%)

(*Ref. 85*)

$$CH_3(CH_2)_3{-}CH{=}CH{-}CH_3 \ [69] \xrightarrow[(C_6H_5CO{-}O{-})_2,\ CCl_4,\ \text{reflux}]{N\text{-bromosuccinimide}} CH_3(CH_2)_2{-}CH(Br){-}CH{=}CH{-}CH_3$$

(58–64%)

(*Ref. 86*)

(e.g., **[67]** from olefin **[68]**) is presumably[73c] an intermediate in these reactions no matter what the actual nature of the brominating agent, a mixture of allylic halides as products is to be expected.[70] The reported formation of only a single structural isomer from bromination of the olefin **[69]** therefore seems most curious; on the other hand, the absence of terminal unsaturation or of a bromomethyl group in the product is in agreement with the generalization[73] that secondary allylic positions are attacked more readily than primary allylic positions.

Examples of the allylic chlorination of olefins with *t*-butyl

$$\text{cis-}(CH_3)_3C{-}CH{=}CH{-}CH_3 \xrightarrow[\text{light},\ -78°]{(CH_3)_3C{-}O{-}Cl} (CH_3)_3C{-}CH{\cdots}CH{\cdots}CH_2 \ [70] \xrightarrow{(CH_3)_3C{-}O{-}Cl} \text{cis-}(CH_3)_3C{-}CH{=}CH{-}CH_2Cl \ (76\%) + (CH_3)_3C{-}CHCl{-}CH{=}CH_2 \ (24\%)$$

(*Ref. 72b*)

$$\text{trans-}(CH_3)_3C{-}CH{=}CH{-}CH_3 \xrightarrow[\text{light},\ -78°]{(CH_3)_3C{-}O{-}Cl} \text{trans-}(CH_3)_3C{-}CH{=}CH{-}CH_2Cl \ (93\%) + (CH_3)_3C{-}CHCl{-}CH{=}CH_2 \ (7\%)$$

(85) H. J. Dauben and L. L. McCoy, *J. Org. Chem.*, **24**, 1577 (1959).

(86) (a) F. L. Greenwood, M. D. Kellert, and J. Sedlak, *Org. Syn.*, **Coll. Vol. 4,** 108 (1963); (b) F. L. Greenwood and M. D. Kellert, *J. Am. Chem. Soc.*, **75**, 4842 (1953).

hypochloric precede. Of special interest is the fact that the intermediate allylic radicals (e.g., **[70]**) offered a sufficient barrier to rotation about the C_2—C_3 bond to preserve their stereochemistry at low temperatures. This chlorination reaction is believed to involve a free-radical chain mechanism comparable to those previously discussed, in which a *t*-butoxy radical abstracts hydrogen from the olefin.

7

· THE ALKYLATION OF ACTIVE METHYLENE COMPOUNDS

THE PRESENCE OF CERTAIN UNSATURATED FUNCTIONS as substituents at a saturated carbon atom—nitro, carbonyl, cyano, sulfone, or phenyl groups, for example—renders any hydrogen atoms bonded to that carbon relatively acidic. In Table 7-1 are listed the pK_a values for representative compounds of this type and, for comparison, for some common solvents and reagents. The acidity of the C—H bond in these substances, often called active methylene compounds, is attributed to a combination of the inductive electron-withdrawing ability of the unsaturated substituents and the ability of these substituents to delocalize the negative charge remaining when a proton has been removed, as illustrated in the accompanying equations. It will be noted from Table 7-1 that the effectiveness of these unsaturated functions as activating groups follows the order $—NO_2 > —CO—R > —SO_2—R > —CO—OR$ and $—C{\equiv}N > —SO—R > —C_6H_5$. Also, the presence of two such unsaturated substituents further enhances the acidity of an active methylene compound. Acidity is increased (about 2 pK_a

$$CH_3{-}C{\equiv}N \xrightarrow{\text{base}} \overset{\ominus}{C}H_2{-}C{\equiv}N \leftrightarrow CH_2{=}C{=}N^{\ominus}$$

$$CH_3{-}\overset{\oplus}{N}(=O)(O^{\ominus}) \xrightarrow{\text{base}} \overset{\ominus}{C}H_2{-}\overset{\oplus}{N}(=O)(O^{\ominus}) \leftrightarrow CH_2{=}\overset{\oplus}{N}(O^{\ominus})(O^{\ominus})$$

units)[1c] by an electron-withdrawing chloro or bromo substituent and is decreased (about 1 to 2 pK_a units)[1c,2] by an alkyl substituent.

TABLE 7-1[1] ▪

Approximate Acidities of Active Methylene Compounds and Other Common Reagents

Compound†	pK_a	Compound†	pK_a
$CH_3CO_2\mathbf{H}$	5	$C_6H_5COC\mathbf{H}_3$	19
$C\mathbf{H}_2(CN)CO_2C_2H_5$	9	$C\mathbf{H}_3COC\mathbf{H}_3$	20
$C\mathbf{H}_2(COCH_3)_2$	9	$C\mathbf{H}_3{-}SO_2{-}C\mathbf{H}_3$	~23
$C_6H_5O\mathbf{H}$	10	$C\mathbf{H}_3CO_2C_2H_5$	~24
$C\mathbf{H}_3NO_2$	10	$C\mathbf{H}_3CO{-}O^{\ominus}$	~24
$CH_3COC\mathbf{H}_2CO_2C_2H_5$	11	$C\mathbf{H}_3CN$	~25
$C\mathbf{H}_2(CN)_2$	11	$C\mathbf{H}_3CONH_2$	~25
$C\mathbf{H}_2(CO_2C_2H_5)_2$	13	$C_6H_5N\mathbf{H}_2$	~30
$CH_3O\mathbf{H}$	16	$(C_6H_5)_3C\mathbf{H}$	~40
$CH_3CH_2O\mathbf{H}$	18	$C\mathbf{H}_3{-}SO{-}C\mathbf{H}_3$	~40
$(CH_3)_2CHO\mathbf{H}$	18	$(C_2H_5)_2N\mathbf{H}$	~40
$(CH_3)_3CO\mathbf{H}$	19	$C_6H_5C\mathbf{H}_3$	>50

†Acidic hydrogen atoms boldface.

Procedures that involve the formation and subsequent reaction of anions derived from active methylene compounds constitute a very important and synthetically useful class of organic reactions. Perhaps the most common of this class are those reactions in which the anion has been derived by removal of a proton from the carbon

(1) (a) J. B. Conant and G. W. Wheland, *J. Am. Chem. Soc.*, **54**, 1212 (1932); (b) W. K. McEwen, *ibid.*, **58**, 1124 (1936); (c) R. G. Pearson and R. L. Dillon, *ibid.*, **75**, 2439 (1953); (d) A. Streitwieser, Jr., W. C. Langworthy, and J. I. Brauman, *ibid.*, **85**, 1761 (1963).

(2) W. L. Rellahan, W. L. Gumby, and H. D. Zook, *J. Org. Chem.*, **24**, 709 (1959).

atom alpha to a carbonyl group. These anions, usually called enolate anions (e.g., [**1**]), are to be distinguished from enols (e.g., [**2**]), which are present in equilibrium with the carbonyl compounds in the presence of either acidic or basic catalysts.[3] In the case of most monoketones and esters the amount of enol present at

$$CH_3—\overset{\overset{\displaystyle O}{\|}}{C}—CH_3 \underset{H^{\oplus}}{\overset{\text{base (slow)}}{\rightleftharpoons}} CH_3—\overset{\overset{\displaystyle O}{\|}}{C}—CH_2^{\ominus} \leftrightarrow CH_3—\overset{\overset{\displaystyle O^{\ominus}}{|}}{C}=CH_2$$

[1a] **[1b]**

$H^{\oplus}$ ⇅ base (left); $H^{\oplus}$ ⇅ base (right)

$$CH_3—\overset{\overset{\displaystyle H—O^{\oplus}}{\|}}{C}—\underset{H}{CH_2} \underset{H^{\oplus}}{\overset{\text{(slow)}}{\rightleftharpoons}} CH_3—\overset{\overset{\displaystyle H—O}{|}}{C}=CH_2$$

OH_2
(or some other
Lewis base)

[2]

equilibrium is small (1 per cent or less)[4]; on the other hand, 1,2- and 1,3-dicarbonyl compounds often contain high percentages (>50 per cent) of their enol tautomer at equilibrium. The extent and stereochemistry of enolization in such systems is dependent on the substituents present and on the solvent in which the equilibrium is measured.[4,5]

Data concerning the rates of proton removal from C—H bonds alpha to carbonyl groups are more plentiful[1,6] than measurements

(3) For a discussion of the relative rates of the steps in these equilibria, see V. J. Shiner, Jr. and B. Martin, *J. Am. Chem. Soc.*, **84**, 4824 (1962).

(4) (a) G. W. Wheland, *Advanced Organic Chemistry*, Wiley, New York, 1949, pp. 580–646; (b) A. Gero, *J. Org. Chem.*, **19**, 1960 (1954); **26**, 3156 (1961).

(5) (a) P. Rumpf and R. La Riviere, *Compt. Rend.*, **244**, 902 (1957); (b) S. T. Yoffe, E. M. Popov, K. V. Vatsuro, E. K. Tulikova, and M. I. Kabachnik, *Tetrahedron*, **18**, 923 (1962).

(6) (a) W. G. Brown and K. Eberly, *J. Am. Chem. Soc.*, **62**, 113 (1940); (b) H. M. E. Cardwell and A. E. H. Kilner, *J. Chem. Soc.*, **1951**, 2430; H. M. E. Cardwell, *ibid.*, **1951**, 2442; (c) A. K. Mills and A. E. Wilder Smith, *Helv. Chim. Acta*, **43**, 1915 (1960); (d) D. J. Cram, B. Rickborn, C. A. Kingsbury, and P. Haberfield, *J. Am. Chem. Soc.*, **83**, 3678 (1961); (e) R. E. Dessy, Y. Okuzumi, and A. Chen, *ibid.*, **84**, 2899 (1962); (f) H. Shechter, M. J. Collis, R. Dessy, Y. Okuzumi, and A. Chen, *ibid.*, **84**, 2905 (1962); (g) A. Schriesheim, R. J. Muller, and C. A. Rowe, Jr., *ibid.*, **84**, 3164 (1962); (h) H. J. Ringold and S. K. Malhotra, *Tetrahedron Letters*, **No. 15,** 669 (1962); H. J. Ringold and S. K. Malhotra, *J. Am. Chem. Soc.*, **84**, 3402 (1962); S. K. Malhotra and H. J. Ringold, *ibid.*, **85**, 1538 (1963); **86**, 1997 (1964).

of the dissociation constants for these weak acids. Proton removal rates involving either acidic or basic catalysis are usually determined by measuring the rate of bromination (see Chapter 6), the rate of deuterium incorporation, or the rate of racemization (if the carbonyl compound is optically active). A qualitative relationship exists between the rate of proton removal and the dissociation constant for the active methylene compounds in that proton removal is usually more rapid for more acidic compounds. However, it is not correct to assume that proton removal rates provide a quantitatively accurate measure of relative acidities (pK_a values) for these compounds.[1c,6b,7] Generally, the rates of proton removal from active methylene compounds are retarded by the presence of alkyl substituents, particularly branched-chain alkyl substituents, at the alpha carbon atom. This effect is attributable in part to an increased steric hindrance to approach of the base for proton abstraction. Also, in the case of methylene groups activated by carbonyl functions (e.g., **[3]**), the presence of alkyl substituents at the alpha carbon atom interferes sterically with attainment of a transition state for proton removal (e.g., **[4]**) that permits continuous overlap of the *p* orbitals involved.[8] This stereoelectronic requirement does not appear to be applicable to carbanions that are stabilized by adjacent sulfone (e.g., **[5]**) or sulfoxide functions, presumably because overlap of the developing *p* orbital on carbon with a *d* orbital of sulfur is possible.[9]

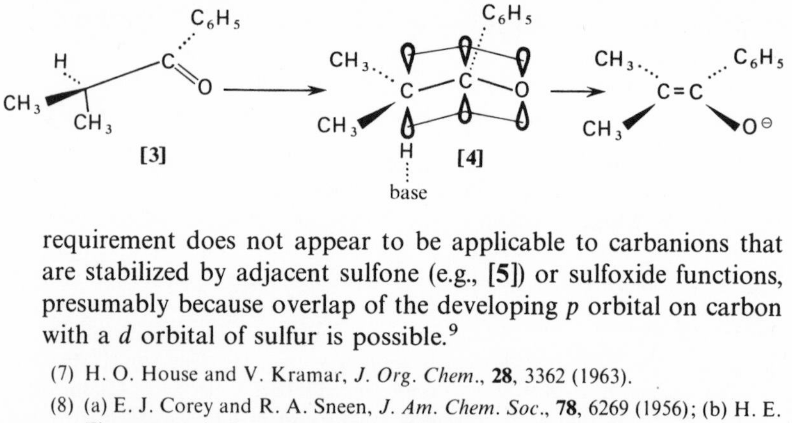

(7) H. O. House and V. Kramar, *J. Org. Chem.*, **28**, 3362 (1963).

(8) (a) E. J. Corey and R. A. Sneen, *J. Am. Chem. Soc.*, **78**, 6269 (1956); (b) H. E. Zimmerman in P. deMayo (ed.), *Molecular Rearrangements*, Vol. 1, Wiley-Interscience, New York, 1963, pp. 345–372.

(9) (a) W. von E. Doering and L. K. Levy, *J. Am. Chem. Soc.*, **77**, 509 (1955); (b) W. von E. Doering and K. C. Schreiber, *ibid.*, **77**, 514 (1955); (c) W. von E. Doering and A. K. Hoffmann, *ibid.*, **77**, 521 (1955); (d) D. J. Cram, D. A. Scott, and W. D. Nielsen, *ibid.*, **83**, 3696 (1961); (e) H. L. Goering, D. L. Towns, and B. Dittmar, *J. Org. Chem.*, **27**, 736 (1962); (f) E. J. Corey, H. König, and T. H. Lowry, *Tetrahedron Letters*, **No. 12,** 515 (1962).

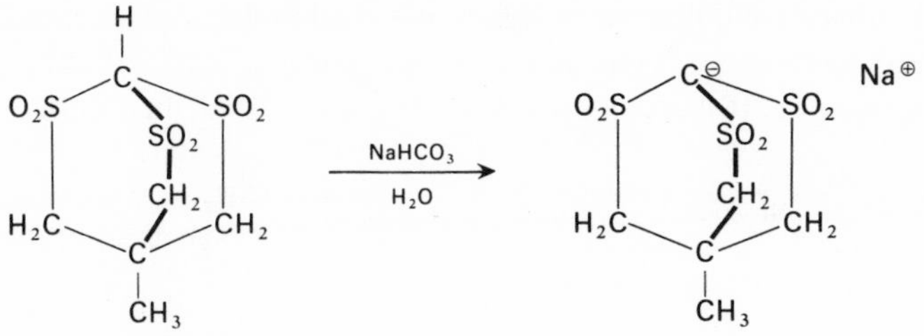

[Structure [5]: bicyclic trisulfone — H–C bridgehead bonded to three SO_2 groups; O_2S–H_2C, SO_2–CH_2, SO_2–CH_2 linking to C–CH_3 bridgehead] $\xrightarrow[H_2O]{NaHCO_3}$ [corresponding carbanion $C^{\ominus}$ with $Na^{\oplus}$] (*Ref. 9a*)

[5]
(pK_a 3.3)

Usually, reactions of active methylene compounds effected in the presence of bases involve enolate anions (or their analogs) as intermediates, whereas acid-catalyzed reactions involve enol intermediates. The majority of the alkylations to be discussed here will involve the formation of enolate anions, which then serve as nucleophiles in bimolecular nucleophilic (S_N2) displacements. An alternative mode of reaction, consisting of attack on the enol by an electrophilic reagent (cf. bromination, Chapter 6) leads to the formation of a new carbon-carbon bond and is occasionally useful for alkylation; more frequently, it is utilized in acid-catalyzed aldol condensations (Chapter 8) and acylations (Chapter 9).

Alkylation of Relatively Acidic Active Methylene Compounds

From the data in Table 7-1 it will be recalled that methylene groups activated by a single nitro group or by two or more carbonyl, ester, or cyano groups are more acidic than are the common aliphatic alcohols. As a result, compounds of these types (e.g., **[6]**) may be converted in large part to their enolate (or analogous) anions (e.g., **[7]**) by treatment with an anhydrous alcoholic solution of a metal alkoxide.[10] (If the product from alkylation of an ester is to be isolated prior to hydrolysis, the alcohol solvent and the metal alkoxide employed should correspond to the alkoxy group of the ester; otherwise the ester interchange that occurs will lead to a mixture of products.) The alcoholic solutions of enolate anions

$$\underset{[6]}{CH_2(CO_2C_2H_5)_2} + Na^{\oplus}\ {}^{\ominus}OC_2H_5 \rightleftharpoons \underset{[7]}{C_2H_5O{-}CO{-}CH{=}\underset{\substack{|\\ O^{\ominus}\\ Na^{\oplus}}}{C}{-}OC_2H_5} + C_2H_5OH$$

(10) A. C. Cope, H. L. Holmes, and H. O. House, *Org. Reactions*, **9**, 107 (1957).

thus obtained are allowed to react with alkyl halides or other alkylating agents, as illustrated in the accompanying equations. β-Diketones (e.g., **[8]**) are often sufficiently acidic that their enolate

$$CH_3{-}CO{-}CH_2CO_2C_2H_5 \xrightarrow[\substack{C_2H_5OH\\ \text{reflux}}]{C_2H_5ONa} CH_3{-}\underset{\substack{|\\ {}^{\ominus}O\\ Na^{\oplus}}}{C}{=}CHCO_2C_2H_5 \xrightarrow[\substack{C_2H_5OH\\ \text{reflux}}]{n\text{-}C_4H_9Br} n\text{-}C_4H_9{-}\underset{\substack{|\\ CO_2C_2H_5}}{CH}{-}CO{-}CH_3$$

(69–72%)

(*Ref. 11*)

$$CH_2(CO_2C_2H_5)_2 \xrightarrow[C_2H_5OH]{C_2H_5ONa} \xrightarrow[\substack{C_2H_5OH\\ \text{reflux}}]{n\text{-}C_4H_9Br} n\text{-}C_4H_9{-}CH(CO_2C_2H_5)_2$$

(80–90%) (*Ref. 12*)

$$CH_2(CO_2C_2H_5)_2 \xrightarrow[C_2H_5OH]{C_2H_5ONa} \xrightarrow[\substack{C_2H_5OH\\ \text{reflux}}]{C_2H_5{-}\overset{\substack{CH_3\\ |}}{CH}{-}Br} C_2H_5{-}\overset{\substack{CH_3\\ |}}{CH}{-}CH(CO_2C_2H_5)_2$$

(83–84%) (*Ref. 13*)

$$\underset{\textbf{[8]}}{CH_3{-}CO{-}CH_2{-}CO{-}CH_3} \xrightarrow[\substack{CH_3COCH_3\\ \text{reflux}}]{\substack{CH_3I\\ K_2CO_3}} CH_3{-}CO{-}\overset{\substack{CH_3\\ |}}{CH}{-}CO{-}CH_3$$

(75–77%) (*Ref. 14*)

anions may be formed with alkali metal hydroxides or alkali metal carbonates in water, aqueous alcohol, or acetone. The alkylation products of malonic esters (e.g., **[6]**) and β-keto esters may be hydrolyzed and decarboxylated, as illustrated in the equations below, to yield acids and ketones, respectively. These

$$C_2H_5{-}\overset{\substack{CH_3\\ |}}{CH}{-}CH(CO_2C_2H_5)_2 \xrightarrow[\substack{H_2O\\ \text{reflux}}]{KOH} C_2H_5{-}\overset{\substack{CH_3\\ |}}{CH}{-}CH(CO_2K)_2 \xrightarrow[\substack{H_2O\\ \text{reflux}}]{H_2SO_4} C_2H_5{-}\overset{\substack{CH_3\\ |}}{CH}{-}CH_2{-}CO_2H$$

(62–65%) (*Ref. 13*)

$$n\text{-}C_4H_9{-}\underset{\substack{|\\ CO_2C_2H_5}}{CH}{-}CO{-}CH_3 \xrightarrow[\substack{H_2O\\ 25^\circ}]{\text{NaOH(5\% soln.)}} n\text{-}C_4H_9{-}\underset{\substack{|\\ CO_2Na}}{CH}{-}CO{-}CH_3 \xrightarrow[\substack{H_2O\\ \text{reflux}}]{H_2SO_4}$$

(*Ref. 15*)

$$n\text{-}C_4H_9{-}CH_2{-}CO{-}CH_3$$

(52–61%)

(11) C. S. Marvel and F. D. Hager, *Org. Syn.*, **Coll. Vol. 1,** 248 (1944).

(12) R. Adams and R. M. Kamm, *ibid.*, **Coll. Vol. 1,** 250 (1944).

(13) (a) C. S. Marvel, *Org. Syn.*, **Coll. Vol. 3,** 495 (1955); (b) E. B. Vliet, C. S. Marvel, and C. M. Hsueh, *Org. Syn.*, **Coll. Vol. 2,** 416 (1943).

(14) A. W. Johnson, E. Markham, and R. Price, *Org. Syn.*, **42,** 75 (1962).

(15) J. R. Johnson and F. D. Hager, *Org. Syn.*, **Coll. Vol. 1,** 351 (1944).

decarboxylations involve the free acids (e.g., **[9]**) and are known to proceed by a six-center transition state (e.g., **[10]**)[16] which initially forms the enol; if the structure of the keto acid (e.g., **[11]**) is such

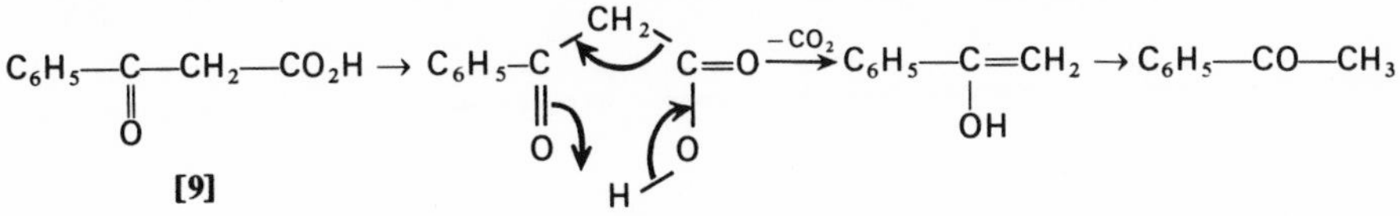

$$C_6H_5—\underset{\underset{O}{\|}}{C}—CH_2—CO_2H \rightarrow C_6H_5—C(=O)—CH_2—C(=O)—O—H \xrightarrow{-CO_2} C_6H_5—\underset{\underset{OH}{|}}{C}=CH_2 \rightarrow C_6H_5—CO—CH_3$$

[9] **[10]**

that the enol (e.g., **[12]**) would be excessively strained, the decarboxylation either fails or takes a different reaction path.[17] Alternative decarboxylation procedures often used include isolation and

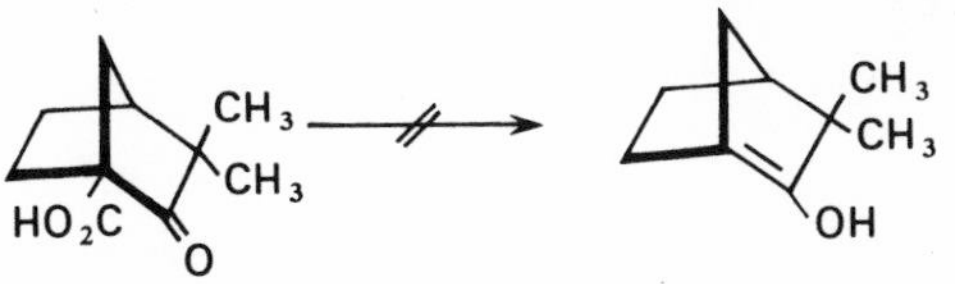

[11] (bicyclic β-keto acid with HO_2C, CH_3, CH_3) ⇸ **[12]** (bridgehead enol with CH_3, CH_3, OH)

subsequent heating of the malonic acid, or heating of the malonic ester or β-keto ester with aqueous constant-boiling hydrochloric acid (20 per cent solution) or hydrobromic acid (48 per cent solution) to effect hydrolysis and decarboxylation in the same reaction. The following equations illustrate the use of these procedures for the preparation of α-substituted carboxylic acids.

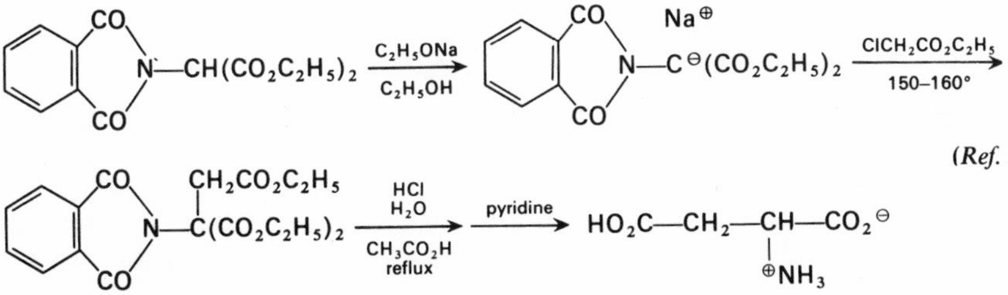

$$C_6H_4(CO)_2N—CH(CO_2C_2H_5)_2 \xrightarrow[C_2H_5OH]{C_2H_5ONa} C_6H_4(CO)_2N—C^{\ominus}(CO_2C_2H_5)_2\ Na^{\oplus} \xrightarrow[150\text{–}160°]{ClCH_2CO_2C_2H_5}$$

(Ref. 18)

$$C_6H_4(CO)_2N—\underset{|}{\overset{CH_2CO_2C_2H_5}{C}}(CO_2C_2H_5)_2 \xrightarrow[CH_3CO_2H,\ reflux]{HCl,\ H_2O} \xrightarrow{pyridine} HO_2C—CH_2—\underset{\underset{^{\oplus}NH_3}{|}}{CH}—CO_2^{\ominus}$$

(95–99%) (42–43%)

(16) C. G. Swain, R. F. W. Bader, R. M. Esteve, Jr., and R. N. Griffin, *J. Am. Chem. Soc.*, **83**, 1951 (1961).

(17) (a) F. S. Fawcett, *Chem. Rev.*, **47**, 219 (1950); (b) H. O. House and H. C. Müller, *J. Org. Chem.*, **27**, 4436 (1962).

(18) (a) M. S. Dunn and B. W. Smart, *Org. Syn.*, **Coll. Vol. 4,** 55 (1963); (b) G. Barger and T. E. Weichselbaum, *Org. Syn.*, **Coll. Vol. 2,** 384 (1943).

$$CH_3CH(CO_2C_2H_5)_2 \xrightarrow[C_2H_5OH]{NaOC_2H_5} \xrightarrow[\text{reflux}]{n\text{-}C_{10}H_{21}Br} n\text{-}C_{10}H_{21}\text{—}C(CH_3)(CO_2C_2H_5)_2 \xrightarrow[H_2O,\ C_2H_5OH,\ \text{reflux}]{KOH}$$

$$\xrightarrow{H_2SO_4} n\text{-}C_{10}H_{21}\text{—}C(CH_3)(CO_2H)_2 \xrightarrow{180\text{–}190^\circ} n\text{-}C_{10}H_{21}\text{—}CH(CH_3)\text{—}CO_2H \quad (61\text{–}74\%)$$

(*Ref. 19*)

The saponification of β-keto esters (e.g., **[13]**) is often complicated by competing attack of the hydroxide anion at the ketone function,

$$\underset{\textbf{[13]}}{\text{2-oxo-1-}(CH_2C_6H_5)\text{-1-}(CO_2C_2H_5)\text{cyclopentane}} \xrightarrow[H_2O,\ \text{reflux}]{NaOH} [\text{tetrahedral adduct: } {}^{\ominus}O,\ OH;\ CH_2C_6H_5,\ CO_2C_2H_5] \longrightarrow [HO\text{–}C(=O)\text{–}(CH_2)_3\text{–}C^{\ominus}(CH_2C_6H_5)\text{–}C(=O)\text{–}OC_2H_5] \quad (\textit{Ref. 20a})$$

$$\longrightarrow Na^{\oplus}\,{}^{\ominus}O_2C(CH_2)_3CH(CH_2C_6H_5)\text{—}CO_2{}^{\ominus}Na^{\oplus} \xrightarrow{H_3O^{\oplus}} HO_2C(CH_2)_3CH(CH_2C_6H_5)\text{—}CO_2H \quad (90\%)$$

leading to cleavage rather than saponification, especially in cases where the alpha position is disubstituted. For this reason hydrolysis and decarboxylation are best accomplished with aqueous acid, as illustrated in the following equation. Other methods that have

$$\text{2-oxo-1-}(CO_2C_2H_5)\text{-1-}(CH_2CH_2CH_2Br)\text{cyclopentane} \xrightarrow[H_2O,\ \text{reflux}]{HBr(48\%\ \text{soln.})} \text{2-}(CH_2CH_2CH_2Br)\text{cyclopentanone} \quad (80\%) \quad (\textit{Ref. 20a})$$

been used for cleavage of the ester function in β-keto esters to permit decarboxylation include hydrogenolysis of benzyl esters[21] (see Chapter 1) and acid-catalyzed cleavage of t-butyl esters (e.g.,

(19) C. F. Allen and M. J. Kalm, *Org. Syn.*, **Coll. Vol. 4,** 618 (1963).

(20) (a) R. Mayer in W. Foerst (ed.), *Newer Methods of Preparative Organic Chemistry*, Vol. 2, Academic, New York, 1963, pp. 101–131; (b) W. B. Renfrow and G. B. Walker, *J. Am. Chem. Soc.*, **70**, 3957 (1948); (c) for a discussion of the structure and alkylation of cyclic β-keto esters as a function of ring size, see S. J. Rhoads and co-workers, *Tetrahedron*, **19**, 1625 (1963).

(21) (a) R. E. Bowman, *J. Chem. Soc.*, **1950**, 325; (b) R. E. Bowman and W. D. Fordham, *ibid.*, **1951**, 2758.

[14])[20b,22] or 2-tetrahydropyranyl esters (e.g., **[15]**).[23] Alternatively, cleavage and subsequent decarboxylation of β-keto esters has been

$$C_6H_5CH_2CH[CO_2C(CH_3)_3]_2 \xrightarrow[C_6H_6,\ reflux]{NaH} \xrightarrow[C_6H_6,\ reflux]{C_6H_5COCl} C_6H_5{-}CO{-}C(CH_2C_6H_5){-}CO_2C(CH_3)_3 \quad (Ref.\ 22)$$

[14]

$$\xrightarrow[CH_3CO_2H,\ reflux]{p\text{-}CH_3C_6H_4SO_3H} (CH_3)_2C{=}CH_2 + [C_6H_5CO{-}C(CH_2C_6H_5)(CO_2H)_2] \xrightarrow{-CO_2} C_6H_5CO{-}CH_2CH_2C_6H_5 \ (80\%)$$

$$n\text{-}C_{11}H_{23}{-}CO{-}C(CH_2C_6H_5)(CO_2\text{-}2\text{-tetrahydropyranyl})_2 \xrightarrow[reflux]{CH_3CO_2H} n\text{-}C_{11}H_{23}COCH_2CH_2C_6H_5\ (60\%) + \text{dihydropyran} + CO_2$$

[15]

(*Ref. 23*)

achieved by passing the materials (e.g., **[16]**) through a glass tube

$$C_6H_{11}{-}CH(CO_2C_2H_5){-}COCH_3\ [16] \xrightarrow[glass\ tube,\ 525^\circ]{-CH_2{=}CH_2} [C_6H_{11}{-}CH(CO_2H){-}COCH_3] \longrightarrow C_6H_{11}{-}CH_2{-}COCH_3\ (72\%)$$

(*Ref. 24*)

heated to 525°.[24] Each of these nonhydrolytic methods enjoys the advantage of minimizing cleavage at the ketone group.

(22) (a) G. S. Fonken and W. S. Johnson, *J. Am. Chem. Soc.*, **74**, 831 (1952); (b) for the preparation of di-*t*-butyl malonate, see A. L. McCloskey, G. S. Fonken, R. W. Kluiber, and W. S. Johnson, *Org. Syn.*, **Coll. Vol. 4,** 261 (1963); (c) for the preparation of *t*-butyl cyanoacetate, see R. E. Ireland and M. Chaykovsky, *Org. Syn.*, **41**, 5 (1961); (d) for the preparation of *t*-butyl acetoacetate, see S. O. Lawesson, S. Gronwall, and R. Sandberg, *ibid.*, **42**, 28 (1962).

(23) R. E. Bowman and W. D. Fordham, *J. Chem. Soc.*, **1952**, 3945.

(24) (a) W. J. Bailey and J. J. Daly, Jr., *J. Org. Chem.*, **22**, 1189 (1957); (b) *ibid.*, **29**, 1249 (1964).

The cleavage of β-keto esters at the ketone function has also been observed during the alkylation reactions leading to their preparation. As was noted earlier, such cleavage is most pronounced when the alkylation product (e.g., **[17]**) has two alpha

$$\text{[18]} \xrightarrow[C_2H_5OH\text{, ice bath}]{NaOC_2H_5} \xrightarrow{CH_3I} \text{[17]}\ (60\%) \xrightarrow[C_2H_5OH\text{, reflux}]{NaOC_2H_5}$$

(*Ref. 20a*)

$$\longrightarrow C_2H_5OCO(CH_2)_3CH(CH_3)-CO_2C_2H_5$$

substituents. With only one alpha substituent, the product exists in the basic solution as a stable enolate anion in which the carbonyl group is relatively resistant to attack by alkoxide ion. The cleavage has been minimized by use of low reaction temperatures with sodium ethoxide; of sterically hindered bases such as potassium *t*-butoxide in *t*-butyl alcohol; or of sodium hydride[20b,22] as a base in a nonhydroxylic solvent such as dioxane, benzene, dimethylformamide or 1,2-dimethoxyethane. Interestingly, it is possible to

$$n\text{-}C_4H_9-CH(CO_2C_2H_5)-COCH_3 \xrightarrow[(CH_3)_3COH]{(CH_3)_3COK} \xrightarrow[(CH_3)_3COH]{n\text{-}C_4H_9I} (n\text{-}C_4H_9)_2C(CO_2C_2H_5)-COCH_3\ (80\%)$$

(*Ref. 25*)

prepare the potassium enolate of 2-carboethoxycyclopentanone **[18]** by reaction of the keto ester with potassium hydroxide in cold aqueous alcohol.[20a] Isolation of the pure potassium enolate, followed by reaction with an alkyl halide in an inert solvent constitutes the best method for alkylating this keto ester. However, alkali metal hydroxides (or other bases in partially aqueous media) normally cannot be used for the alkylation of malonic esters or β-keto esters because the rapid competing saponification of the ester function lowers the yield of alkylated product.[12]

A cleavage mechanistically similar to that previously discussed for β-keto esters, called decarbethoxylation, is almost always a

(25) (a) W. B. Renfrow, Jr., *J. Am. Chem. Soc.*, **66**, 144 (1944); (b) W. B. Renfrow and A. Renfrow, *ibid.*, **68**, 1801 (1946); (c) W. G. Dauben, J. W. McFarland, and J. B. Rogan, *J. Org. Chem.*, **26**, 297 (1961).

significant side reaction when malonic esters (e.g., **[19]**) or cyano-acetic esters are heated with alcoholic sodium ethoxide for long periods of time (i.e., 18 to 24 hr).[10,26] The rate of cleavage is

$$(C_2H_5)_2C(CO_2C_2H_5)_2 \ \textbf{[19]} \xrightleftharpoons[C_2H_5OH,\ 250°]{NaOC_2H_5} (C_2H_5)_2C(CO_2C_2H_5)\text{—}C(O^{\ominus})(OC_2H_5)_2 \rightleftharpoons$$

$$(C_2H_5)_2C^{\ominus}\text{—CO—}OC_2H_5 \ \textbf{[20]} + CO(OC_2H_5)_2$$

$$\rightleftharpoons (C_2H_5)_2CHCO_2C_2H_5 \ (82\%)$$

(*Ref. 26*)

enhanced by aryl or vinyl substituents, which further stabilize the intermediate anion **[20]**. Since the reaction is reversible, it may be suppressed by the use of diethyl carbonate as the reaction solvent.[27]

Comparable cleavage reactions have also been observed during the alkylation of α-substituted β-diketones (e.g., **[21]**). However,

$$\textbf{[21]} \text{ (2-benzylcyclohexane-1,3-dione)} \xrightarrow[CH_3OH]{KOCH_3} \xrightarrow[CH_3OH,\ reflux]{CH_3I} \text{[cyclic adduct: } O^{\ominus},\ OCH_3,\ CH_3,\ CH_2C_6H_5,\ O] \longrightarrow$$

$$CH_3O_2C(CH_2)_3CO\text{—}CH(CH_3)\text{—}CH_2C_6H_5 \ (71\%)$$

(*Ref. 28*)

this cleavage (effected with hydroxide ion) has been used to advantage in the scheme for the synthesis of certain acids, as illustrated in the accompanying equations. A difficulty that frequently arises in the alkylation of 1,3-dicarbonyl compounds (including the diketone **[22]**) is the concurrent formation of both

(26) A. C. Cope and S. M. McElvain, *J. Am. Chem. Soc.*, **54**, 4319 (1932).

(27) (a) V. H. Wallingford, A. H. Homeyer, and D. M. Jones, *ibid.*, **63**, 2056 (1941); (b) V. H. Wallingford, M. A. Thorpe, and A. H. Homeyer, *ibid.*, **64**, 580 (1942).

(28) (a) H. Stetter and W. Dierichs, *Chem. Ber.*, **85**, 1061 (1952); (b) H. Stetter in W. Foerst (ed.), *Newer Methods of Preparative Organic Chemistry*, Vol. 2, Academic, New York, 1963, pp. 51–99.

$\xrightarrow[CH_3OH, H_2O]{KOH}$ $\xrightarrow[reflux]{CH_3I}$ (65%) $\xrightarrow[H_2O, reflux]{Ba(OH)_2}$ $\xrightarrow{H_3O^{\oplus}}$ $HO_2C(CH_2)_3COCH_2CH_3$ (78%) (*Ref. 28b*)

$\xrightarrow[(HOCH_2CH_2—)_2O, 195°]{NH_2NH_2, NaOH}$ $\xrightarrow{H_3O^{\oplus}}$ $CH_3CH_2CH_2(CH_2)_3CO_2H$ (86%)

C-alkylated and O-alkylated products. This possibility becomes apparent when the charge distribution in the intermediate enolate anion **[23]** is examined. A more common example of usually

[22] $\xrightarrow[CH_3OH]{NaOCH_3}$ **[23a]** ⟷ **[23b]** $\xrightarrow{n\text{-}C_4H_9Br}$

(15%) + (37%) (*Ref. 28b*)

predominant O-alkylation is the alkylation of phenols (e.g., **[24]**). In general, O-alkylation competes significantly with C-alkylation

[24] $\xrightarrow[H_2O]{NaOH}$ $\xrightarrow[H_2O, reflux]{(CH_3O)_2SO_2}$ (82–87%) (*Ref. 29*)

only when active methylene compounds are involved in which the equilibrium concentration of the enol is relatively high (e.g., 1,3-dicarbonyl compounds and phenols). Alkylation at the more electronegative atom of the ambient anion (at oxygen rather than at carbon for an enolate anion) is also often favored by the use of a very reactive alkylating agent, where formation of a new bond

(29) J. S. Buck, *Org. Syn.*, **Coll. Vol. 2,** 619 (1943).

to the carbon atom of the alkylating agent is not far advanced in the transition state.[30] However, the choice of reaction conditions may be of prime importance in determining the ratio of O-alkylated to C-alkylated products obtained. The C-alkylation of phenols (e.g., **[25]** and **[26]**), which has been observed as one mode of reaction with a number of phenoxide ions,[31] is favored in some cases by

OH, CH_3, CH_3, t-C_4H_9 **[25]** $\xrightarrow[\text{reflux}]{Na,\ C_6H_5CH_3}$ $O^{\ominus}$ $Na^{\oplus}$, CH_3, CH_3, t-C_4H_9 $\xrightarrow[C_6H_5CH_3,\ \text{reflux}]{C_6H_5CH_2Cl}$ O, CH_3, CH_3, $CH_2C_6H_5$, t-C_4H_9 (46%) + $O—CH_2C_6H_5$, CH_3, CH_3, t-C_4H_9 (5–10%) (*Ref. 31b*)

OH **[26]** $\xrightarrow[H_2O]{NaOH}$ $O^{\ominus}$ $\xrightarrow[H_2O,\ 25°]{CH_3I}$ CH_3, OH (30%) + OCH_3 (66%) (*Ref. 31e*)

heterogeneous rather than homogeneous reaction conditions and by the use of solvents that are able to hydrogen bond with the leaving group of the alkylating agent. Nonhydroxylic polar solvents appear to favor O-alkylation. An interesting illustration of the C-alkylation of phenols is the intramolecular cyclization of the phenol **[27]** to form the indicated tricyclic system. This cyclization has provided a useful synthetic route to comparable ring systems present in certain diterpenes and deterpene alkaloids.[31f]

HO, $CH_2CH_2—OSO_2—C_6H_4CH_3$-*p* **[27]** $\xrightarrow[(CH_3)_3COH,\ \text{reflux}]{KOC(CH_3)_3}$ O, —H

(*Ref. 31f*)

(30) (a) N. Kornblum, R. A. Smiley, R. C. Blackwood, and D. C. Iffland, *J. Am. Chem. Soc.*, **77**, 6269 (1955); (b) see also R. C. Kerber, G. W. Urry, and N. Kornblum, *ibid.*, **86**, 3904 (1964).

(31) (a) D. Y. Curtin, R. J. Crawford, and M. Wilhelm, *ibid.*, **80**, 1391 (1958); (b) D. Y. Curtin and D. H. Dybvig, *ibid.*, **84**, 225 (1962); (c) N. Kornblum and A. Lurie, *ibid.*, **81**, 2705 (1959); (d) N. Kornblum, P. J. Berrigan, and W. J. le Noble, *ibid.*, **85**, 1141 (1963); (e) N. Kornblum, R. Seltzer, and P. Haberfield, *ibid.*, **85**, 1148 (1963); (f) S. Masamune, *ibid.*, **83**, 1009 (1961); **86**, 288–291 (1964);

Recent studies[32] of alkylations in solvents such as dimethylformamide, dimethyl sulfoxide, and 1,2-dimethoxyethane have demonstrated that very substantial increases in the rates of reaction of enolate (or analogous) anions with alkylating agents result from their use in preference to alcohols or inert solvents. Their advantage over protonic solvents (e.g., ethanol) lies in the fact that they presumably do not solvate the enolate anion and, consequently, do not diminish its reactivity as a nucleophile. On the other hand, they do have the ability to solvate the cation, separating it from the cation–enolate anion pair **[28]** and leaving a relatively

$$CH_3{-}C(O^{\ominus}){=}CH{-}C({=}O){-}OC_2H_5 \cdot\cdot\cdot Li^{\oplus}\ \textbf{[28]} + \text{solvent} \rightleftharpoons CH_3{-}C(O^{\ominus}){=}CH{-}C({=}O){-}OC_2H_5\ \textbf{[29]} + Li^{\oplus}\cdots\text{solvent}$$

free anion **[29]** in the reaction mixture, as illustrated in the accompanying equation. This free anion **[29]** would be expected to be a more reactive nucleophile than the ion pair **[28]**. Support for the idea that enolate anions exist as ion pairs with cations is found in observations[32g,33] that the reactivity of an enolate ion is often influenced by the nature of the cation present, the lithium cation forming more tightly associated ion pairs than sodium or potassium.

The alkylating agent frequently employed for reaction with an enolate (or analogous) anion is an alkyl halide. As has been illustrated in previous equations, both primary and secondary halides may be used successfully, as may primary and secondary allylic and benzylic halides. However, tertiary alkyl halides having

---

(g) for other synthetic applications, see E. Wenkert, R. D. Youssefyeh, and R. G. Lewis, *ibid.*, **82**, 4675 (1960); (h) R. Gompper, *Angew. Chem., Internat. Ed.*, **3**, 560 (1964).

(32) (a) H. E. Zaugg, B. W. Horrom, and S. Borgwardt, *J. Am. Chem. Soc.*, **82**, 2895 (1960); (b) H. E. Zaugg, *ibid.*, **82**, 2903 (1960); **83**, 837 (1961); (c) H. E. Zaugg, D. A. Dunnigan, R. J. Michaels, L. R. Swett, T. S. Wang, A. H. Sommers, and R. W. Denet, *J. Org. Chem.*, **26**, 644 (1961); (d) J. J. Bloomfield, *ibid.*, **26**, 4112 (1961); (e) R. Fuchs, G. E. McCrary, and J. J. Bloomfield, *J. Am. Chem. Soc.*, **83**, 4281 (1961); (f) H. D. Zook and T. J. Russo, *ibid.*, **82**, 1258 (1960); (g) H. D. Zook and W. L. Gumby, *ibid.*, **82**, 1386 (1960); (h) A. J. Parker, *Quart. Rev. (London)*, **16**, 163 (1962).

(33) (a) A. Brändström, *Acta Chem. Scand.*, **7**, 223 (1953); A. Brändström, *Arkiv Kemi*, **6**, 155 (1954); **7**, 81 (1954); (b) K. G. Hampton, T. M. Harris, and C. R. Hauser, *J. Org. Chem.*, **28**, 1946 (1963).

at least one beta hydrogen atom (e.g., **[30]**) are usually of little value as alkylating agents because the major reaction that occurs

$$(CH_3)_3C{-}Br + CH_2(CO_2C_2H_5)_2 \xrightarrow[C_2H_5OH,\ 5\text{–}25^\circ]{NaOC_2H_5} (CH_3)_3C{-}CH(CO_2C_2H_5)_2 + (CH_3)_2C{=}CH_2$$

[30] (6%) (*Ref. 34*)

when these materials are treated with enolate anions is a bimolecular elimination (*E*2), leading to formation of an olefin. Dehydrohalogenation may also be a serious side reaction with certain secondary alkyl halides (e.g., **[31]**) and leads to diminished yields of alkylated products.

$$C_6H_{11}Br + CH_2(CO_2C_2H_5)_2 \xrightarrow[C_2H_5OH,\ \text{reflux}]{NaOC_2H_5} C_6H_{11}CH(CO_2C_2H_5)_2 + C_6H_{10}$$

[31] (bromocyclohexane) → cyclohexylmalonate (60%) + cyclohexene (*Ref. 35*)

In certain cases sulfate esters and arylsulfonate esters are more useful alkylating agents than the corresponding alkyl halides. For example, the commercially available methyl *p*-toluenesulfonate, dimethyl sulfate, and diethyl sulfate, being less volatile than the methyl and ethyl halides, can be used to advantage in alkylation reactions that require elevated temperatures, eliminating the need for pressure equipment to prevent the loss of the alkylating agent.[36] Use of the *p*-toluenesulfonate ester rather than the halide also has a very real advantage when the alkylating agent is not commercially available and must be prepared from the corresponding alcohol. Conversion of alcohol to halide may be complicated by molecular rearrangement, and the stereochemical relationship of the alcohol to the halide is frequently uncertain. The following equations exemplify the preparation and use of *p*-toluenesulfonate esters to avoid these difficulties. The reaction of the arylsulfonate ester **[32]** illustrates the general observation[10] that alkylation occurs with inversion of the configuration of the alkylating agent, as expected for an S_N2 reaction. Arylsulfonate esters offer the additional advantage that they are frequently crystalline solids, which may

(34) A. W. Dox and W. G. Bywater, *J. Am. Chem. Soc.*, **58**, 731 (1936).

(35) (a) M. Kopp and B. Tchoubar, *Bull. Soc. Chim. France*, **1951**, 30; (b) J. P. Eykman, *Chem. Weekblad*, **6**, 699 (1909).

(36) E. Bowden, *J. Am. Chem. Soc.*, **60**, 131 (1938).

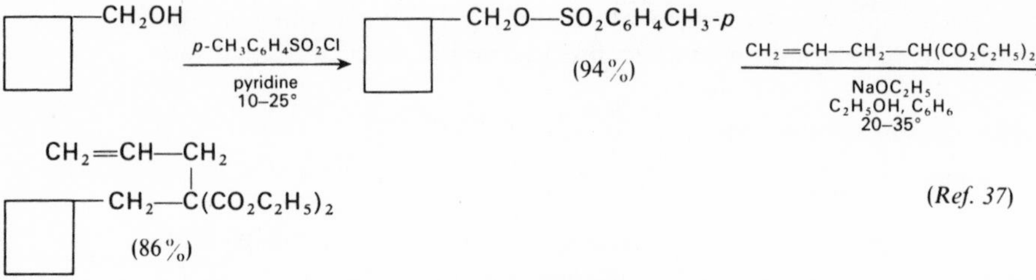

(Ref. 37)

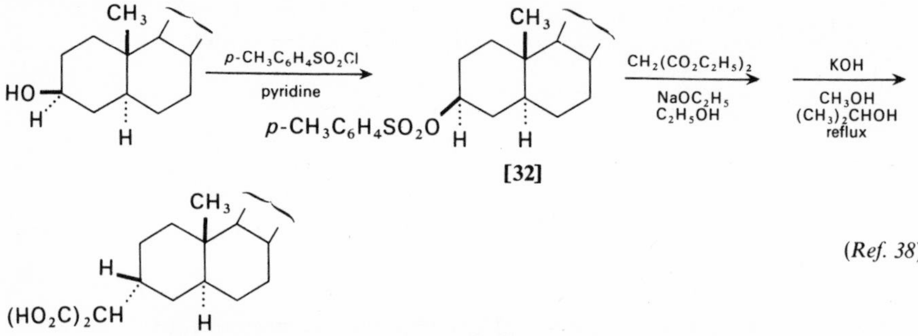

[32]

(Ref. 38)

be readily purified before use. The relative reactivities of the common alkylating agents follow the order R—Cl < R—Br < R—I < R—O—SO_2—$C_6H_5CH_3$-*p* < R—O—SO_2—O—R (for displacement of the first alkyl group).[39]

Since the unsuitability of tertiary halides (and tertiary sulfonates if they can be prepared) as alkylating agents for enolate anions results from a competing dehydrohalogenation reaction, it would appear possible to solve this problem with an acid-catalyzed procedure in which the enol (not enolate) is attacked by a potential tertiary carbonium ion. Although such a reaction has been realized in the alkylation of *β*-keto esters (e.g., [**33**]) by secondary and tertiary alcohols and ethers, the yields with tertiary alkyl derivatives are still very poor (6 to 14 per cent).

As noted previously (Chapter 5), epoxides may also serve as alkylating agents for the anions of active methylene compounds.

(37) (a) W. Braker, E. J. Pribyl, and W. A. Lott, *ibid.*, **69**, 866 (1947); (b) for a study of possible rearrangements during the conversion of alcohols to alkyl halides, see W. Gerrard and H. R. Hudson, *J. Chem. Soc.*, **1964,** 2310; W. Gerrard, H. R. Hudson, and W. S. Murphy, *ibid.*, **1964,** 2314.

(38) C. W. Shoppee and R. J. Stephenson, *J. Chem. Soc.*, **1954**, 2230.

(39) (a) J. M. Conia, *Record Chem. Progr.*, **24**, 43 (1963); (b) J. M. Conia, *Bull. Soc. Chim. France*, **1950**, 533, 537; (c) J. M. Conia, *ibid.*, **1956**, 1040.

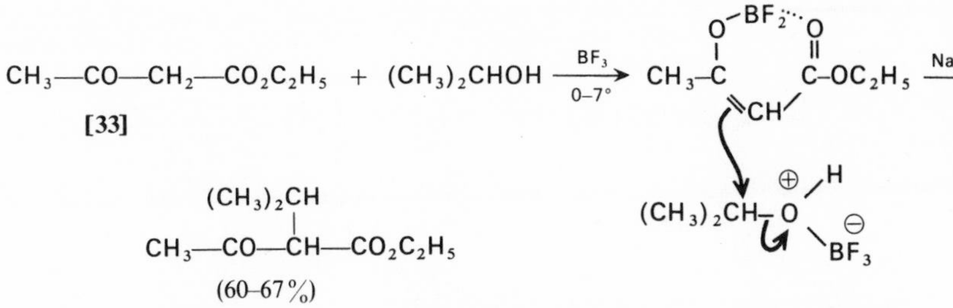

$$CH_3—CO—CH_2—CO_2C_2H_5 + (CH_3)_2CHOH \xrightarrow[0–7°]{BF_3} CH_3—C(—O—BF_2···O=)C—OC_2H_5 \text{ (chelate, =CH— ; attacked by } (CH_3)_2CH—\overset{\oplus}{O}(H)—\overset{\ominus}{B}F_3) \xrightarrow[H_2O]{NaOCOCH_3}$$

[33]

$$CH_3—CO—CH(CH(CH_3)_2)—CO_2C_2H_5$$

(60–67%) (*Ref. 40*)

When an ester function is present (e.g., **[34]**), the product isolated

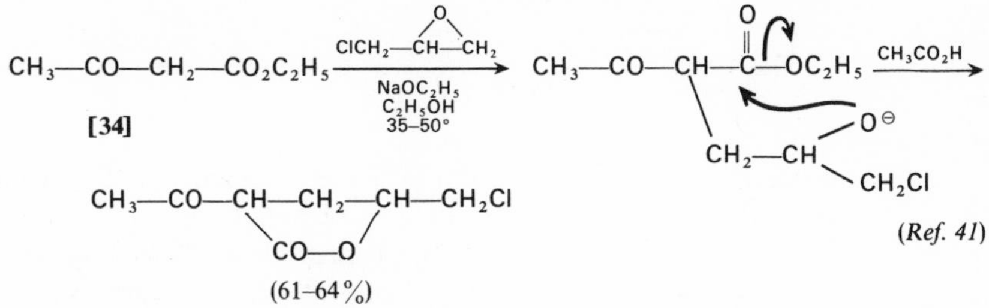

$$CH_3—CO—CH_2—CO_2C_2H_5 \xrightarrow[NaOC_2H_5,\ C_2H_5OH,\ 35–50°]{ClCH_2—CH(O)CH_2} CH_3—CO—CH(CH_2—CH(O^{\ominus})CH_2Cl)—C(=O)—OC_2H_5 \xrightarrow{CH_3CO_2H}$$

[34]

$$CH_3—CO—CH—CH_2—CH—CH_2Cl \text{ (ring closed by } CO—O)$$

(61–64%) (*Ref. 41*)

is usually a lactone. The further conversion of such ketolactones to γ-haloketones is illustrated below.

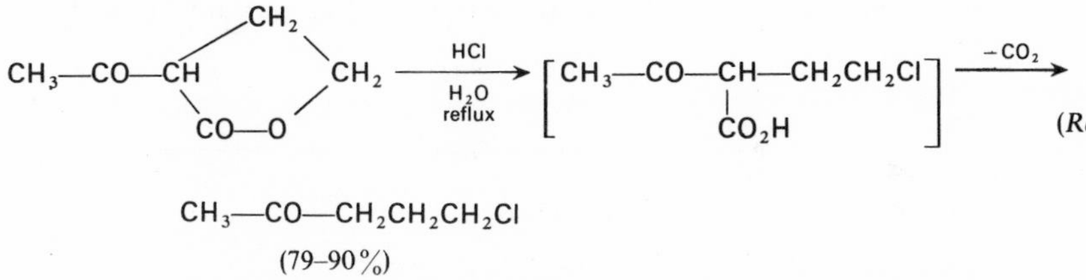

$$CH_3—CO—CH(CH_2CH_2)(CO—O) \xrightarrow[H_2O,\ reflux]{HCl} \left[CH_3—CO—CH(CO_2H)—CH_2CH_2Cl\right] \xrightarrow{-CO_2}$$

$$CH_3—CO—CH_2CH_2CH_2Cl$$

(79–90%) (*Ref. 42*)

Under the normal conditions employed for the alkylation of active methylene compounds, vinyl and aryl halides usually fail to react, a result that would be anticipated from the failure of these halides to undergo other bimolecular nucleophilic displacements. However, aryl halides that are activated by the presence of electron-withdrawing groups at the *ortho* and/or *para* positions (e.g., **[35]**) will act as alkylating agents. Such alkylations are believed to

(40) (a) J. T. Adams, R. Levine, and C. R. Hauser, *Org. Syn.*, **Coll. Vol. 3,** 405 (1955); (b) J. T. Adams, B. Abramovitch, and C. R. Hauser, *J. Am. Chem. Soc.*, **65,** 552 (1943).

(41) G. D. Zuidema, E. van Tamelen, and G. Van Zyl, *Org. Syn.*, **Coll. Vol. 4,** 10 (1963).

(42) G. W. Cannon, R. C. Ellis, and J. R. Leal, *ibid.*, **Coll. Vol. 4,** 597 (1963).

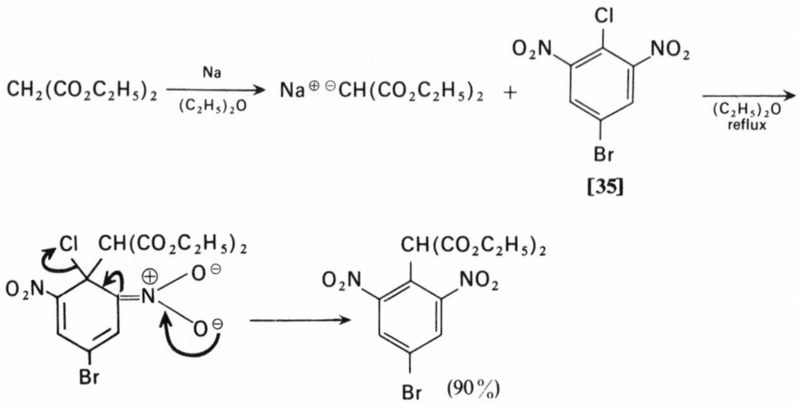

$$CH_2(CO_2C_2H_5)_2 \xrightarrow[(C_2H_5)_2O]{Na} Na^{\oplus}\,{}^{\ominus}CH(CO_2C_2H_5)_2 + \text{[35]} \xrightarrow[\text{reflux}]{(C_2H_5)_2O}$$

(Ref. 43)

(90%)

proceed by the initial addition of the enolate anion to the aromatic system and subsequent elimination of halide ion as illustrated[44]; a mechanistically similar reaction is possible with vinyl halides that have an electron-withdrawing group at the beta carbon atom. A variant of the usual alkylation procedure permits the formation of active methylene compounds having vinyl substituents. The alkylidene derivative (e.g., **[36]**) of the active methylene compound is treated with a metal alkoxide to form the enolate anion **[37]**;

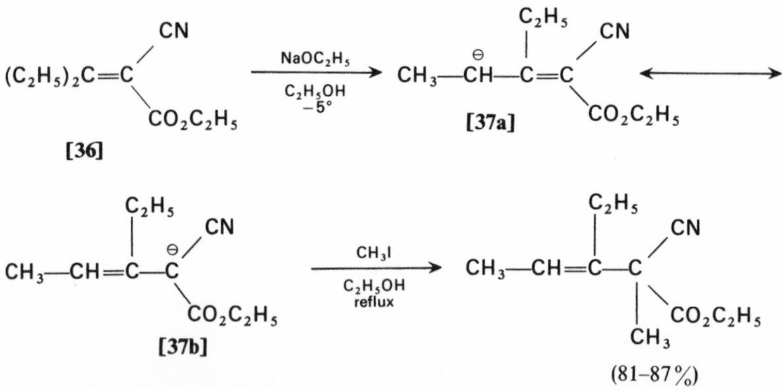

$$(C_2H_5)_2C{=}C(CN)CO_2C_2H_5 \text{ [36]} \xrightarrow[C_2H_5OH,\ -5^\circ]{NaOC_2H_5} CH_3{-}\overset{\ominus}{C}H{-}C(C_2H_5){=}C(CN)CO_2C_2H_5 \text{ [37a]} \longleftrightarrow$$

(Ref. 45)

$$CH_3{-}CH{=}C(C_2H_5){-}\overset{\ominus}{C}(CN)CO_2C_2H_5 \text{ [37b]} \xrightarrow[C_2H_5OH,\ \text{reflux}]{CH_3I} CH_3{-}CH{=}C(C_2H_5){-}C(CH_3)(CN)CO_2C_2H_5$$

(81–87%)

reaction of this anion with an alkylating agent introduces an alkyl substituent at the alpha position, a result reminiscent of the previous discussion (Chapter 3) concerning the site of kinetically controlled

(43) A. B. Sen and P. M. Bhargava, *J. Indian Chem. Soc.*, **24**, 371 (1947).

(44) J. F. Bunnett, *Quart. Rev.* (*London*), **12**, 1 (1958).

(45) E. M. Hancock and A. C. Cope, *Org. Syn.*, **Coll. Vol. 3**, 397 (1955).

protonation of such anions. A comparable result will be found in the subsequently discussed alkylations of α, β-unsaturated ketones.

By using different reaction conditions, namely treatment of an aryl halide (e.g., **[38]**) with a solution of an enolate anion and excess sodium amide in liquid ammonia, it is possible to obtain fair

$$\underset{\text{(2 equiv.)}}{CH_2(CO_2C_2H_5)_2} \xrightarrow[\text{liq. } NH_3]{\text{4 equiv. } NaNH_2} \underset{Na^{\oplus}}{{}^{\ominus}CH(CO_2C_2H_5)_2} + \underset{\textbf{[38]}\ \text{(1 equiv.)}}{C_6H_5Br} \xrightarrow{NaNH_2}$$

(*Ref. 46*)

$$\underset{\textbf{[39]}}{C_6H_4} + {}^{\ominus}CH(CO_2C_2H_5)_2 \longrightarrow {}^{\ominus}C_6H_4CH(CO_2C_2H_5)_2 \longrightarrow$$

$$C_6H_5C^{\ominus}(CO_2C_2H_5)_2 \xrightarrow[H_2O]{HCl} \underset{(51\%)}{C_6H_5CH(CO_2C_2H_5)_2} + \underset{(18\%,\ \text{from } \textbf{[39]} + NH_2^{\ominus})}{C_6H_5NH_2}$$

yields of arylated products. The reaction is not a nucleophilic displacement but rather follows an elimination-addition sequence in which an intermediate **[39]**, called a benzyne or a dehydrobenzene,[44,47] is involved. It will be noted that mixtures of structural isomers will usually be obtained if a substituted aryl halide is employed. A useful synthetic application of this reaction is the intramolecular addition of an anion to a benzyne intermediate as outlined below.

$$o\text{-}ClC_6H_4CH_2CH_2C{\equiv}N \xrightarrow[\text{liq. } NH_3]{KNH_2} C_6H_4CH_2\overset{\ominus}{C}H{-}CN \xrightarrow{NH_4NO_3} \underset{(61\%)}{\text{1-cyanobenzocyclobutene } (C{\equiv}N)}$$

(*Ref. 48*)

The formation of cyclic compounds by the alkylation of active methylene compounds, illustrated in the accompanying equations,

(46) W. W. Leake and R. Levine, *J. Am. Chem. Soc.*, **81**, 1169, 1627 (1959).

(47) (a) R. Huisgen and J. Sauer, *Angew. Chem.*, **72**, 91 (1960); (b) H. Heaney, *Chem. Rev.*, **62**, 81 (1962).

(48) (a) J. F. Bunnett and J. A. Skorcz, *J. Org. Chem.*, **27**, 3836 (1962); (b) J. F. Bunnett, T. Kato, R. R. Flynn, and J. A. Skorcz, *ibid.*, **28**, 1 (1963); (c) see also J. F. Bunnett, B. F. Hrutfiord, and S. M. Williamson, *Org. Syn.*, **40**, 1 (1960); (d) T. M. Harris and C. R. Hauser, *J. Org. Chem.*, **29**, 1391 (1964).

has found widespread use.[10,49] In general, the relative rates of

$$Br(CH_2)_4Br + CH_3COCH_2CO_2C_2H_5 \xrightarrow[C_2H_5OH,\ 100^\circ]{NaOC_2H_5} \text{1-acetyl-1-carbethoxycyclopentane } (COCH_3,\ CO_2C_2H_5) \qquad (Ref.\ 50)$$

$$CH(CO_2C_2H_5)_2-(CH_2)_3-CH(CO_2C_2H_5)_2 + CH_2I_2 \xrightarrow[C_2H_5OH,\ 100^\circ]{NaOC_2H_5} \text{cyclohexane-1,1,3,3-}(CO_2C_2H_5)_4 \qquad (Ref.\ 51)$$

$$CH_3-CO-CH_2CH_2CH_2Cl \xrightarrow[H_2O,\ reflux]{NaOH} CH_3-CO-\text{cyclopropyl} \quad (77\text{–}83\%) \qquad (Ref.\ 42)$$

closure for rings of varying size follow the order three-, five-, and six-membered rings > seven-membered rings > four- and more-than-seven-membered rings and noncyclic compounds (resulting from intermolecular reactions).[52] The fact that four-membered rings are produced at a rate comparable to that of intermolecular reactions requires that they be prepared under carefully controlled conditions[53] to minimize the formation of acylic products. Although the preparation of three-membered rings by alkylation is a kinetically favored process, the initial products are capable of reacting with an additional equivalent of the anion derived from the active methylene compound to form acyclic compounds, as

$$CH_2(CO_2C_2H_5)_2 \xrightarrow[C_2H_5OH]{NaOC_2H_5} {}^{\ominus}CH(CO_2C_2H_5)_2\ Na^{\oplus} \xrightarrow[NaOC_2H_5,\ C_2H_5OH,\ reflux]{Br(CH_2)_3Br} \text{cyclobutane-1,1-}(CO_2C_2H_5)_2\ (55\text{–}65\%) + (C_2H_5O_2C)_2CH-(CH_2)_3-CH(CO_2C_2H_5)_2\ (10\%) \qquad (Ref.\ 53)$$

(49) R. C. Fuson in H. Gilman (ed.), *Organic Chemistry*, Vol. 1, Wiley, New York, 1943, pp. 82–88.

(50) L. J. Goldsworthy, *J. Chem. Soc.*, **1934**, 377.

(51) W. H. Perkin, *ibid.*, **59**, 798 (1891).

(52) (a) E. L. Eliel in M. S. Newman (ed.), *Steric Effects in Organic Chemistry*, Wiley, New York, 1956, pp. 114–120; (b) E. L. Eliel, *Stereochemistry of Carbon Compounds*, McGraw-Hill, New York, 1962, pp. 198–202.

(53) (a) J. Cason and H. Rapoport, *Laboratory Text in Organic Chemistry*, 2d ed., Prentice-Hall, Englewood Cliffs, N.J., 1962, pp. 401–408; (b) for a less satisfactory procedure, see G. B. Heisig and F. H. Stodola, *Org. Syn.*, **Coll. Vol. 3,**

illustrated below. The most successful preparations of cyclopropane derivatives[42,55] utilize the intramolecular alkylation of

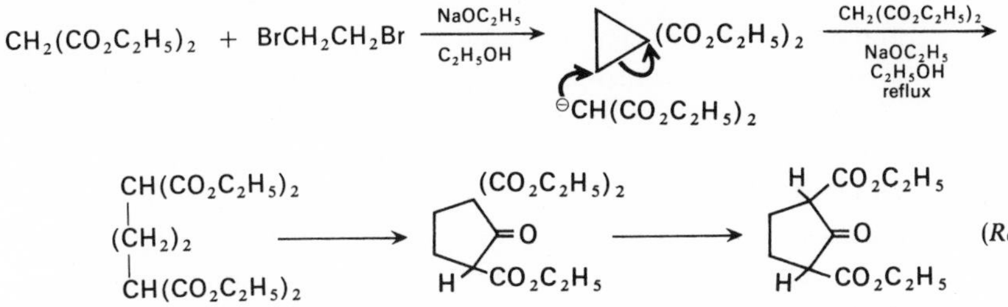

$$CH_2(CO_2C_2H_5)_2 + BrCH_2CH_2Br \xrightarrow[C_2H_5OH]{NaOC_2H_5} \text{cyclopropane}(CO_2C_2H_5)_2 \xrightarrow[\substack{NaOC_2H_5\\C_2H_5OH\\reflux}]{CH_2(CO_2C_2H_5)_2}$$

$$^{\ominus}CH(CO_2C_2H_5)_2$$

$$CH(CO_2C_2H_5)_2-(CH_2)_2-CH(CO_2C_2H_5)_2 \longrightarrow \text{cyclopentanone}(CO_2C_2H_5)_2(H)(CO_2C_2H_5) \longrightarrow \text{cyclopentanone}(H)(CO_2C_2H_5)(H)(CO_2C_2H_5)$$

(*Ref. 54*)

weakly acidic active methylene compounds so that the concentration of enolate anion in solution is kept low and little attack on the cyclopropane ring is observed.

A difficulty always encountered in the alkylation of active methylene compounds having two or more acidic hydrogen atoms is the possibility of dialkylation. This problem, illustrated in the accompanying equations, arises because the monoalkylated product

$$CH_2(CO_2C_2H_5)_2 + C_6H_5CH_2Cl \xrightarrow[\substack{C_2H_5OH\\reflux}]{NaOC_2H_5} \underset{\textbf{[40]}\ (51\text{–}57\%)}{C_6H_5CH_2{-}CH(CO_2C_2H_5)_2} + (C_6H_5CH_2)_2C(CO_2C_2H_5)_2$$

(*Refs. 10, 56*)

$$Na^{\oplus}\,{}^{\ominus}CH(CO_2C_2H_5)_2 + C_2H_5OH \rightleftharpoons CH_2(CO_2C_2H_5)_2 + C_2H_5O^{\ominus}Na^{\oplus}$$

$$C_6H_5CH_2{-}CH(CO_2C_2H_5)_2 + C_2H_5O^{\ominus}Na^{\oplus} \rightleftharpoons \underset{\textbf{[39]}}{C_6H_5CH_2{-}C^{\ominus}(CO_2C_2H_5)_2\ Na^{\oplus}} + C_2H_5OH$$

is also acidic and will be in equilibrium with its enolate anion **[39]**. The possibility is usually not serious for the relatively acidic active methylene compounds being discussed since the solvent (ethanol) and the monoalkylated product are of similar acidic strength and both are weaker acids than the starting compound; as a result,

213 (1955); (c) note that alkylation of acetoacetic ester with 1,3-dibromopropane does not yield a four-membered carbocyclic ring but rather a six-membered dihydropyran derivative that results from a combination of O-alkylation and C-alkylation.

(54) R. W. Kierstead, R. P. Linstead, and B. C. L. Weedon, *J. Chem. Soc.*, **1952**, 3610, 3616.

(55) (a) C. M. McCloskey and G. H. Coleman, *Org. Syn.*, **Coll. Vol. 3,** 221 (1955); (b) M. J. Schlatter, *ibid.*, **Coll. Vol. 3,** 223 (1955).

(56) C. S. Marvel, *ibid.*, **Coll. Vol. 3,** 705 (1955).

the concentration of enolate anion derived from the monoalkylated product is relatively low. However, dialkylation does become a significant side reaction in the alkylation of active methylene compounds with benzyl halides, allyl halides, or α-haloketones, a fact possibly attributable to the greater acidity of the monoalkylated products as compared to that of the corresponding compounds derived from simple alkyl halides. For alkylations carried out with strong bases and nonhydroxylic solvents—such as the subsequently discussed alkylations of ketones and nitriles—dialkylation is almost always a significant side reaction. As would be predicted from the above equilibria, it is possible to reduce the concentration of the monoalkylated enolate anion [**39**] (and consequently the amount of dialkylation) by adding an excess of the starting active methylene compound to the reaction mixture. For example, in the case cited, the yield of the monoalkylated product [**40**] can be increased from 57 per cent to 85 per cent by using two equivalents of diethyl malonate with one equivalent of the halide and one equivalent of base.[10] This procedure is desirable if the starting active methylene compound is readily available and easily separable from the product.

Alkylation of Ketones and Nitriles

From reference to Table 7-1 it will be apparent that a stronger base than sodium ethoxide and a less acidic solvent than ethanol must be used in order to obtain an appreciable concentration of an anion from a methylene group activated only by a nitrile or ketone function. The metal alkoxides derived from tertiary alcohols such as *t*-butyl alcohol or *t*-amyl alcohol are usually sufficiently basic to provide appreciable equilibrium concentrations of enolate anions from ketones, especially in cases where the anion is stabilized both by the carbonyl group and by an alpha vinyl or phenyl substituent. Alternatively, much stronger bases will convert either ketones or nitriles quantitatively to their anions. Table 7-2 lists some of the common bases and solvents that have been employed for the conversion of weakly acidic active methylene compounds to their anions. The accompanying equations illustrate the use of certain of these bases for alkylations.

Among these base-solvent combinations, sodium amide in an inert solvent (usually ether or toluene) and the metal *t*-alkoxides (especially potassium *t*-butoxide in *t*-butyl alcohol) have enjoyed

TABLE 7-2 ▪

Commonly Used Strong Bases

Base	References to preparation and use	Frequently used solvents
$(CH_3)_3C\overset{\ominus}{O}\overset{\oplus}{K}$	6d, 6g, 6h, 57, 58, 59	*t*-Butyl alcohol, dimethyl sulfoxide, ether,* 1,2-dimethoxyethane,* benzene,* tetrahydrofuran
$(CH_3)_2C(C_2H_5)—\overset{\ominus}{O}\overset{\oplus}{Na}$	39, 60	Ether, benzene, toluene
$Na^{\oplus}\overset{\ominus}{N}H_2$	61, 62	Liquid ammonia, ether,* benzene,* toluene,* 1,2-dimethoxyethane*
$K^{\oplus}\overset{\ominus}{N}H_2$	33b, 63, 64	Liquid ammonia, ether*
$(C_2H_5)_2\overset{\ominus}{N}\overset{\oplus}{Li}$	65	1,2-Dimethoxyethane, ether
NaH	7, 22, 32a, 32c, 32g, 66, 67	Ether,* benzene,* toluene,* xylene,* 1,2-dimethoxyethane,* dimethylformamide*
LiH	2, 32g, 66	Ether*
$CH_3SO—\overset{\ominus}{C}H_2\overset{\oplus}{Na}$	32d, 68	Dimethyl sulfoxide (prepared by reaction of sodium hydride with excess dimethyl sulfoxide)
$(C_6H_5)_3\overset{\ominus}{C}\overset{\oplus}{Li}$	7, 65d, 69	Ether, 1,2-dimethoxyethane
$(C_6H_5)_3\overset{\ominus}{C}\overset{\oplus}{Na}$	2, 70, 71b	Ether, benzene, toluene, liquid ammonia
$(C_6H_5)_3\overset{\ominus}{C}\overset{\oplus}{K}$	7, 65d, 71	1,2-Dimethoxyethane
[naphthalene radical anion]$^{\ominus}$ $Na^{\oplus}$	72	1,2-Dimethoxyethane

*Solvents in which base is only slightly soluble.

(57) Commercially available from the MSA Research Corp., Callery, Pennsylvania.

(58) For preparations see (a) W. S. Johnson and W. P. Schneider, *Org. Syn.*, **Coll. Vol. 4**, 132 (1963); (b) W. S. Johnson and G. H. Daub, *Org. Reactions*, **6**, 41 (1951); (c) Ref. 6d.

(59) (a) H. Rinderknecht, *J. Am. Chem. Soc.*, **73**, 5770 (1951); (b) F. Sondheimer and Y. Mazur, *ibid.*, **79**, 2906 (1957); (c) Y. Mazur and F. Sondheimer, *ibid.*, **80**, 5220, 6296 (1958); (d) H. J. Ringold and G. Rosenkrantz, *J. Org. Chem.*, **22**, 602 (1957); (e) M. Yanagita, M. Hirakura, and F. Seki, *ibid.*, **23**, 841 (1958); (f) N. W. Atwater, *J. Am. Chem. Soc.*, **82**, 2847 (1960).

(60) (a) J. M. Conia and P. Gosselin, *Bull. Soc. Chim. France*, **1961**, 836; (b) J. M. Conia and F. Rouessac, *Tetrahedron*, **16**, 45 (1961); (c) J. M. Conia and A. Sandre-Le Craz, *Tetrahedron Letters*, **No. 12**, 505 (1962); (d) J. M. Conia and F. Rouessac, *Bull. Soc. Chim. France*, **1963**, 1925, 1930.

(61) Commercially available from Roberts Chemicals, Inc., Nitro, West Virginia.

(62) (a) F. W. Bergstrom, *Org. Syn.*, **Coll. Vol. 3**, 778 (1955); (b) C. A. Vanderwerf and L. F. Lemmerman, *ibid.*, **Coll. Vol. 3**, 44 (1955); (c) E. M. Hancock and A. C. Cope, *ibid.*, **Coll. Vol. 3**, 219 (1955); (d) C. R. Hauser and W. R. Dunnavant, *Org. Syn.*, **40**, 38 (1960); (e) G. Wash, B. Shive, and H. L. Lochte, *J. Am. Chem. Soc.*, **63**, 2975 (1941); (f) A. Haller and E. Bauer, *Ann. Chim. (Paris)*, **(8)28**, 373 (1913).

(63) C. R. Hauser and W. R. Dunnavant, *Org. Syn.*, **39**, 73 (1959).

(64) (a) C. R. Hauser and T. M. Harris, *J. Am. Chem. Soc.*, **80**, 6360 (1958); **81**, 1154, 1160 (1959); (b) R. B. Meyer and C. R. Hauser, *J. Org. Chem.*, **25**, 158 (1960); (c) W. G. Kofron, W. R. Dunnavant, and C. R. Hauser, *ibid.*, **27**, 2737 (1962); (d) T. M. Harris and C. R. Hauser, *J. Am. Chem. Soc.*, **84**, 1750 (1962).

(65) (a) K. Ziegler and H. Ohlinger, *Ann. Chem.*, **495**, 84 (1932); (b) J. Cason, G. Sumrell, and R. S. Mitchell, *J. Org. Chem.*, **15**, 850 (1950); (c) A. C. Cope and B. D. Tiffany, *J. Am. Chem. Soc.*, **73**, 4158 (1951); (d) H. O. House and B. M. Trost, *J. Org. Chem.*, **30**, 1341 (1965); (e) H. Gilman, N. N. Crounse, S. P. Massie, Jr., R. A. Benkeser, and S. M. Spatz, *J. Am. Chem. Soc.*, **67**, 2106 (1945); (f) C. H. Horning and F. W. Bergstrom, *ibid.*, **67**, 2110 (1945).

(66) Commercially available from Metal Hydrides, Inc., Beverley, Massachusetts; see Ref. 58b for precautions in handling dry sodium hydride. The currently available sodium hydride is sold as a dispersion in mineral oil. It is almost always desirable to wash this dispersion with ether or pentane (see Ref. 32g) prior to use in order to remove the mineral oil.

(67) (a) M. D. Soffer, R. A. Stewart, J. C. Cavagnol, H. E. Gellerson, and E. A. Bowler, *J. Am. Chem. Soc.*, **72**, 3704 (1950); (b) J. H. Fried, G. E. Arth, and L. H. Sarett, *ibid.*, **82**, 1684 (1960); (c) J. H. Fried, A. N. Nutile, and G. E. Arth, *ibid.*, **82**, 5704 (1960).

(68) (a) E. J. Corey and M. Chaykovsky, *ibid.*, **84**, 866 (1962); (b) for a study of the thermal decomposition of dimethylsulfoxide, see V. J. Traynelis and W. L. Hergenrother, *J. Org. Chem.*, **29**, 221 (1964); (c) A. Ledwith and N. McFarlane, *Proc. Chem. Soc.*, 108 (1964).

(69) (a) P. Tomboulian, *J. Org. Chem.*, **24**, 229 (1959); (b) H. Gilman and B. J. Gaj, *ibid.*, **28**, 1725 (1963).

Cyclohexanone $\xrightarrow[(C_2H_5)_2O,\ \text{reflux}]{NaNH_2}$ sodium enolate ($O^{\ominus}Na^{\oplus}$) $\xrightarrow[(C_2H_5)_2O,\ \text{reflux}]{CH_2{=}CHCH_2Cl}$ 2-($CH_2CH{=}CH_2$)cyclohexanone (54–62%) + ($CH_2CH{=}CH_2)_2$-cyclohexanone (*Ref. 62b*)

$$C_6H_5{-}CH_2{-}C{\equiv}N \xrightarrow[\text{liq. } NH_3]{NaNH_2} C_6H_5{-}C^{\ominus}H{-}C{\equiv}N\ Na^{\oplus} \xrightarrow[C_6H_5CH_3,\ \text{reflux}]{\text{cyclohexyl-Br}} C_6H_5{-}CH(C_6H_{11}){-}C{\equiv}N$$

(65–77%) (*Ref. 62c*)

$$(C_6H_5)_2CH{-}C{\equiv}N \xrightarrow[\text{liq. } NH_3]{KNH_2} (C_6H_5)_2C^{\ominus}{-}C{\equiv}N\ K^{\oplus} \xrightarrow[\text{liq. } NH_3]{C_6H_5CH_2Cl} (C_6H_5)_2C(CH_2{-}C_6H_5){-}C{\equiv}N$$

(95–99%) (*Ref. 63*)

β-Tetralone + $BrCH_2CO_2CH_3$ $\xrightarrow[C_6H_6]{NaH}$ 1-($CH_2{-}CO_2CH_3$)-2-tetralone (94%) (*Ref. 67a*)

$$C_6H_5{-}CO{-}CH_2CH_2CH_3 \xrightarrow[(C_2H_5)_2O]{(C_6H_5)_3C^{\ominus}Na^{\oplus}} C_6H_5{-}C(O^{\ominus})\!{=}CHCH_2CH_3\ Na^{\oplus} \xrightarrow[(C_2H_5)_2O]{C_2H_5Br} C_6H_5{-}CO{-}CH(C_2H_5)_2$$

(62%) (*Ref. 70a*)

---

(70) (a) H. D. Zook and W. L. Rellahan, *J. Am. Chem. Soc.*, **79**, 881 (1957); (b) C. R. Hauser and W. B. Renfrew, Jr., *Org. Syn.*, **Coll. Vol. 2,** 268 (1943); (c) H. Adkins and W. Zartman, *ibid.*, **Coll. Vol. 2,** 607 (1943).

(71) (a) H. O. House and V. Kramar, *J. Org. Chem.*, **27**, 4146 (1962); (b) D. F. Thompson, P. L. Bayless, and C. R. Hauser, *ibid.*, **19**, 1490 (1954); C. R. Hauser, D. S. Hoffenberg, W. H. Puterbaugh, and F. C. Frostick, Jr., *ibid.*, **20**, 1531 (1955).

(72) (a) N. D. Scott, J. F. Walker, and V. L. Hansley, *J. Am. Chem. Soc.*, **58**, 2442 (1936); (b) H. Normant and B. Angelo, *Bull. Soc. Chim. France*, **1960**, 354; see also (c) J. J. Eisch and W. C. Kaska, *J. Org. Chem.*, **27**, 3745 (1962).

CH_3I, $(CH_3)_3COK$, $(CH_3)_3COH$, reflux (*Ref. 59c*)

$C_2H_5—C(CH_3)_2ONa$, C_6H_6, reflux (55%) (*Ref. 60b*)

the most widespread use. The *t*-alkoxide bases suffer one major disadvantage: at equilibrium, most ketones are only partially converted to their enolate anions; as a result, an aldol condensation (see Chapter 8) may occur between the free ketone and its enolate anion,[39] especially if the intermediate aldol condensation product can be dehydrated by base to form an α,β-unsaturated ketone. Although the other bases listed in Table 7-2 are capable of converting ketones essentially quantitatively to their enolate anions, competing aldol condensation may also be a problem with sodium hydride[7] or sodium amide[39] in an inert solvent. When either of these is used, the enolate is formed relatively slowly in the heterogeneous reaction mixture, with the result that appreciable concentrations of both the free ketone and its enolate anion are present at some point. This difficulty may be mitigated, at least in part, by allowing a mixture of the ketone and the alkylating agent to react with sodium hydride in 1,2-dimethoxyethane, instead of attempting to form the enolate anion before the alkylating agent is added.

The various metal derivatives of triphenylmethane offer the advantage that addition of the ketone to solutions of the triphenylmethide anion results in immediate formation of the enolate anion, so that little, if any aldol condensation is observed. Furthermore, the dropwise addition of the ketone until the intense red color of the triphenylmethide anion is just discharged allows conversion to the enolate anion in the absence of excess base and excess ketone. Similarly, the addition of a few milligrams of triphenylmethane as an indicator to solutions of lithium diethylamide in 1,2-dimethoxyethane,[65d] of sodium amide in liquid ammonia, or of the dimethyl sulfoxide anion in dimethyl sulfoxide permits these bases to be titrated with a ketone. This procedure for establishing the complete conversion of an active methylene compound to its anion is decidedly simpler than following the evolution of hydrogen when sodium hydride is employed as the base.[7,67a] The major objection to the use of metal triphenylmethides is the fact that the reaction products must be separated from a substantial quantity of triphenylmethane. Utilization of the dimethyl sulfoxide anion as a base is frequently objectionable because this anion may add to the carbonyl function instead of abstracting an alpha hydrogen atom.[68,73] Furthermore, the facts that dimethyl sulfoxide reacts slowly with alkylating agents and is sometimes difficult to separate from the products make this an undesirable solvent for alkylation reactions. At the present time, 1,2-dimethoxyethane, dimethylformamide, or liquid ammonia appear to be the best solvents to employ. Although the selection of the base will depend on the properties of the compound to be alkylated, sodium *t*-amyloxide, sodium amide, sodium hydride, and lithium diethylamide seem to offer the most advantages. In spite of its lower solubility in ethereal solvents, potassium *t*-butoxide does offer the practical advantage of being commercially available.[57]

The alkylation of nitriles, of symmetrical ketones, and of ketones that can enolize in only one direction usually presents no problem other than the separation of the monoalkylated product from any unchanged starting material or dialkylated product. The O-alkylation of ketone enolates is only rarely observed.[59a,62e] The alkylation of nitriles (e.g., **[41]**) and subsequent hydrolysis often provides a good synthetic route to α-substituted acetic acids in spite of the rather vigorous conditions required for the hydrolysis.

$$\underset{\textbf{[41]}}{n\text{-}C_4H_9\text{—}CH_2\text{—}CN} \xrightarrow[\substack{NaNH_2\\ C_6H_5CH_3\\ \text{reflux}}]{n\text{-}C_4H_9Br} \underset{(81\%)}{(n\text{-}C_4H_9)_3C\text{—}C\equiv N} \xrightarrow[\substack{H_2O\\ \text{reflux}}]{H_2SO_4(80\%)}$$

(*Ref. 74*)

$$\underset{(90\%)}{(n\text{-}C_4H_9)_3C\text{—}CO\text{—}NH_2} \xrightarrow[\substack{HCl\\ CH_3CO_2H}]{n\text{-}C_4H_9\text{—}ONO} \underset{(79\%)}{(n\text{-}C_4H_9)_3C\text{—}CO_2H}$$

(73) (a) G. A. Russel, E. G. Janzen, H. D. Becker, and F. J. Smentowski, *J. Am. Chem. Soc.*, **84**, 2652 (1962); (b) M. Chaykovsky and E. J. Corey, *J. Org. Chem.*, **28**, 254 (1963); (c) C. Walling and L. Bollyky, *ibid.*, **28**, 256 (1963).

(74) (a) N. Sperber, D. Papa, and E. Schwenk, *J. Am. Chem. Soc.*, **70**, 3091 (1948); (b) the N-alkylation of very hindered nitriles to form ketimines has been observed: see M. S. Newman, T. Fukunaga, and T. Miwa, *ibid.*, **82**, 873 (1960).

The alkylation of ketones that can form structurally isomeric enolate anions raises two questions: which enolate will predominate in the equilibrium mixture and which monoalkylated structure will predominate in the product. As illustrated previously in this chapter, if only one of the structurally isomeric enolate anions is stabilized by an alpha substituent such as a carboalkoxy, cyano, or carbonyl group, then essentially only this highly stabilized enolate is formed and alkylation occurs at the position activated by both functional groups. Interestingly, if such stabilized enolates are treated with an excess of potassium amide in liquid ammonia, dianions may be formed[64]; as the accompanying equations show, reaction of these dianions with only one equivalent of an alkylating agent results in the predominant alkylation of the less stable of the two enolate anions present.

$\xrightarrow[\text{liq. } NH_3]{KNH_2}$ $\xrightarrow[\text{liq. } NH_3,\ (C_2H_5)_2O]{\text{1 equiv. } C_6H_5CH_2Cl}$ $\xrightarrow[H_2O]{NH_4Cl}$

$CO—CH_2CH_2C_6H_5$ (62%)

(Ref. 64a)

$\xrightarrow[\text{liq. } NH_3]{KNH_2}$ $\xrightarrow[\text{liq. } NH_3]{\text{1 equiv. } CH_3I}$ $\xrightarrow[H_2O]{Cu(OCOCH_3)_2}$

(Ref. 64d)

(60%) $\xrightarrow{H_3O^{\oplus}}$ $\xrightarrow[H_2O]{OH^{\ominus}}$

[85% of mixture of *cis* (44%) and *trans* (56%) isomers]

Even an α-phenyl group[7,39] or an α-vinyl group[6h,39,60c] provides sufficient stabilization to determine the structure of an enolate anion derived from an unsymmetrical ketone. This selectivity is illustrated by the accompanying examples. As noted previously, the anion [**44**] derived from an α,β-unsaturated ketone [**43**] by abstraction of a gamma proton is alkylated at the alpha position

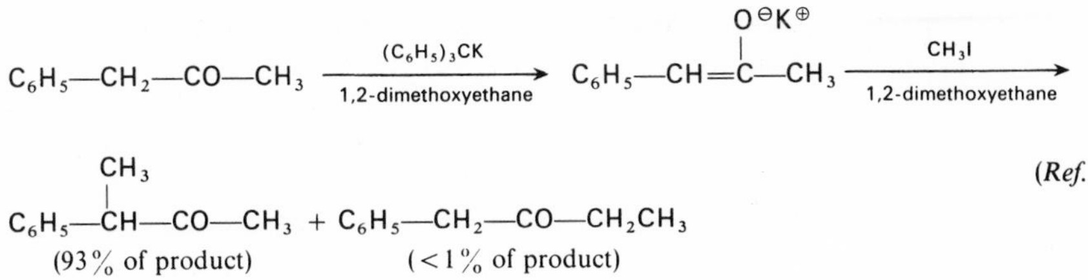

$$C_6H_5{-}CH_2{-}CO{-}CH_3 \xrightarrow[\text{1,2-dimethoxyethane}]{(C_6H_5)_3CK} C_6H_5{-}CH{=}\overset{O^{\ominus}K^{\oplus}}{\overset{|}{C}}{-}CH_3 \xrightarrow[\text{1,2-dimethoxyethane}]{CH_3I}$$

$$\underset{(93\%\ \text{of product})}{C_6H_5{-}\overset{CH_3}{\overset{|}{C}H}{-}CO{-}CH_3} + \underset{(<1\%\ \text{of product})}{C_6H_5{-}CH_2{-}CO{-}CH_2CH_3}$$

(*Ref. 7*)

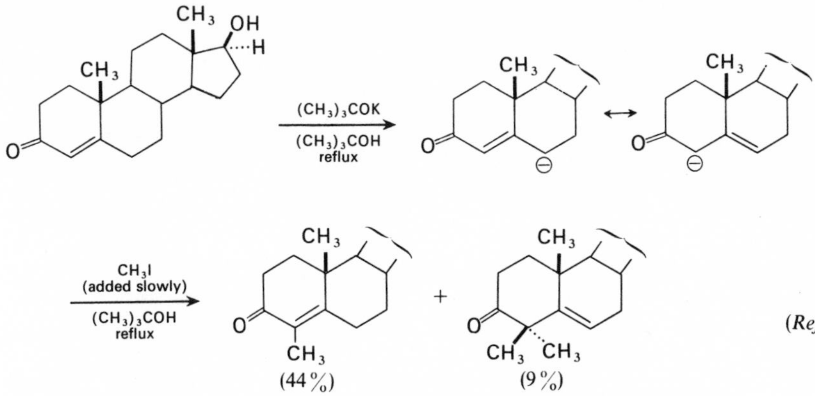

(CH$_3$)$_3$COK, (CH$_3$)$_3$COH, reflux; then CH$_3$I (added slowly), (CH$_3$)$_3$COH, reflux → (44%) + (9%)

(*Ref. 59f*)

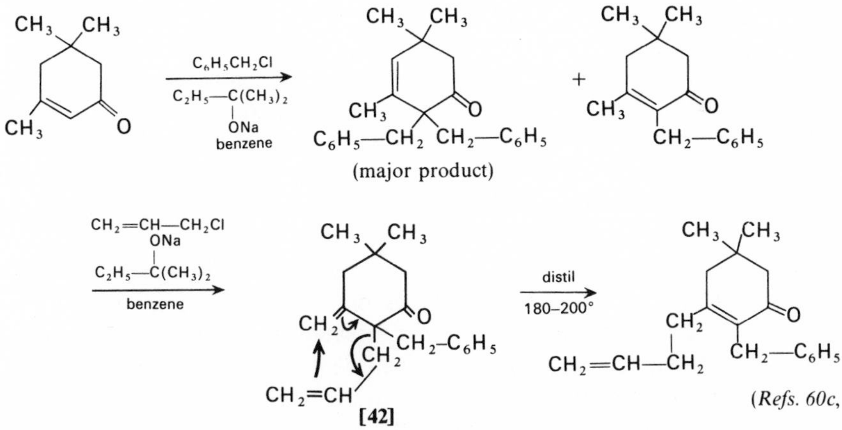

C$_6$H$_5$CH$_2$Cl, C$_2$H$_5$—C(CH$_3$)$_2$ONa, benzene → C$_6$H$_5$—CH$_2$, CH$_2$—C$_6$H$_5$ (major product) + CH$_2$—C$_6$H$_5$

CH$_2$=CH—CH$_2$Cl, C$_2$H$_5$—C(CH$_3$)$_2$ONa, benzene → [42] → distil 180–200° → CH$_2$=CH—CH$_2$, CH$_2$—C$_6$H$_5$

(*Refs. 60c, 75*)

to form a β,γ-unsaturated ketone [**45**]. This initial product [**45**] may be isomerized to an α-alkyl-α,β-unsaturated ketone [**46**] or

(75) (a) J. M. Conia, *Bull. Soc. Chim. France*, **1954,** 690; (b) J. M. Conia and C. Nevot, *ibid.*, **1959,** 493; (c) J. M. Conia and A. Le Craz, *ibid.*, **1960,** 1929, 1934; (d) J. M. Conia and P. Le Perchec, *Tetrahedron Letters*, **No. 39,** 2791 (1964).

$$R_2CH\text{—}CH{=}CH\text{—}CO\text{—}R \underset{(slow)}{\overset{base}{\rightleftharpoons}} R_2C^{\ominus}\text{—}CH{=}CH\text{—}CO\text{—}R \longleftrightarrow$$
[43] **[44a]**

$$R_2C{=}CH\text{—}CH^{\ominus}\text{—}CO\text{—}R \xrightarrow{CH_3I} R_2C{=}CH\text{—}CH(CH_3)\text{—}CO\text{—}R \underset{(fast)}{\overset{base}{\rightleftharpoons}}$$
[44b] **[45]**

$$R_2C{=}CH\text{—}\overset{\ominus}{C}(CH_3)\text{—}CO\text{—}R \longleftrightarrow R_2\overset{\ominus}{C}\text{—}CH{=}C(CH_3)\text{—}CO\text{—}R$$
[47a] **[47b]**

$$R_2C{=}CH\text{—}C(CH_3)_2\text{—}CO\text{—}R \xleftarrow{CH_3I} [47] \underset{(slow)}{\overset{H^+}{\rightleftharpoons}} R_2CH\text{—}CH{=}C(CH_3)\text{—}CO\text{—}R$$
[48] **[46]**

may undergo further alkylation ([**48**]). Dialkylation has often been the major reaction in such cases[6h,59b,59d–59f,76] because a proton is abstracted more readily from the intermediate β,γ-unsaturated ketone [**45**] than from the starting material [**43**] or the alkylated α,β-unsaturated ketone [**46**].[6h] Dialkylation may be diminished either by the slow addition of the alkylating agent[59f] or by the use of a less reactive alkylating agent (e.g., methyl chloride).[6h] Such procedures permit the isomerization of the β,γ-unsaturated ketone [**45**] (to the less acidic α,β-unsaturated ketone [**46**]) to occur more rapidly than alkylation of the intermediate anion [**47**]. The ready thermal isomerization of the α-allyl-β,γ-unsaturated ketone [**42**], an example of the Cope rearrangement, is also noteworthy as a possible complication in the alkylation of an α,β-unsaturated ketone with an allyl halide.

Unsymmetrical ketones with only alkyl groups as alpha substituents usually yield mixtures of the two possible structurally isomeric enolate anions when treated with base. The various potential effects of α-alkyl substituents, including destabilization of resonance structure [**49**] (for electrostatic reasons) and stabilization of resonance structure [**50**] (by hyperconjugation) appear to

$$R\text{—}C({=}O)\text{—}CH^{\ominus}\text{—}CH_3 \longleftrightarrow R\text{—}C(O^{\ominus}){=}CH\text{—}CH_3$$
[49] **[50]**

(76) R. B. Woodward, A. A. Patchett, D. H. R. Barton, D. A. J. Ives, and R. B. Kelly, *J. Chem. Soc.*, **1957**, 1131.

be approximately balanced. As a result, the equilibrium between structurally isomeric enolates of this type may be influenced not only by the structure of the ketone but also by factors usually considered of minor importance, among them the identity of the cation and the nature of the solvent.[6b,7] Table 7-3 summarizes the

TABLE 7-3 ▪
Equilibrium Positions for Solutions of Potassium Enolates in 1,2-Dimethoxyethane

Ketone	Less highly substituted enolate, %	Ketone	Less highly substituted enolate, %
$n\text{-}C_4H_9—CH_2—CO—CH_3$	58	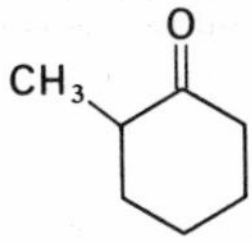 CH_3, O	30–40
$(CH_3)_2CH—CH_2—CO—CH_3$	82	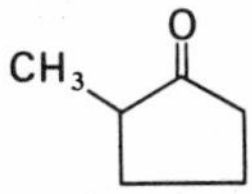 CH_3, O	25–30
$(CH_3)_2CH—CO—CH_2—CH_3$	90		
$(C_2H_5)_2CH—CO—CH_2—C_2H_5$	97		

equilibrium concentrations for a number of potassium enolates as solutions in 1,2-dimethoxyethane.[7,65d] In general, changing from a lithium to a potassium enolate shifts the equilibrium toward the less highly substituted enolate anion, whereas changing the solvent from 1,2-dimethoxyethane to the more polar dimethyl sulfoxide shifts the equilibrium toward the more highly substituted enolate.[7,65d] Since the rate of reaction of an enolate anion with a given alkylating agent is usually not markedly altered by changing the number of alkyl substituents on the enolate anion,[39,70a] the amounts of monoalkylated products formed often follow closely the compositions of the enolate anion mixtures. However, this generalization is only valid provided that further alkylation of the initial products can be avoided, since monoalkylated products may subsequently react with base at different rates to form anions that are themselves alkylated. Although di- and polyalkylation may sometimes be diminished by the slow addition of a solution of the enolate anion to a large excess of the alkylating agent, such procedure is not practical in the usual preparative alkylation experiments (e.g., with **[51]**). As a result, rather complex mixtures may be formed in the alkylation of unsymmetrical ketones; and if the physical

[51] $\xrightarrow[\text{1,2-dimethoxyethane}]{\text{1. } (C_6H_5)_3CK \text{ 2. } CH_3I}$ (9%) + (41%) + (21%) + (6%) *(Ref. 7)*

properties of the mono- and dialkylated products are similar (as is often the case when a methyl or ethyl group is being introduced), isolation of pure compounds from the mixture frequently requires chemical transformation of some of the components prior to separation.[77]

Two general procedures have been followed to avoid this problem in the alkylation of unsymmetrical ketones. One approach involves the introduction of an activating functional group alpha to the carbonyl group to stabilize the desired enolate anion. Aside from the previously illustrated α-aryl substituents or α-vinyl substituents (an α,β-unsaturated ketone with a gamma proton is equivalent), the commonly used activating groups are carbethoxy, formyl,[78] and ethoxyoxalyl.[59c] As in the example below, these activating groups may be introduced by acylation of the enolate anion, usually a thermodynamically controlled process (see Chapter 9). After alkylation the activating group is removed by base-catalyzed cleavage.

(77) (a) H. Sobotka and J. D. Chanley, *J. Am. Chem. Soc.*, **71**, 4136 (1949); (b) W. J. Bailey and M. Madoff, *ibid.*, **76**, 2707 (1954); (c) F. E. King, T. J. King, and J. G. Topliss, *J. Chem. Soc.*, **1957**, 919.

(78) R. B. Woodward, F. Sondheimer, D. Taub, K. Heusler, and W. M. McLamore, *J. Am. Chem. Soc.*, **74**, 4223 (1952).

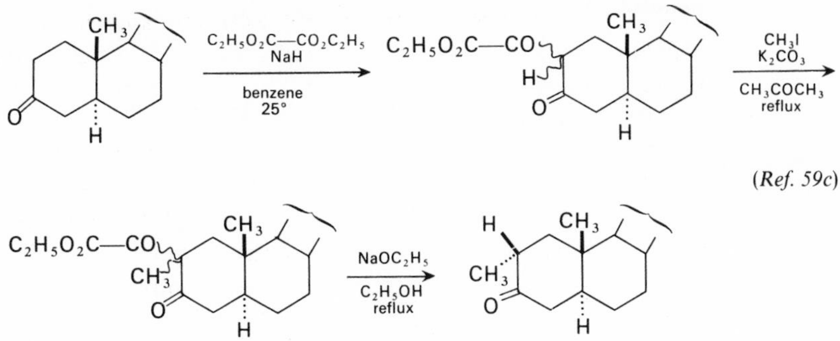

(*Ref.* 59c)

An alternative approach to selective alkylation involves the introduction of a blocking group at a methyl or methylene group alpha to the carbonyl function, thus preventing the formation of the corresponding enolate. One such type of blocking is achieved by an aldol condensation (Chapter 8) between the ketone and an aromatic aldehyde (usually benzaldehyde or furfural).[79] Although this procedure has the advantage of often producing easily crystallized ketone derivatives, it suffers from the difficulty that the arylidene blocking group is frequently difficult to remove after alkylation. A second type of blocking involves the initial acylation of a

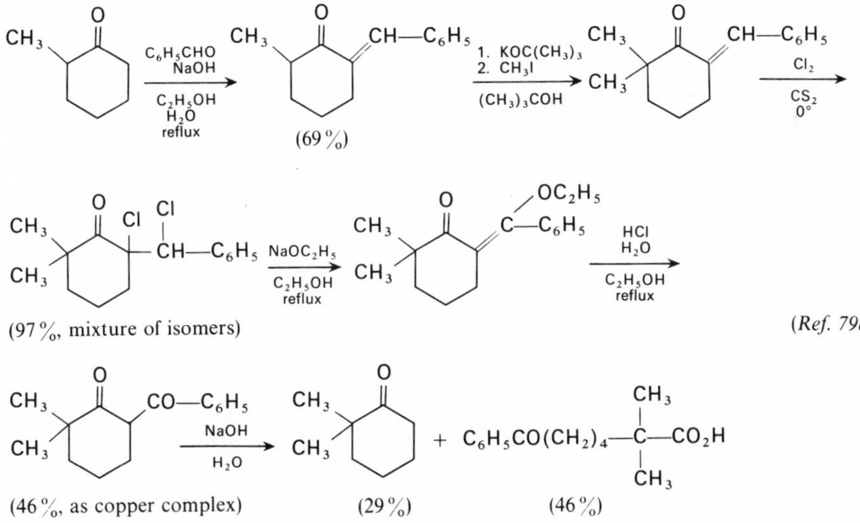

(69 %)

(97 %, mixture of isomers)

(*Ref.* 79a)

(46 %, as copper complex) (29 %) (46 %)

(79) (a) W. S. Johnson, *ibid.*, **65**, 1317 (1943); **66**, 215 (1944); (b) W. S. Johnson, D. S. Allen, Jr., R. R. Hindersinn, G. H. Sausen, and R. Pappo, *ibid.*, **84**, 2181 (1962).

methyl or methylene group with ethyl formate and the subsequent transformation of the resulting formyl (or hydroxymethylene) substituent to a grouping that is stable to base. Three different procedures have been used: reaction of the formyl group with N-methylaniline (or some other secondary amine) to form an enamine (e.g., **[52]**)[80a]; O-alkylation of the formyl substituent with isopropyl iodide to form an isopropoxy ether (e.g., **[53]**)[80b]; and reaction of the formyl group with *n*-butyl mercaptan to form a thioether (e.g., **[54]**).[81] The latter, illustrated in the accompanying equations, appears to have the greatest synthetic utility of the three. The

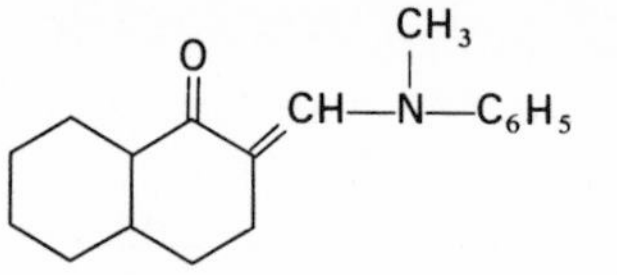

$CH—N(CH_3)—C_6H_5$

[52]

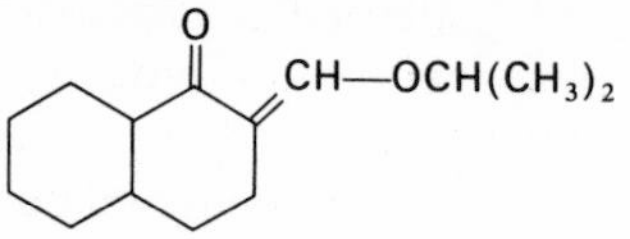

$CH—OCH(CH_3)_2$

[53]

$\xrightarrow[C_6H_6]{HCO_2C_2H_5,\ NaOCH_3}$ $\xrightarrow{H_3O^{\oplus}}$ CHO $\xrightarrow[\text{benzene, reflux with separation of } H_2O]{n\text{-}C_4H_9SH,\ p\text{-}CH_3C_6H_4SO_3H}$

(*Ref. 81*)

$CH—S—C_4H_9\text{-}n$ $\xrightarrow[(CH_3)_3COH]{1.\ KOC(CH_3)_3\quad 2.\ CH_3I}$ CH_3 $CH—S—C_4H_9\text{-}n$ H

[54] (84%)

(85%, mixture of *cis* and *trans* isomers)

$\xrightarrow[\text{diethylene glycol, reflux}]{KOH,\ H_2O}$ CH_3 H

(78%, mixture of approximately equal amounts of *cis* and *trans* isomers)

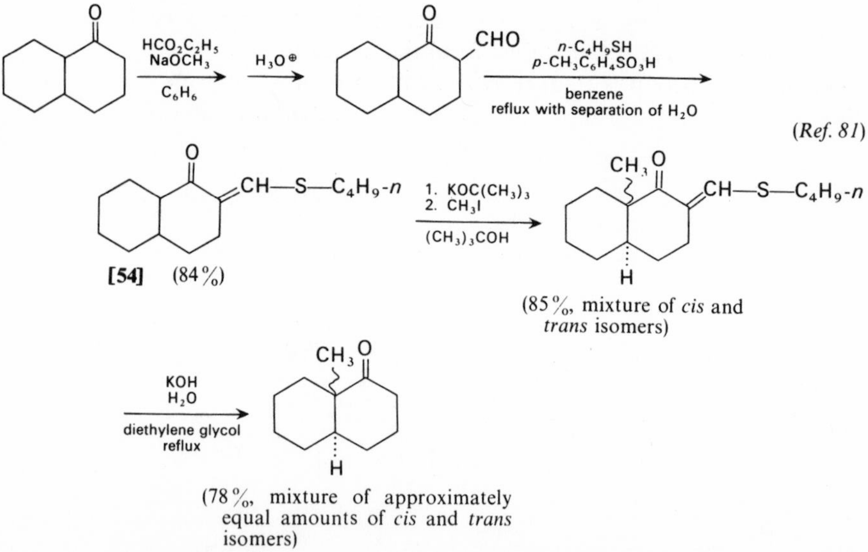

thioether blocking group (as in **[55]**) has also proved useful by virtue of its reducibility with Raney nickel or with lithium in liquid ammonia to form an α-methylketone. Reaction of an

(80) (a) A. J. Birch and R. Robinson, *J. Chem. Soc.*, **1944**, 501; (b) W. S. Johnson and H. Posvic, *J. Am. Chem. Soc.*, **69**, 1361 (1947).

(81) R. E. Ireland and J. A. Marshall, *J. Org. Chem.*, **27**, 1615, 1620 (1962).

[55] $\xrightarrow[\text{C}_2\text{H}_5\text{OH, 65°}]{\text{Ra—Ni (excess)}}$ (94%) (*Ref. 81*)

α-formylketone with 1,3-propanedithiol di-*p*-toluenesulfonate in alcoholic potassium acetate yields a keto dithioketal (e.g., **[56]**), in which the dithioketal function serves to block a methylene group during alkylation[76]; it is removed by hydrogenolysis over Raney nickel (see Chapter 1). The previously discussed monoalkylation of the dianion derived from an α-formylketone can also be considered an example of the use of a blocking group.

$\xrightarrow[\text{C}_2\text{H}_5\text{OH, reflux}]{\text{CH}_2(\text{CH}_2\text{—S—SO}_2\text{C}_6\text{H}_4\text{—CH}_3\text{-}p)_2,\ \text{KOCOCH}_3}$ **[56]** (*Ref. 76*)

A method for selectively generating a specific enolate anion that has received limited application thus far consists of reduction of an α,β-unsaturated ketone or of an α-halo- or α-acetoxyketone with a metal such as lithium, sodium, or calcium in liquid ammonia[82] (see Chapter 3). As illustrated in the equation below, enolate anions generated in this way can be alkylated before equilibration occurs.

$\xrightarrow[\text{liq. NH}_3]{\text{Li}}$ $\xrightarrow[\text{liq. NH}_3]{n\text{-C}_4\text{H}_9\text{I}}$ (*Ref. 82a*)

An indirect procedure for the selective alkylation (or acylation: see Chapter 9) of an aldehyde or ketone involves the initial reaction of the carbonyl compound with a secondary amine to form an intermediate enamine.[83] Typical enamine preparations are outlined in the accompanying equations. It will be noted that the less

(82) (a) G. Stork, P. Rosen, and N. L. Goldman, *J. Am. Chem. Soc.*, **83**, 2965 (1961); (b) R. E. Schaub and M. J. Weiss, *Chem. Ind.* (*London*), **1961**, 2003; (c) M. J. Weiss, R. E. Schaub, J. F. Poletto, G. R. Allen, Jr., and C. J. Coscia, *ibid.*, **1963,** 118; (d) M. J. Weiss and co-workers, *Tetrahedron*, **20**, 357 (1964).

(83) (a) G. Stork, A. Brizzolara, H. Landesman, J. Szmuszkovicz, and R. Terrell, *J. Am. Chem. Soc.*, **85**, 207 (1963); (b) J. Szmuszkovicz in R. A. Raphael, E. C.

highly substituted enamine is usually the predominant product unless the enamine function can be stabilized by conjugation with an adjacent functional group. The electronic distribution in enamines, as exemplified by the resonance structures **[57]** and

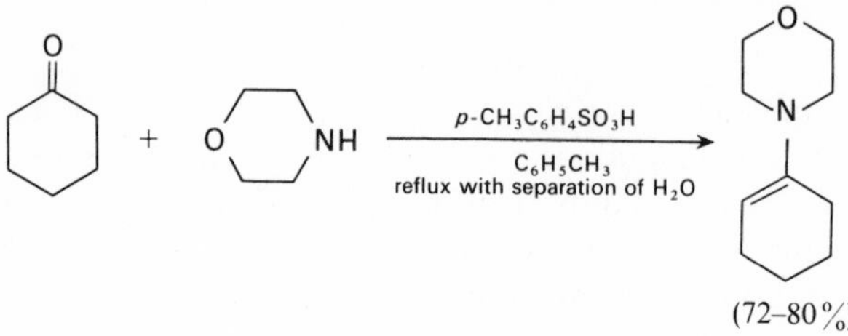

Cyclohexanone + morpholine (O, NH) $\xrightarrow[C_6H_5CH_3 \text{ reflux with separation of } H_2O]{p\text{-}CH_3C_6H_4SO_3H}$ 1-morpholinocyclohexene (N, O) (72–80%) (*Ref. 84*)

Cyclohexanone (O) + $(CH_3)_2NH$ $\xrightarrow[(C_2H_5)_2O]{CaCl_2}$ 1-(dimethylamino)cyclohexene, $N(CH_3)_2$ (52%) (*Ref. 85*)

$(CH_3)_2CH—CH_2—CHO$ + piperidine (N—H) $\xrightarrow{K_2CO_3}$ $(CH_3)_2CH—CH_2—CH(—N\text{piperidino})_2$

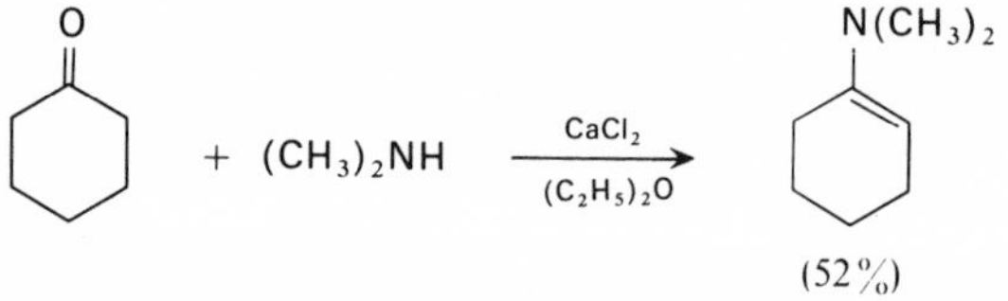

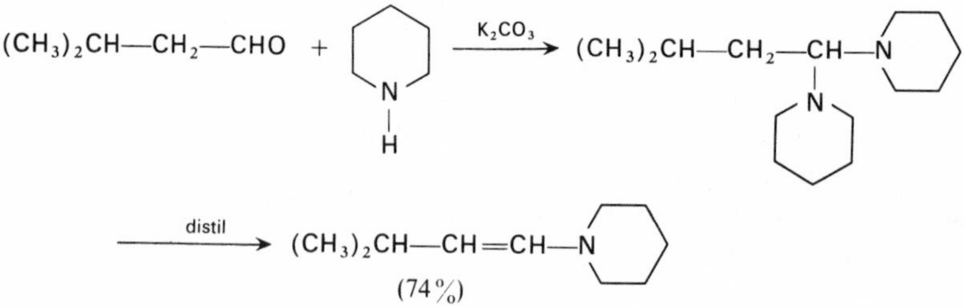

$\xrightarrow{\text{distil}}$ $(CH_3)_2CH—CH{=}CH—N$(piperidino) (74%) (*Ref. 83a*)

2-Methylcyclohexanone (CH_3, O) + pyrrolidine (N—H) $\xrightarrow[C_6H_6 \text{ reflux with separation of } H_2O]{p\text{-}CH_3C_6H_4SO_3H}$ 1-pyrrolidino-6-methylcyclohexene (CH_3, N) + 1-pyrrolidino-2-methylcyclohexene (CH_3, N)

(85% of mixture) (15% of mixture)

(53%) (*Ref. 86*)

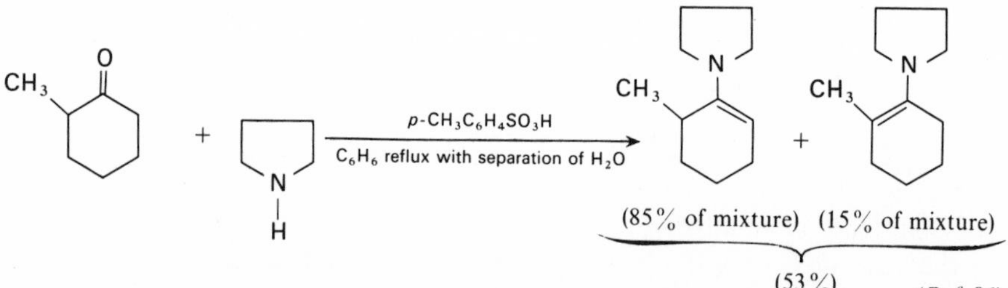

Taylor, and H. Wynberg (ed.), *Advances in Organic Chemistry: Methods and Results*, Vol. 4, Wiley-Interscience, New York, 1963, pp. 1–113.

(84) S. Hünig, E. Lücke, and W. Brenninger, *Org. Syn.*, **41**, 65 (1961).

(85) E. P. Blanchard, Jr., *J. Org. Chem.*, **28**, 1397 (1963).

(86) (a) M. E. Kuehne, *J. Am. Chem. Soc.*, **81**, 5400 (1959); (b) H. O. House and M. Schellenbaum, *J. Org. Chem.*, **28**, 34 (1963).

[58], is such that the beta carbon atom bears an appreciable negative charge and may serve as a nucleophile. When enamines (e.g., **[59]**)

$$\mathrm{R{-}CH{=}CH{-}\ddot{N}R_2} \longleftrightarrow \mathrm{R{-}C^{\ominus}H{-}CH{=}N^{\oplus}R_2}$$

[57] **[58]**

are treated with alkylating agents, reaction paths leading to C-alkylation or N-alkylation are possible. Subsequent hydrolysis of the C-alkylated iminium salt **[60]** yields an alkylated ketone, whereas the N-alkylated product **[61]** is usually water soluble, and relatively inert to hydrolysis. This alkylation procedure does not

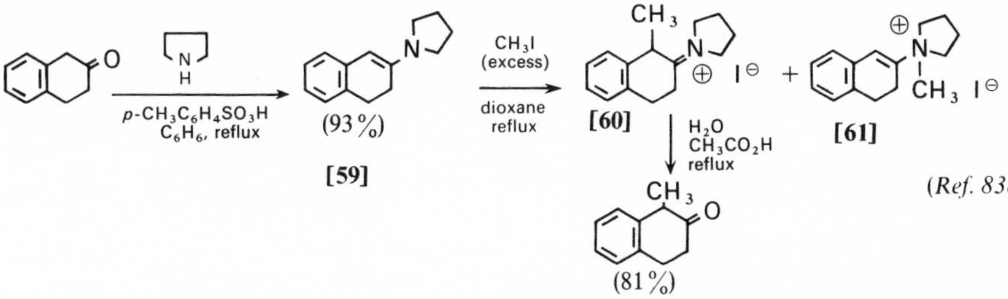

preclude the possibility of alkylation since the iminium salt (e.g., **[62]**) can react with the original enamine (e.g., **[63]**) to form a new enamine (e.g., **[64]**), which can react with the alkylating agent. In

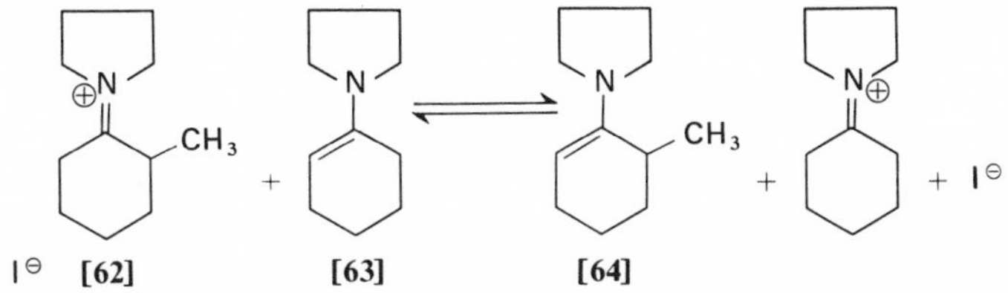

such cases, hydrolysis of the reaction mixture yields, as neutral products, a mixture of the starting ketone (from the salt of the starting enamine), the monoalkylated product, and the dialkylated product(s). Frequently, the alkylation of enamines with simple alkylating agents is not a good preparative method because the major reaction is N-alkylation rather than C-alkylation.[83] However, good yields of C-alkylated products have been obtained with such very reactive alkylating agents as allyl halides, benzyl halides, or α-halocarbonyl compounds. The successful use of these reagents (e.g., **[67]**) may be attributable to the ability of initially formed

N-alkylated products to undergo either an intramolecular (e.g., **[65]**) or an intermolecular (e.g., **[66]**) transfer of the alkyl group to carbon.[87]

1-(pyrrolidin-1-yl)cyclohexene + $Br—CH_2CO_2C_2H_5$ **[67]** $\xrightarrow[\text{reflux}]{CH_3OH}$ $\xrightarrow[\text{reflux}]{H_2O}$ 2-($CH_2CO_2C_2H_5$)cyclohexanone (58%) (*Ref. 83b*)

$(CH_3)_2C{=}CH—N(CH_3)_2 \xrightarrow[\substack{CH_3CN \\ \text{reflux}}]{CH_3CH{=}CHCH_2Br}$ $(CH_3)_2C{=}CH—N^{\oplus}(CH_3)_2(CH_2—CH{=}CH—CH_3)$ $Br^{\ominus}$ **[65]** $\rightarrow$ $(CH_3)_2C(CH(CH_3)—CH{=}CH_2)—CH{=}N^{\oplus}(CH_3)_2$ $Br^{\ominus}$ $\xrightarrow{H_2O}$ $CH_2{=}CH—CH(CH_3)—C(CH_3)_2—CHO$ (67%) (*Ref. 87*)

$(CH_3)_2C{=}CH—N(CH_3)(CH_2—C_6H_5) \xrightarrow[CH_3CN]{CH_3I}$ $(CH_3)_2C{=}CH—N^{\oplus}(CH_3)_2(CH_2—C_6H_5)$ $I^{\ominus}$ + $(CH_3)_2C{=}CH—N(CH_3)CH_2C_6H_5$ **[66]** $\longrightarrow$ (*Ref. 87*)

$I^{\ominus}$ $(CH_3)_2C(CH_2C_6H_5)—CH{=}N^{\oplus}(CH_3)(CH_2—C_6H_5) \xrightarrow{H_2O} C_6H_5—CH_2—C(CH_3)_2—CHO$ (47%)

In a recent modification of the enamine alkylation procedure,[88] an aldehyde (e.g., **[68]**) or ketone was allowed to react with an aliphatic amine (*t*-butylamine and cyclohexylamine were used) to form an imine (e.g., **[69]**). Subsequent reaction with ethylmagnesium

(87) K. C. Brannock and R. D. Burpitt, *J. Org. Chem.*, **26**, 3576 (1961). Unpublished experiments of Dr. K. C. Brannock suggest that the kinetically favored N-alkylated product is attacked by iodide ion to form benzyl iodide. This halide then reacts rapidly, but reversibly, at nitrogen and slowly, but irreversibly, at carbon.

(88) G. Stork and S. R. Dowd, *J. Am. Chem. Soc.*, **85**, 2178 (1963).

$$(CH_3)_2CH{-}CHO + (CH_3)_3C{-}NH_2 \longrightarrow (CH_3)_2CH{-}CH{=}N{-}C(CH_3)_3 \xrightarrow[\text{THF}]{C_2H_5MgBr}$$

[68] **[69]**

$$(CH_3)_2C{=}CH{-}N^{\ominus}(^{\oplus}MgBr){-}C(CH_3)_3 \xrightarrow[\text{THF}]{C_6H_5CH_2Cl} C_6H_5{-}CH_2{-}C(CH_3)_2{-}CH{=}N{-}C(CH_3)_3$$

$$\xrightarrow{H_3O^{\oplus}} C_6H_5{-}CH_2{-}C(CH_3)_2{-}CHO \quad (80\%)$$

(*Ref. 88*)

bromide formed a magnesium salt that underwent C-alkylation when treated with alkylating agents. This modification appears to be distinctly superior to the original enamine procedure for the alkylation of aldehydes and ketones.

As noted earlier in this chapter, the reaction of an alkylating agent with the anion of an active methylene compound is usually a typical bimolecular nucleophilic displacement (S_N2) reaction, which results in inversion of configuration at the carbon atom of the alkylating agent where displacement occurs. The stereochemistry at the carbon atom alpha to the carbonyl function in the alkylated product cannot be predicted with such certainty. If the alkylated alpha position still retains one hydrogen atom, the alkaline reaction conditions used will usually permit isomerization at this position and the more stable epimer will predominate, irrespective of the initial direction of attack on the enolate anion. A case in point is the previously described methylation of 3-cholestanone[59e] to form 2α-methyl-3-cholestanone, the epimer in which the methyl group occupies the more stable equatorial position.[89] If the alkylated product has no hydrogen atom at the alkylated position, the stereochemical problem presented is similar to that encountered in the halogenation of ketones (see Chapter 6). In other words, the direction of attack on the enolate anion by the alkylating agent will be perpendicular to the plane of the enolate anion and, if one side of the enolate anion (e.g., **[70]**) is clearly less hindered, the predominant product will usually be the one resulting from introduction of the alkyl group from the less hindered side.

(89) For a case where part of the less stable isomer was isolated before isomerization occurred, see J. L. Beton, T. H. Halsall, E. R. H. Jones, and P. C. Phillips, *J. Chem. Soc.*, **1957**, 753.

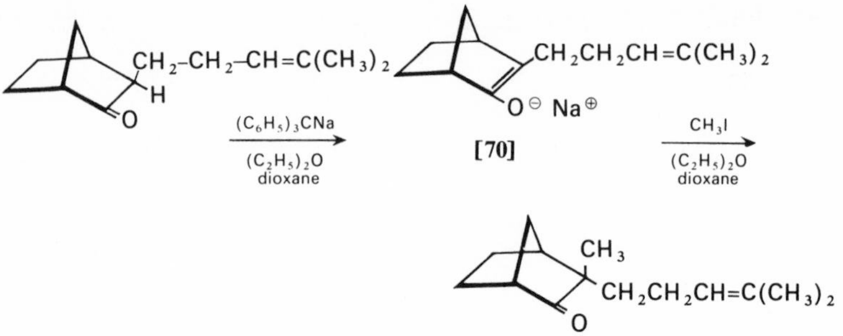

CH_2–CH_2–$CH{=}C(CH_3)_2$; H ; O

$\xrightarrow[(C_2H_5)_2O \text{ dioxane}]{(C_6H_5)_3CNa}$

$CH_2CH_2CH{=}C(CH_3)_2$; $O^{\ominus}$ $Na^{\oplus}$

[70]

$\xrightarrow[(C_2H_5)_2O \text{ dioxane}]{CH_3I}$

CH_3 ; $CH_2CH_2CH{=}C(CH_3)_2$; O

(67%) (*Ref. 90*)

If an enolate anion derived from a cyclohexanone is being alkylated, two factors need to be considered: steric hindrance to approach of the alkylating agent and stereoelectronic control, the latter favoring the initial formation of a cyclohexanone in the chair form with the entering alkyl group in an axial position. As was the case with bromination, it is clear that if one side of a cyclohexanone enolate anion is substantially more hindered than the other side, alkylation will occur from the less hindered side.[67b,79b] Even the alkylation of relatively simple 1-decalone systems (e.g., [**54**] and [**71**]) leads to 9-methyl-1-decalone mixtures in which the *cis* and *trans* isomers are formed in approximately equal amounts or in which a slight preference for the *cis* isomer is observed. These results suggest that the geometry of the transition state (e.g., [**72**])

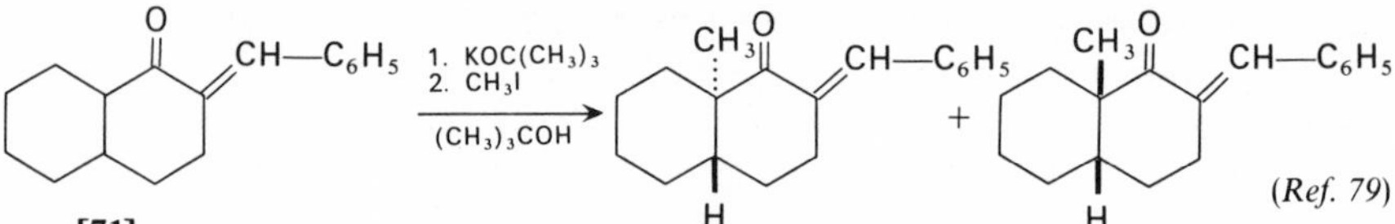

O ; CH—C_6H_5

[71]

$\xrightarrow[(CH_3)_3COH]{1.\ KOC(CH_3)_3 \quad 2.\ CH_3I}$

CH_3 O ; CH—C_6H_5 ; H

(23%)

\+

CH_3 O ; CH—C_6H_5 ; H

(68%)

(*Ref. 79*)

I ; CH_3 ; H ; O

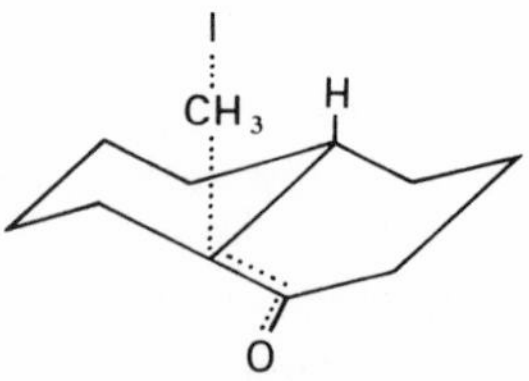

[72]

for alkylation is similar to the geometry of the enolate anion and, consequently, that stereoelectronic control is less important than

(90) E. J. Corey, R. Hartmann, and P. A. Vatakencherry, *J. Am. Chem. Soc.*, **84**, 2611 (1962).

steric hindrance in determining the direction of attack on an enolate anion. The presence of a 6,7–double bond in a 1-decalone system (as in [73] and [74]) favors the formation of a *trans*-fused ring system

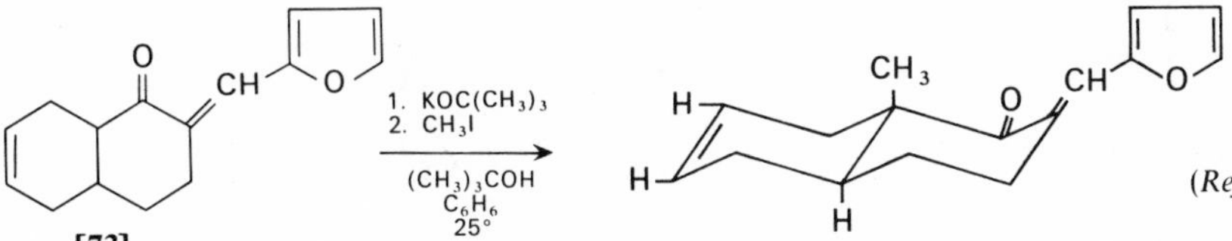

[73]

1. $KOC(CH_3)_3$
2. CH_3I
$(CH_3)_3COH$
C_6H_6
25°

(56%; only product isolated)

(*Ref. 79b*)

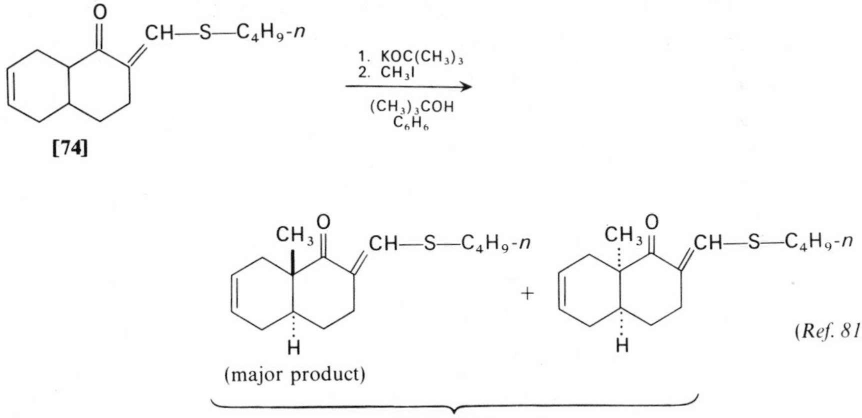

[74]

1. $KOC(CH_3)_3$
2. CH_3I
$(CH_3)_3COH$
C_6H_6

$CH—S—C_4H_9$-*n*

(major product)

(89% of mixture)

(*Ref. 81*)

on alkylation. This could be considered evidence for stereo-electronic control, which becomes more important as one of the 1,3-diaxial interactions (that between the axial hydrogen atom at C-7 and the methyl group) in a 9-methyl-*trans*-1-decalone is removed. However, the force of this argument is diminished by the fact that introduction of double bonds elsewhere in the 1-decalone system (which also diminishes the number of 1,3-diaxial interactions in the alkylated product) does not favor the formation of a *trans*-fused product with an axial methyl group.[79b] The alkylation of the monocyclic ketone [75] appears to offer no support for the idea of preferential alkylation of a cyclohexanone enolate anion from a direction permitting introduction of the alkyl group as an axial substituent. Furthermore, although the previously illustrated intramolecular alkylation with the bromoketone [76] to form

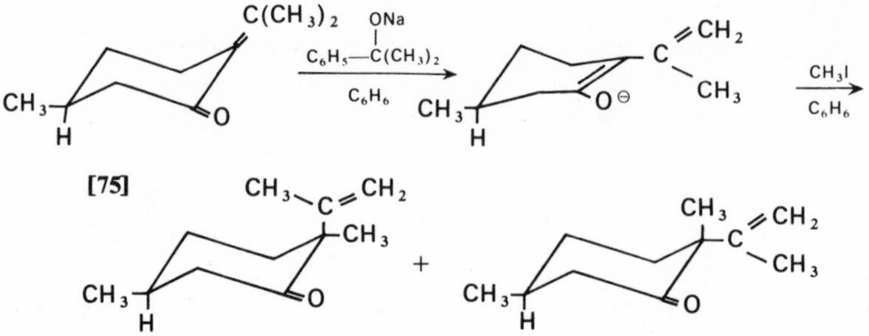

[75]

(Ref. 91)

(83% of product) (17% of product)

9-methyl-*cis*-1-decalone has been interpreted as evidence for a preferential axial attack on the enolate anion (i.e., **[77]**),[39a,60b,60d] the geometry of the enolate anion **[78]** favors the formation of the *cis*-fused decalone in any event.

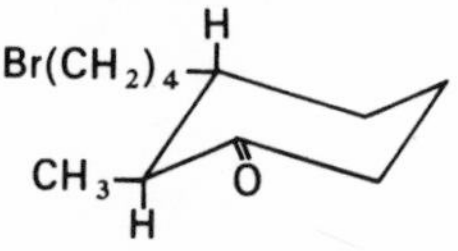

[76] 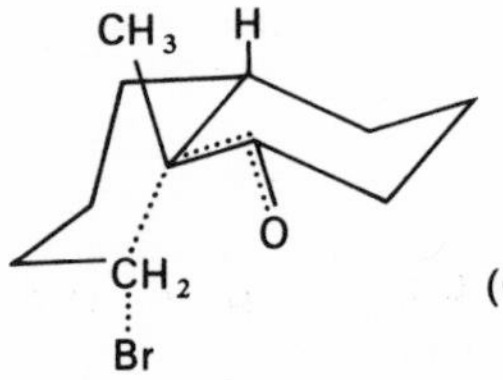 [77] 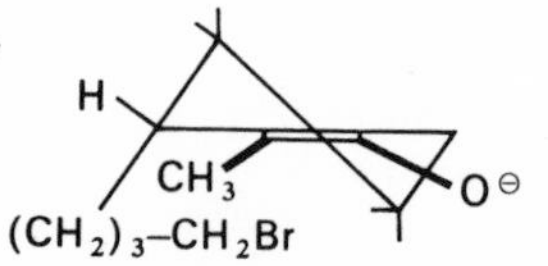 [78]

The Michael Reaction

The nucleophilic addition of enolate (or analogous) anions (e.g., **[79]**) to the carbon-carbon double bond of α,β-unsaturated ketones, aldehydes, or carboxylic acid derivatives, a process known as the Michael reaction,[92] also constitutes a method for the alkylation of active methylene compounds. The unsaturated compounds used in the reaction, often called Michael acceptors, may include any unsaturated system having a functional group capable of stabilizing the carbanionic intermediate (e.g., **[80]**). The Michael reaction differs from previously discussed alkylation reactions in that the base which generates the enolate anion is regenerated, so that

(91) (a) C. Djerassi, J. Osiecki, and E. J. Eisenbraun, *J. Am. Chem. Soc.*, **83**, 4433 (1961); (b) for a discussion of the influence of polar substituents on the stereochemistry of alkylation, see F. J. McQuillin and P. L. Simpson, *J. Chem. Soc.*, **1963,** 4726; (c) see also J. M. Conia and P. Briet, *Tetrahedron Letters*, **No. 39,** 2797 (1964); (d) L. Velluz, J. Valls, and G. Nominé, *Angew. Chem., Intern. Ed. Engl.*, **4**, 181 (1965).

(92) (a) E. D. Bergmann, D. Ginsburg, and R. Pappo, *Org. Reactions*, **10**, 179 (1959); (b) H. A. Bruson, *ibid.*, **5**, 79 (1949).

$$CH_2(CO_2C_2H_5)_2 \xrightarrow[C_2H_5OH,\ 25\text{–}35^\circ]{NaOC_2H_5} {}^{\ominus}CH(CO_2C_2H_5)_2\ \textbf{[79]} \xrightarrow{CH_2{=}CH{-}CN}$$ (*Ref. 93*)

$$\left[\begin{array}{c} N{\equiv}C{-}\overset{\ominus}{C}H{-}CH_2{-}CH(CO_2C_2H_5)_2\ \textbf{[80]} \\ \Updownarrow \\ N{\equiv}C{-}CH_2{-}CH_2{-}C^{\ominus}(CO_2C_2H_5)_2 \end{array}\right] \xrightarrow{H_2O} N{\equiv}C{-}CH_2{-}CH_2{-}CH(CO_2C_2H_5)_2\ (57\text{–}63\%)$$

usually only a catalytic amount is required. Furthermore, the reaction step (i.e., **[79]** → **[80]**) which forms a new carbon-carbon bond is reversible, and the product, usually a 1,5-dicarbonyl compound, is frequently capable of further transformation in the presence of base. Because these differences permit a variety of side reactions[92a] not encountered in the previously discussed alkylations, it is generally desirable to use the mildest reaction conditions possible for effecting any given Michael reaction.

It will be noted that many Michael products may, in principle, be obtained from either of two different pairs of reactants. For example, a combination either of benzalacetophenone and diethyl malonate or of diethyl benzalmalonate (**[81]**) and acetophenone (**[82]**) could theoretically effect preparation of the adduct **[83]**. Of these possibilities, diethyl malonate rather than acetophenone as the active methylene component is the proper choice because formation of its anion can be accomplished with a weaker base and less vigorous reaction conditions. When possible, relatively

$$C_6H_5{-}CH{=}CH{-}CO{-}C_6H_5 + CH_2(CO_2C_2H_5)_2 \xrightarrow[C_2H_5OH,\ reflux]{piperidine} C_6H_5{-}CO{-}CH_2{-}\underset{|}{\overset{C_6H_5}{C}}H{-}CH(CO_2C_2H_5)_2\ \textbf{[83]}\ (98\%)$$ (*Ref. 94*)

$$\underset{\textbf{[81]}}{C_6H_5{-}CH{=}C(CO_2C_2H_5)_2} \qquad \underset{\textbf{[82]}}{C_6H_5{-}CO{-}CH_3}$$

weak basic catalysts such as piperidine, pyridine, triethylamine, benzyltrimethylammonium hydroxide (Triton B), or potassium hydroxide should be selected. If stronger bases (e.g., sodium

(93) N. F. Albertson and J. F. Fillman, *J. Am. Chem. Soc.*, **71**, 2818 (1949).

(94) R. Connor and D. B. Andrews, *ibid.*, **56**, 2713 (1934).

ethoxide or potassium *t*-butoxide) are required, it is normally appropriate to use only 0.1 to 0.3 equivalent of the base and to employ low reaction temperatures (25° or less) and short reaction times in order to minimize side reactions.[95] Also, use of an excess of the active methylene compound is recommended if dialkylation and reverse Michael reactions are to be minimized. Examples of these various procedures are illustrated in the previous and following equations.

$$(CH_3)_2CH{-}NO_2 + CH_2{=}CH{-}CO_2CH_3 \xrightarrow[\text{H}_2\text{O, dioxane, } 70\text{–}100°]{C_6H_5CH_2{-}\overset{\oplus}{N}(CH_3)_3\ \overset{\ominus}{O}H} O_2N{-}C(CH_3)_2{-}CH_2CH_2CO_2CH_3$$

(80–86%) (*Ref. 96*)

$$C_6H_5{-}CH(C{\equiv}N){-}CO_2C_2H_5 + CH_2{=}CH{-}C{\equiv}N \xrightarrow[(CH_3)_3COH,\ 40\text{–}45°]{KOH} C_6H_5{-}C(C{\equiv}N)(CO_2C_2H_5){-}CH_2CH_2C{\equiv}N$$

(69–83%) (*Ref. 97*)

$$CH_3{-}CO{-}NH{-}CH(C{\equiv}N){-}CO_2C_2H_5 + CH_2{=}CH{-}CHO \xrightarrow[C_2H_5OH,\ 25°\text{ or less}]{NaOC_2H_5} CH_3{-}CO{-}NH{-}C(C{\equiv}N)(CO_2C_2H_5){-}CH_2CH_2CHO$$

(66%) (*Ref. 92a*)

$$(CH_3{-}CO)_2CH_2 + CH_2{=}CH{-}C{\equiv}N \xrightarrow[(CH_3)_3COH,\ H_2O,\ 25°]{(C_2H_5)_3N} (CH_3{-}CO)_2C(CH_2CH_2C{\equiv}N)_2$$

(77%) (*Ref. 98*)

(95) (a) R. Connor and W. R. McClellan, *J. Org. Chem.*, **3**, 570 (1939); (b) J. A. Gardner and H. N. Rydon, *J. Chem. Soc.*, **1938**, 45; (c) H. Wachs and O. F. Hedenburg, *J. Am. Chem. Soc.*, **70**, 2695 (1948).

(96) R. B. Moffett, *Org. Syn.*, **Coll. Vol. 4,** 652 (1963).

(97) E. C. Horning and A. F. Finelli, *ibid.*, **Coll. Vol. 4,** 776 (1963).

(98) J. A. Adamcik and E. J. Miklasiewicz, *J. Org. Chem.*, **28**, 336 (1963).

The use of a full equivalent of base, elevated reaction temperatures, and long reaction times frequently promotes reversal of the Michael reaction (called a retrograde Michael reaction) or further transformation of the initial product. Since a retrograde Michael reaction may lead to compounds other than the original starting materials (e.g., **[81]** and **[82]** from **[83]**), complex mixtures may result. Examples of further transformations of Michael products are provided in the accompanying equations; it will be noted that these transformations always lead to a product more acidic than the initial Michael adduct.

$$(CH_3)_2C{=}CH{-}CO{-}CH_3 + CH_2(CO_2C_2H_5)_2 \xrightarrow[C_2H_5OH,\ reflux]{NaOC_2H_5} (CH_3)_2C(CH^{\ominus}{-}CO{-}CH_3\ Na^{\oplus})(CH(CO_2C_2H_5){-}CO_2C_2H_5)$$

(*Ref. 99*)

$$\longrightarrow (CH_3)_2C\begin{cases} CH_2{-}C(O^{\ominus}){=}CH \\ CH(CO_2C_2H_5){-}CO \end{cases} Na^{\oplus} \xrightarrow[H_2O]{KOH} \xrightarrow[-CO_2]{H_3O^{\oplus}} (CH_3)_2C\begin{cases} CH_2{-}CO \\ CH_2{-}CO \end{cases}CH_2$$

(67–85%)

$$CH_3{-}CH{=}CH{-}CO_2C_2H_5 + CH_3{-}CH(CO_2C_2H_5)_2 \xrightarrow[C_2H_5OH,\ (C_2H_5)_2O,\ reflux]{NaOC_2H_5} CH_3{-}CH(C(CH_3)(CO_2C_2H_5)_2){-}CH^{\ominus}{-}CO_2C_2H_5$$

(*Refs. 92a, 100*)

$$\xrightarrow{-C_2H_5O^{\ominus}} \left[\begin{matrix} CH_3{-}CH{-}CH{-}CO_2C_2H_5 \\ CH_3{-}C(CO_2C_2H_5){-}C{=}O \end{matrix}\right] \xrightarrow{NaOC_2H_5} \xrightarrow{H_3O^{\oplus}} \begin{matrix} CH_3{-}CH{-}CH(CO_2C_2H_5)_2 \\ CH_3{-}CH{-}CO_2C_2H_5 \end{matrix}$$

(60%)

A variant of the usual procedure for the Michael reaction consists of treating the active methylene compound with a β-halocarbonyl compound, a β-dialkylaminocarbonyl compound, or the quaternary salt from a β-dialkylaminocarbonyl compound. These reactants are rapidly converted to α,β-unsaturated carbonyl

(99) R. L. Shriner and H. R. Todd, *Org. Syn.*, **Coll. Vol. 2,** 200 (1943).

(100) A. Michael and J. Ross, *J. Am. Chem. Soc.*, **52**, 4598 (1930).

compounds in the reaction mixture by base-catalyzed elimination,[101] and a normal Michael reaction then occurs. The β-halocarbonyl compounds and corresponding quaternary ammonium salts consume a full equivalent of base during the elimination reaction; consequently, Michael reactions using these materials are often run like conventional alkylation reactions. Perhaps the most useful precursors of Michael acceptors are the β-dialkylaminocarbonyl compounds and corresponding quaternary salts,[102] which are readily available from Mannich reactions (see Chapter 8) involving a ketone, formaldehyde, and a secondary amine. Since vinylketones are frequently unstable liquids that tend to dimerize or polymerize on standing, the generation of these materials from β-aminoketones in the reaction mixture is advantageous.

2-(dimethylaminomethyl)cyclohexanone ($CH_2N(CH_3)_2$) + CH_3NO_2 $\xrightarrow[\text{CH}_3\text{OH, reflux}]{\text{NaOCH}_3}$ 2-methylenecyclohexanone (CH_2) + $^{\ominus}CH_2NO_2$ ⟶ $\xrightarrow{H_3O^{\oplus}}$ 2-(2-nitroethyl)cyclohexanone ($CH_2CH_2NO_2$) (72%)

(*Ref. 102*)

An interesting and useful synthetic procedure, which would appear to be related to the Michael reaction, is the condensation of a 6-hydroxy- or 6-alkoxy-1-vinyl-1-tetralol with a 1,3-dicarbonyl compound.[103] As illustrated below, the reaction may involve attack of an enolate anion on the oxonium salt **[84]** (or the corresponding ketone if a 6-hydroxytetralin derivative is employed).

Although monoketones may be used as active methylene compounds in the Michael reaction with very reactive Michael acceptors such as acrylonitrile **[85]**, the reaction conditions required with less reactive unsaturated systems are sufficiently vigorous that further transformations of the initial Michael adducts are often observed. From the accompanying examples it will be noted that

(101) N. Ferry and F. J. McQuillin, *J. Chem. Soc.*, **1962**, 103.

(102) J. H. Brewster and E. L. Eliel, *Org. Reactions*, **7**, 99 (1953).

(103) (a) S. N. Ananchenko, V. Y. Limanov, V. N. Leonov, V. N. Rzhezniko, and I. V. Torgov, *Tetrahedron*, **18**, 1355 (1962); (b) A. B. Zakharichev, S. N. Ananchenko, and J. V. Torgov, *Tetrahedron Letters*, **No. 3**, 171 (1964); (c) T. B. Windholz, J. H. Fried, and A. A. Patchett, *J. Org. Chem.*, **28**, 1092 (1963).

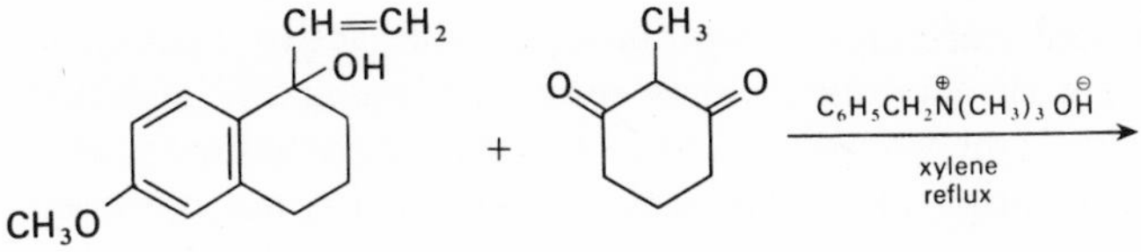

$C_6H_5CH_2\overset{\oplus}{N}(CH_3)_3\ \overset{\ominus}{OH}$, xylene, reflux

(*Ref. 103*)

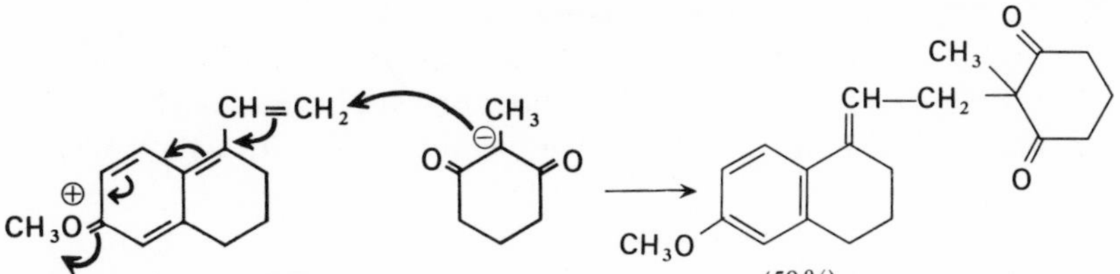

[84] (50%)

the Michael acceptor is normally introduced largely, if not exclusively, at the more highly substituted position of unsymmetrical ketones. Since neither the relative stabilities nor the rates of formation of the enolate anions derived from these ketones[7] account

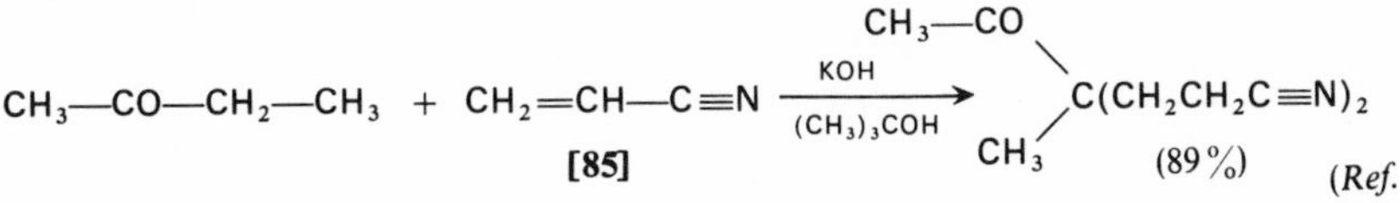

$$CH_3{-}CO{-}CH_2{-}CH_3 + CH_2{=}CH{-}C{\equiv}N \xrightarrow[(CH_3)_3COH]{KOH} (CH_3{-}CO)(CH_3)C(CH_2CH_2C{\equiv}N)_2$$

[85] (89%) (*Ref. 104a*)

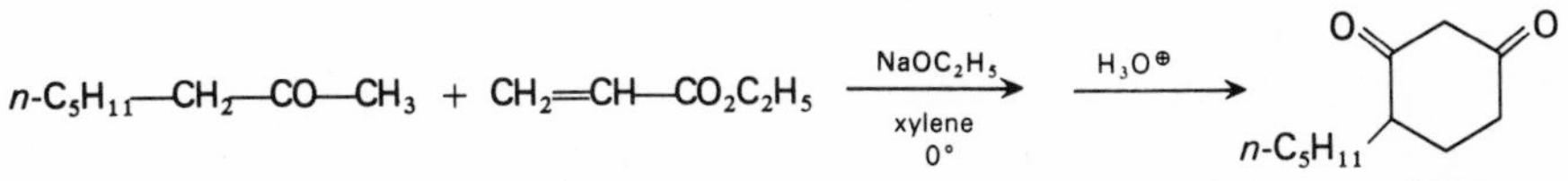

$$n\text{-}C_5H_{11}{-}CH_2{-}CO{-}CH_3 + CH_2{=}CH{-}CO_2C_2H_5 \xrightarrow[\text{xylene, } 0°]{NaOC_2H_5} \xrightarrow{H_3O^{\oplus}}$$

(27%) (*Ref. 104b*)

$$+ CH_2{=}CH{-}CO_2CH_3 \xrightarrow[(CH_3)_3COH,\ 30°]{KOC(CH_3)_3} CH_2CH_2CO_2CH_3$$

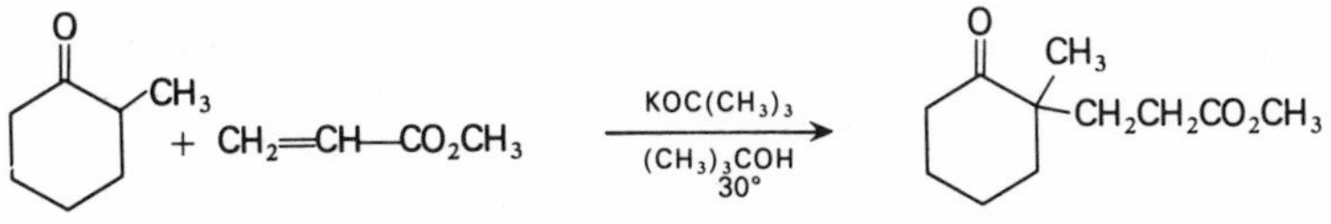

(57%) (*Refs. 86b, 105*)

for the results observed, the reason for this selectivity in Michael reactions remains to be established. The reaction of enolizable

(104) (a) H. A. Bruson and T. W. Riener, *J. Am. Chem. Soc.*, **64**, 2850 (1942); R. Bertocchio and J. Dreux, *Bull. Soc. Chim. France*, **1962**, 823, 1809; (b) J. J. Miller and P. L. deBenneville, *J. Org. Chem.*, **22**, 1268 (1957).

(105) (a) R. L. Frank and R. C. Pierle, *J. Am. Chem. Soc.*, **73**, 726 (1951); (b) see also V. Boekelheide, *ibid.*, **69**, 790 (1947); W. E. Bachmann and L. B. Wick, *ibid.*, **72**, 3388 (1950).

α,β-unsaturated carbonyl compounds (as the active methylene component) with acrylonitrile has resulted both in the expected reaction at the alpha position and in reaction at the gamma position.[106] Substitution at the latter position, which is not observed in normal alkylations, may well be a consequence of the fact that the Michael reaction is reversible.

One of the most useful synthetic applications of the Michael reaction has been the Robinson annelation reaction,[92a,102,107] illustrated by the accompanying equations. The formation of the

CO_2CH_3 — $NaOCH_3$ / CH_3OH, C_6H_6, reflux → CO_2CH_3, $O^{\ominus}Na^{\oplus}$ — $(C_2H_5)_2\overset{\oplus}{N}(CH_3)$—$CH_2CH_2COCH_3$ $I^{\ominus}$ / CH_3OH, 25° → CO_2CH_3, $CH_2CH_2COCH_3$, O (92%)

(*Ref. 108*)

KOH / CH_3OH, H_2O, reflux → $H_3O^{\oplus}$ → O (90%)

$CH_2\overset{\oplus}{N}(CH_3)_3$ $I^{\ominus}$, O + CH_3CO—$CH(CH_3)$—$CO_2C_2H_5$ — $NaOCH(CH_3)_2$ / $(CH_3)_2CHOH$ → [$CO_2C_2H_5$, CH_2—C—CH_3, CO—CH_3, O] (*Ref. 109*)

→ CH_3, O (59%) + CH_3, O

(106) (a) H. A. Bruson and T. W. Riener, *J. Am. Chem. Soc.*, **75**, 3585 (1953): correction of the structural assignments is made in Ref. 92a; (b) C. R. Engel and J. Lessard, *J. Am. Chem. Soc.*, **85**, 638 (1963).

(107) (a) E. C. duFeu, F. J. McQuillin, and R. Robinson, *J. Chem. Soc.*, **1937**, 53; (b) F. J. McQuillin and R. Robinson, *ibid.*, **1938**, 1097; (c) J. W. Cornforth and R. Robinson, *ibid.*, **1949**, 1855; (d) N. C. Ross and R. Levine, *J. Org. Chem.*, **29**, 2341, 2346 (1964).

(108) A. L. Wilds and C. H. Shunk, *J. Am. Chem. Soc.*, **65**, 469 (1943).

(109) A. V. Logan, E. N. Marvell, R. LaPore, and D. C. Bush, *ibid.*, **76**, 4127 (1954).

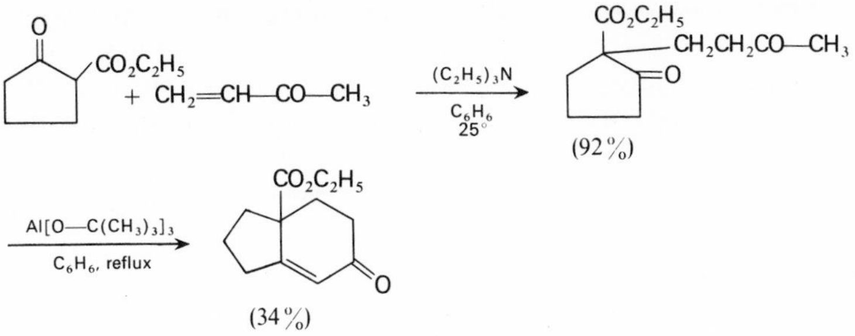

$+ CH_2{=}CH{-}CO{-}CH_3 \xrightarrow[C_6H_6,\ 25°]{(C_2H_5)_3N}$ (92%)

$\xrightarrow[C_6H_6,\ reflux]{Al[O{-}C(CH_3)_3]_3}$ (34%)

(Refs. 25c, 110)

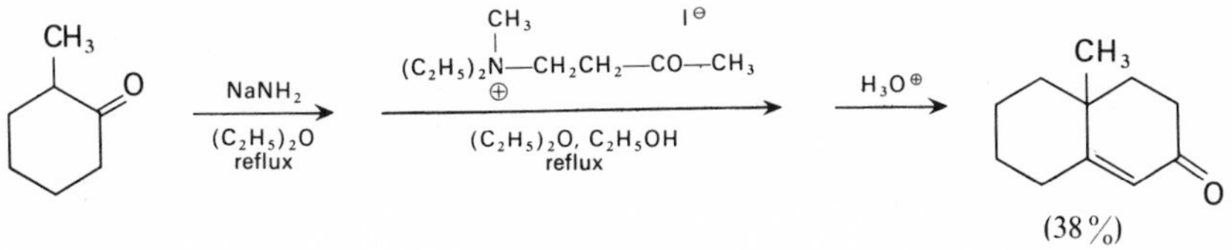

$\xrightarrow[(C_2H_5)_2O,\ reflux]{NaNH_2} \xrightarrow[(C_2H_5)_2O,\ C_2H_5OH,\ reflux]{CH_3(C_2H_5)_2\overset{\oplus}{N}{-}CH_2CH_2{-}CO{-}CH_3\ I^{\ominus}} \xrightarrow{H_3O^{\oplus}}$ (38%)

(Refs. 102, 107a)

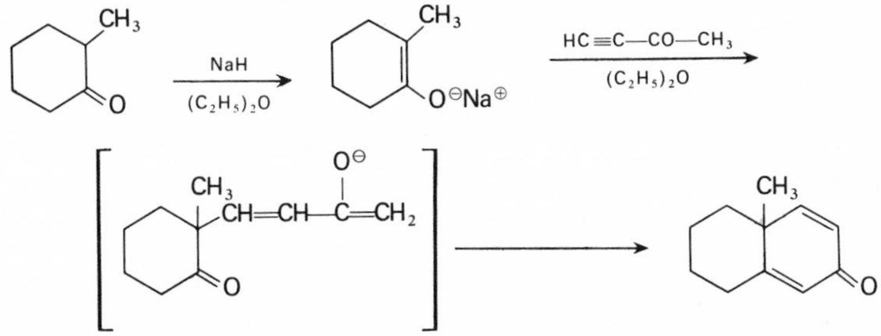

$\xrightarrow[(C_2H_5)_2O]{NaH}$ $O^{\ominus}Na^{\oplus}$ $\xrightarrow[(C_2H_5)_2O]{HC{\equiv}C{-}CO{-}CH_3}$ (Ref. 111)

$CH{=}CH{-}C(O^{\ominus}){=}CH_2$ ⟶

$+ CH_2{=}CH{-}CO{-}CH_3 \xrightarrow[CH_3OH,\ reflux]{KOH}$ $CH_2CH_2{-}CO{-}CH_3$

$\xrightarrow[C_6H_6,\ reflux\ with\ removal\ of\ H_2O]{pyrrolidine} \xrightarrow{H_3O^{\oplus}}$ (63–65%)

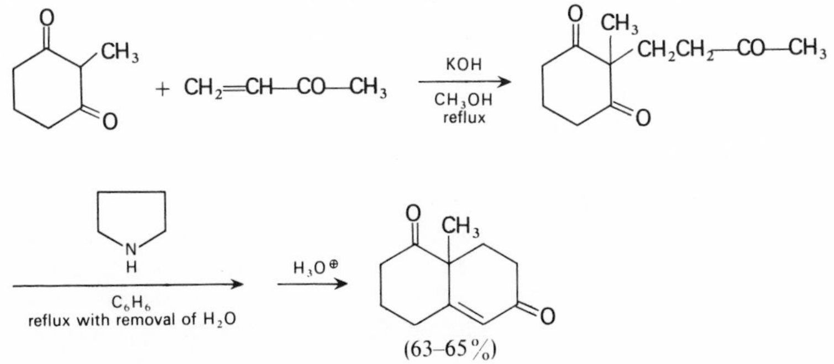

(Ref. 112)

(110) W. G. Dauben and J. W. McFarland, *ibid.*, **82**, 4245 (1960).

(111) R. B. Woodward and T. Singh, *ibid.*, **72**, 494 (1950).

(112) S. Ramachandran and M. S. Newman, *Org. Syn.*, **41**, 38 (1961); A. B. Mekler, S. Ramachandran, S. Swaminathan, and M. S. Newman, *ibid.*, **41**, 56 (1961).

new six-membered ring involves the intramolecular aldol condensation (see Chapter 8) of the initial Michael adduct and subsequent dehydration. Recently, two different modes of intramolecular aldol condensation have been found to occur as shown below.

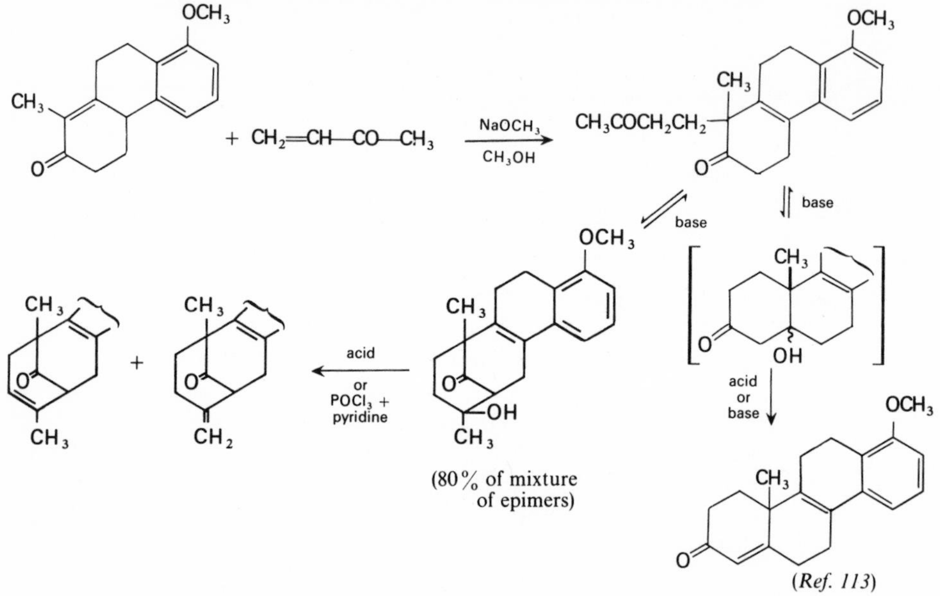
OCH3
CH3
+ CH2=CH—CO—CH3
NaOCH3
CH3OH
CH3COCH2CH2
OCH3
CH3
base
base
OCH3
CH3
OH
acid
or
POCl3 +
pyridine
CH3
CH3
CH3
CH2
CH3
CH3
OH
acid
or
base
OCH3
CH3
(80% of mixture of epimers)
(Ref. 113)

The reaction of α,β-unsaturated carbonyl compounds with enamines provides a useful alternative route to Michael adducts.[83] Unlike the reaction of enamines with alkylating agents, the introduction of a Michael acceptor at the nitrogen atom of an enamine to form **[86]** is not a serious problem because this reaction is reversible. The initial adduct **[87]** from reaction at carbon can either undergo ring closure[114] to form **[88]** or proton transfer to

(113) (a) W. S. Johnson, J. Ackerman, J. F. Eastham, and H. A. DeWalt, Jr., *J. Am. Chem. Soc.*, **78**, 6302 (1956); (b) W. S. Johnson, J. J. Korst, R. A. Clement, and J. Dutta, *ibid.*, **82**, 614 (1960); (c) for the use of pyrrolidine and acetic acid to effect the final aldol condensation in the Robinson annelation reaction, see T. A. Spencer and K. K. Schmiegel, *Chem. Ind.* (*London*), **1963**, 1765; T. A. Spencer, K. K. Schmiegel, and K. L. Williamson, *J. Am. Chem. Soc.*, **85**, 3785 (1963).

(114) (a) K. C. Brannock, A. Bell, R. D. Burpitt, and C. A. Kelly, *J. Org. Chem.*, **26**, 625 (1961); (b) K. C. Brannock, R. D. Burpitt, V. W. Goodlett, and J. G. Thweatt, *ibid.*, **28**, 1464 (1963); (c) G. A. Berchtold and G. F. Uhlig, *ibid.*, **28**, 1459 (1963); (d) C. F. Huebner and co-workers, *ibid.*, **28**, 3134 (1963); (e) I. Fleming and J. Harley-Mason, *J. Chem. Soc.*, **1964,** 2165.

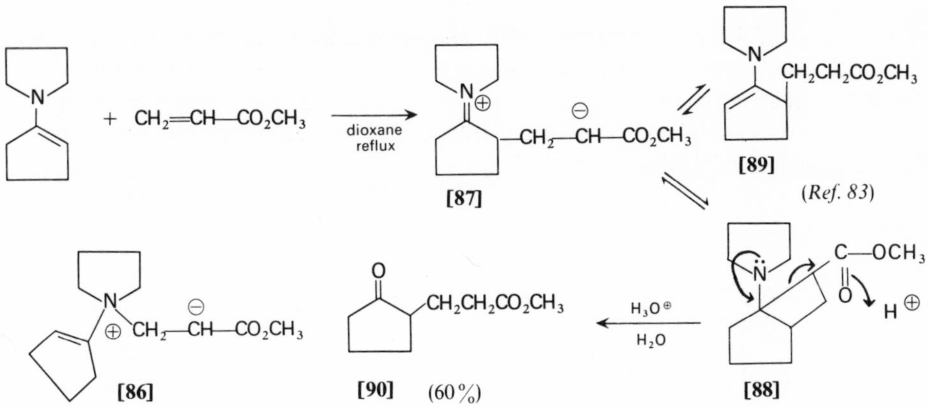

$+ CH_2{=}CH{-}CO_2CH_3 \xrightarrow[\text{reflux}]{\text{dioxane}}$ [87] ⇌ [89] (*Ref. 83*)

[86] [90] (60%) $\xleftarrow[H_2O]{H_3O^{\oplus}}$ [88]

form [**89**]. In either case, acid-catalyzed hydrolysis leads to the Michael adduct [**90**]. Other examples of the use of enamines with Michael acceptors are provided in the following equations. If

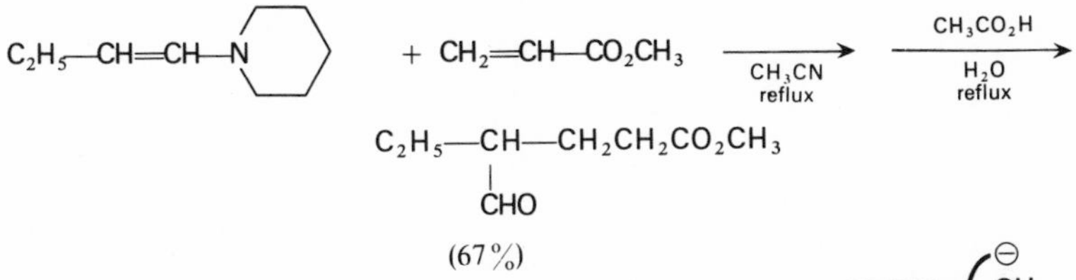

$$C_2H_5{-}CH{=}CH{-}N(C_5H_{10}) + CH_2{=}CH{-}CO_2CH_3 \xrightarrow[\text{reflux}]{CH_3CN} \xrightarrow[\substack{H_2O\\ \text{reflux}}]{CH_3CO_2H} C_2H_5{-}CH(CHO){-}CH_2CH_2CO_2CH_3$$

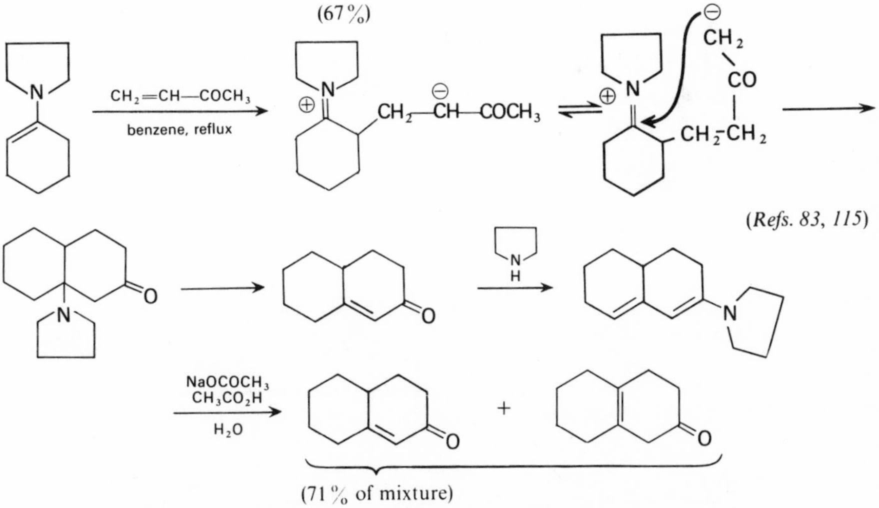

(67%) (*Ref. 83*)

$\xrightarrow[\text{benzene, reflux}]{CH_2{=}CH{-}COCH_3}$ (*Refs. 83, 115*)

$\xrightarrow[H_2O]{NaOCOCH_3,\ CH_3CO_2H}$ (71% of mixture)

(115) R. L. Augustine and H. V. Cortez, *Chem. Ind.* (*London*), **1963**, 490. The initial enamine product is a mixture of double bond isomers. H. O. House and co-workers, *J. Org. Chem.*, to be published.

acetylenic esters (e.g., **[91]**) are employed as Michael acceptors with enamines, the intermediate cyclic product **[92]** is capable of thermal isomerization. Should this rearrangement occur prior to hydrolysis, the resulting product **[93]** does not correspond to a Michael adduct.

$CO_2CH_3-C{\equiv}C-CO_2CH_3$ **[91]** $\xrightarrow[\text{50° or less}]{\text{toluene}}$ **[92]** $\longrightarrow$

(*Refs. 114b, c*)

(42%) $\xrightarrow[\text{CH}_3\text{OH, reflux}]{\text{HCl, H}_2\text{O}}$ **[93]** (86%)

A reaction closely related to the Michael reaction in mechanism is the conjugate addition of cyanide ion to various unsaturated systems. Some typical examples of this reaction are provided in the accompanying equations. A modification of the usual reaction

$$C_6H_5-CH{=}C(C{\equiv}N)-C_6H_5 \xrightarrow[\text{CH}_3\text{OH, (C}_2\text{H}_5)_2\text{O, reflux}]{\text{KC}\equiv\text{N, H}_2\text{O}} C_6H_5-CH(C{\equiv}N)-\overset{\ominus}{C}(C{\equiv}N)-C_6H_5 \xrightarrow[\text{H}_2\text{O}]{\text{NH}_4\text{OCOCH}_3}$$

$$C_6H_5-CH(C{\equiv}N)-CH(C{\equiv}N)-C_6H_5$$

(92–94%, mixture of stereoisomers) (*Ref. 116*)

$$C_6H_5-CO-CH_2CH_2-N(CH_3)_2 \xrightarrow[\text{H}_2\text{O, reflux}]{\text{KCN}} C_6H_5-CO-CH_2CH_2-C{\equiv}N \quad (67\%)$$ (*Ref. 102*)

(116) J. A. McRae and R. A. B. Bannard, *Org. Syn.*, **Coll. Vol. 4,** 393 (1963).

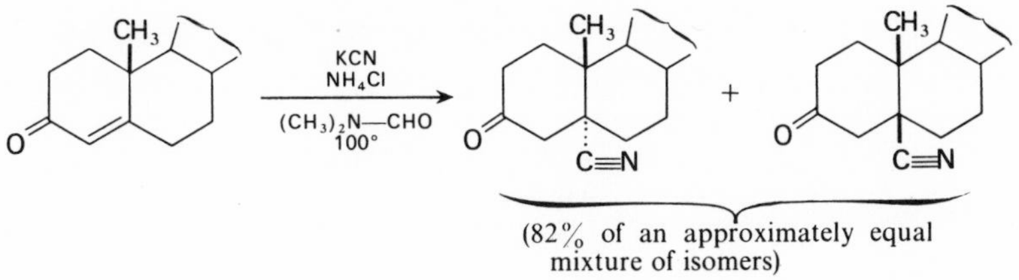
CH3
KCN
NH4Cl
(CH3)2N—CHO
100°
O
CH3
C≡N
+
CH3
C≡N
(82% of an approximately equal mixture of isomers)

(*Ref. 117*)

conditions—the use of hydrogen cyanide and triethylaluminum in an inert solvent such as ether, tetrahydrofuran, or benzene—has been found to increase markedly the stereoselectivity of this addition,[118] apparently favoring the product with the cyano group in an axial position.

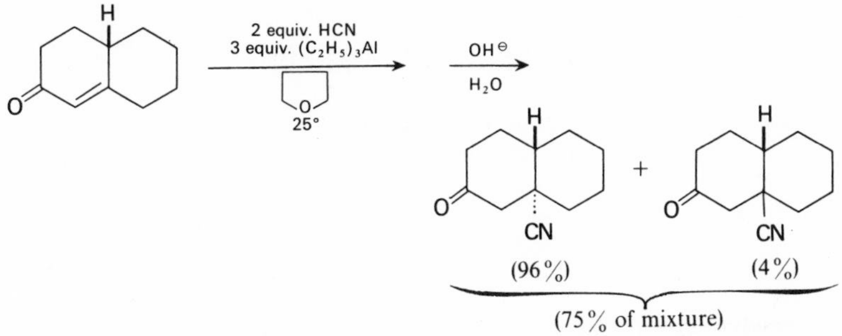
H
O
2 equiv. HCN
3 equiv. (C2H5)3Al
O
25°
OH⊖
H2O
H
CN
(96%)
+
H
CN
(4%)
(75% of mixture)

(*Ref. 118a*)

(117) (a) W. Nagata, S. Hirai, H. Itazaki, and K. Takeda, *J. Org. Chem.*, **26**, 2413 (1961); see also (b) W. Nagata, *Tetrahedron*, **13**, 278 (1961); (c) A. Bowers, *J. Org. Chem.*, **26**, 2043 (1961); (d) W. L. Meyer and N. G. Schnautz, *ibid.*, **27**, 2011 (1962); (e) C. Djerassi, R. A. Schneider, H. Vorbrueggen, and N. L. Allinger, *ibid.*, **28**, 1632 (1963); (f) for a discussion of comparable additions of cyanide ion to tetrahydroindanone systems, see W. L. Meyer and J. F. Wolfe, *ibid.*, **29**, 170 (1964).

(118) (a) W. Nagata, M. Yoshioka, and S. Hirai, *Tetrahedron Letters*, **No. 11,** 461 (1962); (b) W. Nagata, T. Terasawa, and T. Aoki, *Tetrahedron Letters*, **No. 14,** 865 (1963).

8

THE ALDOL CONDENSATION AND RELATED REACTIONS ·

TOGETHER WITH THE PREVIOUSLY DISCUSSED (Chapter 7) reactions of enolate anions with alkylating agents and additions of enolate anions to the carbon-carbon double bonds of conjugated systems (the Michael reaction), additions of enolate anions to carbonyl functions constitute an important group of organic reactions. If the carbonyl function is part of a carboxylic acid derivative, such an addition leads to the introduction of an acyl group (Chapter 9), whereas addition of an enolate anion to the carbonyl group of an aldehyde or ketone followed by protonation constitutes a reaction known as aldol condensation. The series of equilibria involved in base-catalyzed aldol condensation are illustrated in the accompanying equations. If relatively weak bases (e.g., hydroxide ion, ethoxide ion) are employed as catalysts, the first equilibrium is usually unfavorable and the last is usually favorable to the formation of the aldol product (e.g., [**1**]). A successful reaction in the presence of relatively weak bases is therefore normally dependent on the position of the second equilibrium, that forming the alkoxide (e.g., [**3**]); this equilibrium is usually unfavorable if the carbonyl compound to which the enolate anion adds (e.g., [2]) is a ketone rather than an aldehyde. In spite of this fact reasonable

$$CH_3{-}CHO + RO^{\ominus} \rightleftharpoons CH_2{=}C(O^{\ominus}){-}H + ROH$$

$$CH_3{-}CH{=}O\ (\text{[2]}) + CH_2{=}C(H){-}O^{\ominus} \rightleftharpoons CH_3{-}CH(O^{\ominus}){-}CH_2{-}CHO\ (\text{[3]})$$

$$CH_3{-}CH(O^{\ominus}){-}CH_2{-}CHO + ROH \rightleftharpoons CH_3{-}CH(OH){-}CH_2{-}CHO\ (\text{[1]}) + RO$$

yields of aldol products may occasionally be obtained from ketones (e.g., [4]) if the reaction conditions employed permit the continuous separation of the product (e.g., [5]) from the catalyst as it is formed.

$$\underset{[4]}{CH_3{-}CO{-}CH_3} \xrightarrow[\text{refluxing acetone}]{Ba(OH)_2 \text{ contained in the thimble of a Soxhlet extractor}} \underset{[5]\ (71\%)}{(CH_3)_2C(OH){-}CH_2{-}CO{-}CH_3} \quad (\textit{Ref. 1})$$

As mentioned previously (Chapter 7), aldol condensations may also be catalyzed by acids, in which case the reaction is believed to follow the path indicated below. The enol (e.g., [6]) undergoes

$$CH_3{-}CO{-}CH_3 \underset{}{\overset{H^{\oplus}}{\rightleftharpoons}} CH_3{-}C(={}^{\oplus}OH){-}CH_3 \overset{-H^{\oplus}}{\rightleftharpoons} CH_3{-}C(OH){=}CH_2$$

$$\underset{[6]}{CH_3{-}C(\ddot{O}H){=}CH_2} + \underset{[7]}{CH_3{-}C(CH_3){=}\overset{\oplus}{O}H} \rightleftharpoons CH_3{-}C(={}^{\oplus}O{-}H){-}CH_2{-}C(CH_3)_2(OH)$$

$$CH_3{-}C(={}^{\oplus}O{-}H){-}CH_2{-}C(CH_3)_2(OH) \overset{-H^{\oplus}}{\rightleftharpoons} CH_3{-}CO{-}CH_2{-}C(CH_3)_2(OH)$$

(1) J. B. Conant and N. Tuttle, *Org. Syn.*, **Coll. Vol. 1,** 199 (1944).

an electrophilic attack by the conjugate acid (e.g., [**7**]) of the carbonyl component. It will become apparent in the subsequent discussion that the success of most of the preparatively useful reactions involving aldol condensation is attributable to further transformations (e.g., dehydration) of the initial aldol product, which serve to displace the various prior equilibria in favor of the final product.

Condensations in which Equilibrium Is favored by Dehydration of the Intermediate Aldol Product: The Claisen-Schmidt and Knoevenagel Reactions

In the presence of strongly acidic or strongly basic catalysts, the β-hydroxycarbonyl compounds resulting from aldol condensation may often be dehydrated to form α,β-unsaturated carbonyl compounds. Although this dehydration step is reversible, it is usually energetically favorable to the production of the conjugated product (e.g., [**8**]) and may serve to displace preceding unfavorable equilibria. The base-catalyzed dehydration reaction is believed to proceed by formation of an enolate anion (e.g., [**9**]) and subsequent elimination of hydroxide ion as illustrated. The use of a relatively strong base as catalyst to effect dehydration and force an aldol

$$C_6H_5{-}CO{-}CH_3 \xrightleftharpoons[\text{xylene, } 133\text{–}137^\circ]{Al[O{-}C(CH_3)_3]_3} C_6H_5{-}\underset{OH}{\overset{CH_3}{C}}{-}CH_2{-}CO{-}C_6H_5 \rightleftharpoons C_6H_5{-}\underset{OH}{\overset{CH_3}{C}}{-}CH{=}\underset{O^{\ominus}}{C}{-}C_6H_5 \; [\mathbf{9}]$$

$$\rightleftharpoons C_6H_5{-}\overset{CH_3}{C}{=}CH{-}CO{-}C_6H_5$$

[**8**] (77–82%) *(Ref. 2)*

$$(CH_3)_2C{=}CH{-}CH_2CH_2{-}\overset{CH_3}{C}{=}CH{-}CHO + CH_3{-}CO{-}CH_3 \xrightarrow[C_2H_5OH,\ -5^\circ]{NaOC_2H_5} \xrightarrow{H_3O^{\oplus}}$$

$$(CH_3)_2C{=}CH{-}(CH_2)_2{-}\overset{CH_3}{C}{=}CH{-}CH{=}CH{-}CO{-}CH_3$$

(45–49%) *(Ref. 3)*

condensation to completion is not universally successful because α,β-unsaturated carbonyl compounds having gamma hydrogen

(2) (a) W. Wayne and H. Adkins, *Org. Syn.*, **Coll. Vol. 3,** 367 (1955); (b) W. Wayne and H. Adkins, *J. Am. Chem. Soc.*, **62**, 3401 (1940).

(3) A. Russell and R. L. Kenyon, *Org. Syn.*, **Coll. Vol. 3,** 747 (1955).

atoms (e.g., [**10**]) may be converted to enolate anions (e.g., [**11**]), which can undergo further condensation and lead ultimately to polymeric products (e.g., [**12**]). However, this method for forcing

$$CH_3—CH(OH)—CH_2—CHO \underset{}{\overset{base}{\rightleftharpoons}} \underset{[10]}{CH_3—CH{=}CH—CHO} \overset{base}{\rightleftharpoons}$$

$$\underset{[11]}{\overset{\ominus}{C}H_2—CH{=}CH—CHO} \overset{CH_3CHO}{\rightleftharpoons} CH_3—CH(OH)—CH_2—CH{=}CH—CHO \xrightarrow{\text{repeated dehydration and condensation}}$$

$$\underset{[12]}{CH_3—(CH{=}CH)_n—CHO} + \text{other products}$$

aldol condensations to completion is more often useful when one of the carbonyl components is an aromatic aldehyde because the resulting α,β-unsaturated product (e.g., [**13**]) has no gamma hydrogen atoms and cannot undergo further condensation. The condensation of an aromatic aldehyde with an aliphatic aldehyde or ketone in the presence of a relatively strong base (hydroxide or alkoxide ion)

$$C_6H_5—CHO + CH_3—CO—C(CH_3)_3 \xrightarrow[\substack{H_2O \\ C_2H_5OH \\ 25°}]{NaOH} \underset{[13]\quad (88\text{–}93\%)}{C_6H_5—CH{=}CH—CO—C(CH_3)_3}$$ (*Ref. 4*)

to form an α,β-unsaturated aldehyde or ketone is known as the Claisen-Schmidt reaction and has been widely used in synthesis. The following examples are illustrative. Some workers prefer the use of methanol rather than ethanol as a co-solvent in these reactions to avoid the aldol polymers that may result if any of the ethanol present is oxidized by air to acetaldehyde during the course of the reaction.

$$\text{(2-furyl)}—CHO + CH_3—CO—CH_3 \xrightarrow[H_2O]{NaOH} \xrightarrow{H_3O^{\oplus}} \underset{(60\text{–}66\%)}{\text{(2-furyl)}(H)C{=}C(H)COCH_3}$$ (*Ref. 5*)

(4) G. A. Hill and G. M. Bramann, *Org. Syn.*, **Coll. Vol. 1,** 81 (1944).

(5) (a) G. J. Leuck and L. Cejka, *ibid.*, **Coll. Vol. 1,** 283 (1944); (b) see also N. L. Drake and P. Allen, Jr., *ibid.*, **Coll. Vol. 1,** 77 (1944); (c) when the arylidene group is being introduced as a blocking group (see Chapter 7), the use of furfural rather than benzaldehyde is desirable because the Claisen-Schmidt condensation is more rapid: cf. W. S. Johnson, B. Bannister, and R. Pappo, *J. Am. Chem. Soc.*, **78**, 6331 (1956).

$$C_6H_5\text{—CHO} + CH_3\text{—CO—}CH_3 \xrightarrow[\substack{H_2O\\C_2H_5OH\\20\text{–}25°}]{NaOH} C_6H_5CH{=}CH\text{—CO—}CH{=}CHC_6H_5 \quad (90\text{–}94\%)$$ (*Ref. 6*)

$$C_6H_5\text{—CHO} + C_6H_5\text{—}CH_2\text{—}C{\equiv}N \xrightarrow[C_2H_5OH]{NaOC_2H_5} C_6H_5CH{=}C(C_6H_5)C{\equiv}N \quad (83\text{–}91\%)$$ (*Ref. 7*)

$$\text{cycloheptanone} + C_6H_5\text{-CHO} \xrightarrow[\substack{H_2O\\\text{reflux}}]{KOH} \text{2-benzylidenecycloheptanone} \quad (75\%)$$ (*Ref. 8*)

The stereochemistry of the Claisen-Schmidt reaction is of interest in that the unsaturated product normally has the carbonyl function *trans* to the larger group at the beta carbon atom. This stereoselectivity appears to be attributable to the preferential dehydration of the enolate anion in conformation **[14]** rather than in conformation **[15]**. Conformation **[14]**, in which there is less steric

$$C_6H_5\text{—CHO} + C_6H_5\text{—CO—}CH_3 \xrightarrow[\substack{H_2O\\C_2H_5OH\\15\text{–}30°}]{NaOH} C_6H_5\text{—CH(OH)—}CH_2\text{—CO—}C_6H_5 \overset{OH^{\ominus}}{\rightleftharpoons}$$ (*Ref. 9*)

[15] $\rightleftharpoons$ **[14]** $\longrightarrow$ **[16]** $\xrightarrow{-OH^{\ominus}}$ $C_6H_5CH{=}CH\text{—CO—}C_6H_5$ **[17]** (85%)

(6) C. R. Conard and M. A. Dolliver, *Org. Syn.*, **Coll. Vol. 2,** 167 (1943).
(7) S. Wawzonek and E. M. Smolin, *Org. Syn.*, **Coll. Vol. 3,** 715 (1955).
(8) R. Baltzly, E. Lorz, P. B. Russell, and F. M. Smith, *J. Am. Chem. Soc.*, **77,** 624 (1955).
(9) E. P. Kohler and H. M. Chadwell, *Org. Syn.*, **Coll. Vol. 1,** 78 (1944).

interference between the planar enolate anion system and the substituent at the beta carbon atom, is energetically favored.[10] Furthermore, the transition state **[16]** leading to the *trans* product **[17]** is favored, since two large substituents do not bear a *cis* coplanar relationship to one another[11] and there is no interference with coplanarity of the enolate system in the transition state. Of the two, the latter factor is in general the more important.[10]

Reaction of the intermediate aldol condensation products with base may lead either to the previously discussed dehydration reaction or to reversal of the aldol condensation (called a retrograde aldol reaction). Usually dehydration (i.e., the Claisen-Schmidt reaction) predominates when aromatic aldehydes are condensed with methyl ketones or with the methylene group of cyclic ketones. However, condensation at the methylene group of acyclic ketones having alpha substituents often fails because the intermediate aldol product (e.g., **[18]**) undergoes a retrograde aldol reaction more rapidly than it dehydrates.[12] For this reason the Claisen-Schmidt condensation of aromatic aldehydes with methyl alkyl

$$CH_3\text{—CO—}CH(CH_3)\text{—}CO_2C_2H_5 \xrightarrow[\text{2. } H_3O^{\oplus}]{\text{1. dilute NaOH, } H_2O} CH_3\text{—CO—}CH(CH_3)\text{—}CO_2H \xrightarrow[\substack{H_2O \text{ buffered to pH 7} \\ 25°}]{C_6H_5\text{—CHO}}$$

$$\underset{\textbf{[18]}\ (22\%)}{C_6H_5\text{—}CH(OH)\text{—}CH(CH_3)\text{—CO—}CH_3} \xrightarrow[\substack{H_2O \\ CH_3CH_2COCH_3 \\ 25°}]{\text{NaOH}} [C_6H_5\text{—CHO} + CH_3CH_2COCH_3] \longrightarrow$$

$$C_6H_5\text{—CH=CH—}COCH_2CH_3$$

(31% isolated; major product as determined spectrophotometrically)

(*Ref. 12c*)

$$\textbf{[18]} \xrightarrow[\substack{CH_3OH \\ 25°}]{H_2SO_4} C_6H_5\text{—CH=}C(CH_3)\text{—CO—}CH_3$$

(9% isolated; 48% as determined spectrophotometrically)

(10) (a) H. E. Zimmerman, L. Singer, and B. S. Thyagarajan, *J. Am. Chem. Soc.*, **81**, 108 (1959); (b) H. E. Zimmerman and L. Ahramjian, *ibid.*, **81**, 2086 (1959); (c) H. E. Zimmerman and L. Ahramjian, *ibid.*, **82**, 5459 (1960).

(11) D. Y. Curtin, *Record Chem. Progr.*, **15**, 111 (1954).

(12) (a) J. D. Gettler and L. P. Hammett, *J. Am. Chem. Soc.*, **65**, 1824 (1943); (b) D. S. Noyce and W. L. Reed, *ibid.*, **81**, 624 (1959); (c) M. Stiles, D. Wolf, and G. V. Hudson, *ibid.*, **81**, 628 (1959).

ketones normally yields the product of condensation at the methyl group, as is illustrated by the accompanying examples. In acid solution both dehydration and retrograde aldol condensation of the hydroxyketone [**18**] have been observed, but under the reaction conditions used the retrograde aldol products did not recondense.

$$C_6H_5\text{—}CHO + CH_3\text{—}CO\text{—}CH_2\text{—}CH_3 \xrightarrow[H_2O]{NaOH} C_6H_5\text{—}CH{=}CH\text{—}CO\text{—}CH_2\text{—}CH_3$$

(99%) (*Ref. 12a*)

$$C_6H_5\text{—}CHO + C_6H_5\text{—}CH_2\text{—}CO\text{—}CH_3 \xrightarrow[H_2O,\ 55°]{KOH} C_6H_5\text{—}CH{=}CH\text{—}CO\text{—}CH_2\text{—}C_6H_5$$

(48%) (*Ref. 13*)

The successful condensation of aldehydes at the methylene group of methyl alkyl ketones is most readily accomplished with acid catalysis. This process involves the intermediate enol,[12,14] and, as noted previously (Chapters 6 and 7), the more highly substituted enol derived from an unsymmetrical ketone is usually the more stable. As a result, condensation in the presence of acid catalysts occurs predominantly at the methylene group.[12] Although the intermediate aldol condensation product may be dehydrated by the acid present in the original reaction mixture, a more common method for effecting this condensation involves reaction of the carbonyl compound with dry hydrogen chloride to form a β-chloroketone; subsequent heating or treatment with base produces the α,β-unsaturated ketone. These procedures are illustrated below.

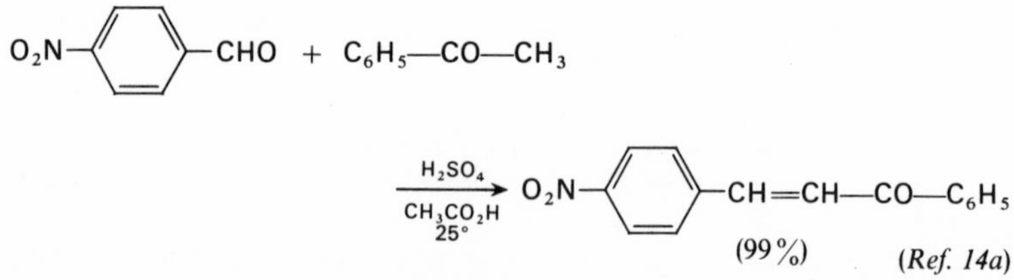

$$O_2N\text{—}C_6H_4\text{—}CHO + C_6H_5\text{—}CO\text{—}CH_3 \xrightarrow[CH_3CO_2H,\ 25°]{H_2SO_4} O_2N\text{—}C_6H_4\text{—}CH{=}CH\text{—}CO\text{—}C_6H_5$$

(99%) (*Ref. 14a*)

(13) P. L. Southwick, L. A. Pursglove, and P. Numerof, *ibid.*, **72**, 1604 (1950).

(14) (a) D. S. Noyce and W. A. Pryor, *ibid.*, **77**, 1397 (1955); **81**, 618 (1959); (b) D. S. Noyce, W. A. Pryor, and A. H. Bottini, *ibid.*, **77**, 1402 (1955); (c) D. S. Noyce and L. R. Snyder, *ibid.*, **80**, 4033, 4324 (1958); **81**, 620 (1959); (d) D. S. Noyce and W. L. Reed, *ibid.*, **80**, 5539 (1958).

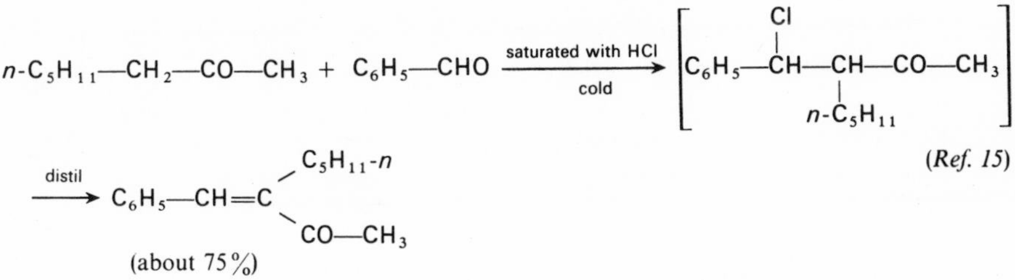

$$n\text{-}C_5H_{11}\text{—}CH_2\text{—}CO\text{—}CH_3 + C_6H_5\text{—}CHO \xrightarrow[\text{cold}]{\text{saturated with HCl}} \left[C_6H_5\text{—}\underset{}{\overset{Cl}{CH}}\text{—}\underset{n\text{-}C_5H_{11}}{CH}\text{—}CO\text{—}CH_3\right]$$

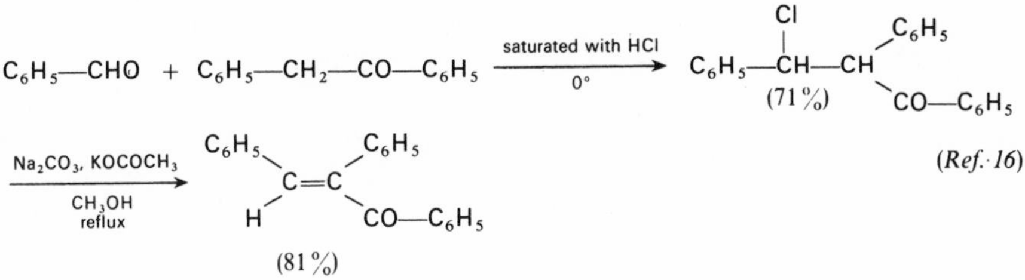

$$\xrightarrow{\text{distil}} C_6H_5\text{—}CH{=}C\begin{matrix}C_5H_{11}\text{-}n\\ CO\text{—}CH_3\end{matrix}$$

(about 75%) (*Ref. 15*)

$$C_6H_5\text{—}CHO + C_6H_5\text{—}CH_2\text{—}CO\text{—}C_6H_5 \xrightarrow[0^\circ]{\text{saturated with HCl}} C_6H_5\text{—}\overset{Cl}{CH}\text{—}CH\begin{matrix}C_6H_5\\ CO\text{—}C_6H_5\end{matrix}$$

(71%)

$$\xrightarrow[\text{CH}_3\text{OH reflux}]{Na_2CO_3,\ KOCOCH_3} \begin{matrix}C_6H_5\\ H\end{matrix}C{=}C\begin{matrix}C_6H_5\\ CO\text{—}C_6H_5\end{matrix}$$

(81%) (*Ref. 16*)

Cyclohexanone $\xrightarrow[\text{cold}]{\text{HCl}}$ 2-(1-chlorocyclohexyl)cyclohexanone (Cl) $\xrightarrow[\text{CH}_3\text{OH, }10^\circ]{\text{NaOCH}_3}$ 2-cyclohexylidenecyclohexanone (*Ref. 17*)

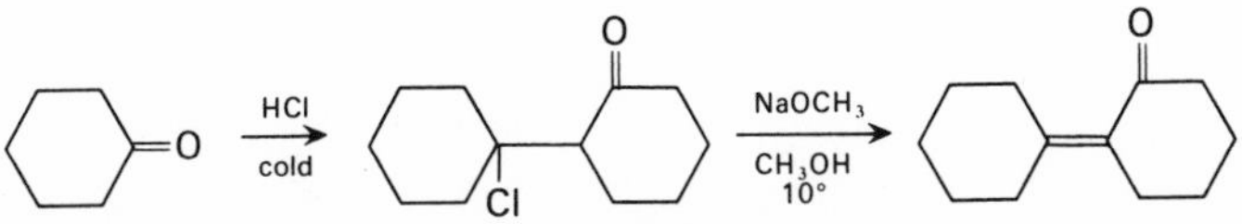

Intramolecular base- or acid-catalyzed aldol condensation followed by dehydration for the preparation of cyclic α,β-unsaturated ketones is a widely used synthetic sequence, especially in cases where a five- or six-membered cyclic ketone is to be formed. The second or ring-closure step in the Robinson anellation reaction (see Chapter 7) provides a number of examples of the preparation of cyclohexanone derivatives. Others, are illustrated below.

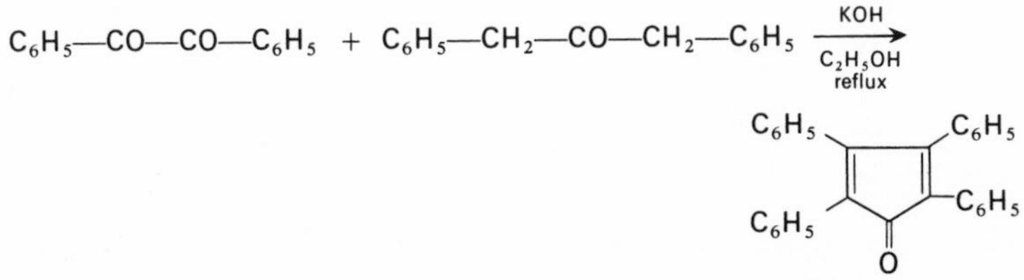

$$C_6H_5\text{—}CO\text{—}CO\text{—}C_6H_5 + C_6H_5\text{—}CH_2\text{—}CO\text{—}CH_2\text{—}C_6H_5 \xrightarrow[\text{C}_2\text{H}_5\text{OH reflux}]{\text{KOH}}$$

Tetraphenylcyclopentadienone (C_6H_5 ×4, C=O)

(91–96%) (*Ref. 18*)

(15) M. T. Bogert and D. Davidson, *ibid.*, **54**, 334 (1932).
(16) E. P. Kohler and E. M. Nygaard, *ibid.*, **52**, 4128 (1930).
(17) J. Reese, *Ber.*, **75**, 384 (1942).
(18) J. R. Johnson and O. Grummitt, *Org. Syn.*, **Coll. Vol. 3,** 806 (1955).

$CH_3—CHO + CH_3—CO—CH_2—CO_2C_2H_5 \xrightarrow[C_2H_5OH,\ 0°]{\text{piperidine (NH)}} CH_3—CH(CH(COCH_3)(CO_2C_2H_5))_2 \xrightarrow[CH_3CO_2H,\ reflux]{H_2SO_4}$ (Ref. 19)

O, CH_3, CH_3, $CO_2C_2H_5$ (47–50%) $\xrightarrow[H_2O,\ C_2H_5OH,\ reflux]{NaOH} \xrightarrow[reflux,\ -CO_2]{H_3O^{\oplus}}$ O, CH_3, CH_3 (52–55%)

$CH_3—CO—CH_2—CH_2—CO—CH_3 \xrightarrow[H_2O,\ reflux]{NaOH}$ CH_3, O (42%) (Ref. 20)

$CH_3—CO—CH_2—CH_2—CO—CH_2—C_5H_{11}\text{-}n \xrightarrow[H_2O,\ C_2H_5OH,\ reflux]{NaOH}$ CH_3, $C_5H_{11}\text{-}n$, O (92%) (Ref. 20b)

$HO_2C—CH_2—CH_2$, CH_3, O $\xrightarrow[(CH_3CO)_2O,\ reflux]{CH_3COCl}$ CH_3, O, O (92%) $\xrightarrow[(C_2H_5)_2O,\ 25°]{CH_3MgI} \xrightarrow[H_2O]{NH_4Cl}$

(Ref. 21)

$CH_3—C(=O)—CH_2—CH_2$, CH_3, O (45–65%) $\xrightarrow[H_2O,\ CH_3OH]{NaOH}$ CH_3, O (52–60% based on enol lactone)

(19) (a) E. C. Horning, M. O. Denekas, and R. E. Field, *ibid.*, **Coll. Vol. 3,** 317 (1955); (b) E. C. Horning, M. O. Denekas, and R. E. Field, *J. Org. Chem.*, **9**, 547 (1944); (c) E. C. Horning and R. E. Field, *J. Am. Chem. Soc.*, **68**, 384 (1946).

(20) (a) R. M. Acheson and R. Robinson, *J. Chem. Soc.*, **1952,** 1127; (b) H. Hunsdiecker, *Ber.*, **75**, 447, 455, 460 (1942).

(21) (a) G. I. Fujimoto, *J. Am. Chem. Soc.*, **73**, 1856 (1951); (b) R. B. Turner, *ibid.*, **72**, 579 (1950); (c) R. B. Woodward, F. Sondheimer, D. Taub, K.

A reaction related to the Claisen-Schmidt reaction, in the sense that condensation is forced to completion by dehydration of the intermediate aldol product, is the Knoevenagel reaction.[22] It is effected by treating an aldehyde or ketone with an active methylene compound in the presence of a catalytic amount of ammonia or a primary or secondary amine and at least a catalytic amount of a carboxylic acid.[23] The active methylene compounds commonly employed include esters of malonic, cyanoacetic, and acetoacetic acid, as well as phenylacetonitrile, benzyl ketones, and aliphatic nitro compounds. Although malonic esters may be used with aldehydes and such reactive ketones as acetone and cyclohexanone, less reactive ketones require the use of cyanoacetic esters if good yields of condensation products are to be obtained. The reactions are normally run in refluxing benzene or toluene solution with provision for the continuous separation of water as it is formed. The following examples illustrate the utility of this reaction.

$$C_6H_5\text{—}CHO + CH_2(CO_2C_2H_5)_2 \xrightarrow[\text{C}_6\text{H}_6\text{, reflux with separation of H}_2\text{O}]{\text{piperidine (NH), C}_6\text{H}_5\text{CO}_2\text{H}} C_6H_5\text{—}CH{=}C(CO_2C_2H_5)_2 \quad (89\text{–}91\%)$$

(*Ref. 24*)

$$\text{2,3-(CH}_3\text{O)}_2C_6H_3\text{—}CHO + CH_3\text{—}CO\text{—}CH_2\text{—}CO_2C_2H_5 \xrightarrow[\text{C}_6\text{H}_6\text{, reflux with separation of H}_2\text{O}]{\text{piperidine (NH), CH}_3\text{CO}_2\text{H}}$$

$$\text{2,3-(CH}_3\text{O)}_2C_6H_3\text{—}CH{=}C(COCH_3)(CO_2C_2H_5) \quad (64\text{–}72\%)$$

(*Ref. 25*)

Heusler, and W. M. McLamore, *ibid.*, **74**, 4223 (1952); (d) C. F. H. Allen, J. W. Gates, Jr., and J. A. VanAllan, *Org. Syn.*, **Coll. Vol. 3**, 353 (1955).

(22) J. R. Johnson, *Org. Reactions*, **1**, 210 (1942).

(23) (a) A. C. Cope, *J. Am. Chem. Soc.*, **59**, 2327 (1937); (b) A. C. Cope, C. M. Hofmann, C. Wyckoff, and E. Hardenbergh, *ibid.*, **63**, 3452 (1941).

(24) (a) C. F. H. Allen and F. W. Spangler, *Org. Syn.*, **Coll. Vol. 3**, 377 (1955); (b) see also G. Billek, *ibid.*, **43**, 49 (1963).

(25) E. C. Horning, J. Koo, M. S. Fish, and G. N. Walker, *Org. Syn.*, **Coll. Vol. 4**, 408 (1963).

$$CH_3{-}CO{-}C_2H_5 + \underset{\displaystyle C{\equiv}N}{CH_2}{-}CO_2C_2H_5 \xrightarrow[\substack{C_6H_6 \\ \text{reflux with separation} \\ \text{of } H_2O}]{\substack{H_3N^{\oplus}{-}CH_2CH_2{-}CO_2^{\ominus} \\ CH_3CO_2H}} (C_2H_5)(CH_3)C{=}C(CN)CO_2C_2H_5 \quad (81\text{–}88\%)$$

(*Ref. 26*)

$$C_6H_5{-}CO{-}CH_3 + \underset{\displaystyle C{\equiv}N}{CH_2}{-}CO_2C_2H_5 \xrightarrow[\substack{C_6H_6 \\ \text{reflux with separation} \\ \text{of } H_2O}]{\substack{NH_4OCOCH_3 \\ CH_3CO_2H}} (C_6H_5)(CH_3)C{=}C(CN)CO_2C_2H_5 \quad (52\text{–}58\%)$$

(*Ref. 27*)

$$o\text{-}CH_3O{-}C_6H_4{-}CHO + CH_3{-}CH_2{-}NO_2 \xrightarrow[\substack{C_6H_5CH_3, \\ \text{reflux with separation of } H_2O}]{n\text{-}C_4H_9{-}NH_2} o\text{-}CH_3O{-}C_6H_4{-}CH{=}C(CH_3){-}NO_2$$

(*Ref. 28*)

$$\xrightarrow[\substack{H_2O,\ C_6H_5CH_3 \\ 75^\circ}]{\substack{Fe,\ FeCl_3 \\ HCl}} \left[o\text{-}CH_3O{-}C_6H_4{-}CH_2{-}C(CH_3){=}NOH\right] \xrightarrow{H_3O^{\oplus}} o\text{-}CH_3O{-}C_6H_4{-}CH_2{-}CO{-}CH_3 \quad (63\text{–}73\%)$$

$$C_6H_5{-}CHO + C_6H_5{-}CH_2{-}CO{-}CH_3 \xrightarrow[\substack{C_6H_6 \\ \text{reflux with separation of } H_2O}]{\text{piperidine (NH)}} (C_6H_5)(H)C{=}C(C_6H_5)(CO{-}CH_3) \quad (81\%)$$

(*Ref. 10a*)

Similar condensations have been effected employing either an ion-exchange resin[29] or potassium fluoride[30] as a reaction catalyst.

Although these condensations were formerly considered to occur by a mechanism comparable to that previously discussed for the Claisen-Schmidt reaction, it appears probable that the initial

(26) F. S. Prout, R. J. Hartman, E. P. Y. Huang, C. J. Korpics, and G. R. Tichelaar, *ibid.*, **Coll. Vol. 4,** 93 (1963); see also F. S. Prout, *J. Org. Chem.*, **18**, 928 (1953).

(27) (a) S. M. McElvain and D. H. Clemens, *Org. Syn.*, **Coll. Vol. 4**, 463 (1963); see also (b) A. C. Cope and E. M. Hancock, *Org. Syn.*, **Coll. Vol. 3**, 399 (1955).

(28) R. V. Heinzelman, *Org. Syn.*, **Coll. Vol. 4,** 573 (1963).

(29) (a) M. J. Astle and W. C. Gergel, *J. Org. Chem.*, **21**, 493 (1956); (b) R. W. Hein, M. J. Astle, and J. R. Shelton, *ibid.*, **26**, 4874 (1961).

(30) L. Rand, J. V. Swisher, and C. J. Cronin, *ibid.*, **27**, 3505 (1962).

stage in the Knoevenagel condensations involves the formation of an imine or imminium salt (e.g., [**19**]) from the ketone or aldehyde and the amine.[31] Subsequent reaction of this imine (or imminium salt) with the enolate anion (or enol) derived from the active methylene compound produces an intermediate amino compound (e.g., [**20**]), which in turn forms the unsaturated product by elimination of the amine. It will be noted that the position of condensation of an aldehyde with an unsymmetrical ketone (e.g., benzaldehyde with benzyl methyl ketone) is sometimes not the same in the Knoevenagel reaction as in the Claisen-Schmidt reaction.

$$CH_3—CO—CH_3 + C_5H_{10}N—H \underset{}{\overset{H^{\oplus},\ -H_2O}{\rightleftharpoons}} (CH_3)_2C{=}\overset{\oplus}{N}C_5H_{10} \ [\mathbf{19}] \xrightarrow{CH^{\ominus}(CO_2C_2H_5)_2}$$

$$(CH_3)_2C(NC_5H_{10})—CH(CO_2C_2H_5)_2 \ [\mathbf{20}] \xrightarrow{-C_5H_{10}N—H} (CH_3)_2C{=}C(CO_2C_2H_5)_2$$

Malonic acid, the monoesters of malonic acid, and cyanoacetic acid are sufficiently reactive as active methylene compounds to permit successful Knoevenagel condensations with aldehydes

$$\text{cyclohexanone } [\mathbf{21}] + CH_2(C{\equiv}N)—CO_2H \xrightarrow[C_6H_6,\ \text{reflux with separation of } H_2O]{NH_4OCOCH_3} \text{cyclohexylidene}{=}C(C{\equiv}N)CO_2H \ [\mathbf{22}]\ (65–76\%)$$

$$\xrightarrow{165–175^\circ} \left[\text{1-cyclohexenyl}—CH(C{\equiv}N)CO_2H\right] [\mathbf{24}] \xrightarrow{-CO_2} \text{1-cyclohexenyl}—CH_2C{\equiv}N \ [\mathbf{23}]\ (76–91\%)$$

(*Ref. 32*)

(31) (a) T. I. Crowell and D. W. Peck, *J. Am. Chem. Soc.*, **75**, 1075 (1953); (b) E. H. Cordes and W. P. Jencks, *ibid.*, **84**, 826 (1962); (c) D. N. Robertson, *J. Org. Chem.*, **25**, 47 (1960); (d) C. Schroeder, S. Preis, and K. P. Link, *Tetrahedron Letters*, **No. 13**, 23 (1960); (e) G. Charles, *Bull. Soc. Chim. France*, **1963**, 1559, 1566, 1573, 1576; (f) for the use of the anion derived from an imine as one component in an aldol condensation, see G. Wittig, H. D. Frommeld, and P. Suchanek, *Angew, Chem., Intern. Ed. Engl.*, **2**, 683 (1963).

(32) A. C. Cope, A. A. D'Addieco, D. E. Whyte, and S. A. Glickman, *Org. Syn.*, **Coll. Vol. 4,** 234 (1963).

and very reactive ketones (e.g., [**21**]). As indicated in the accompanying equations, thermal decarboxylation of the condensation product (e.g., [**22**]) leads predominantly to the formation of a *β,γ*-unsaturated acid derivative (e.g., [**23**]), presumably by the initial isomerization of the conjugated acid (e.g., [**22**]) to the unconjugated acid (e.g., [**24**]) and the usual subsequent decarboxylation of the nonconjugated cyanoacetic acid.[33] If condensations of this type are run in pyridine solution (the Doebner modification), decarboxylation usually occurs in the reaction mixture, leading to formation of *α,β*-unsaturated carboxylic acid derivatives as shown in the following equations. This procedure is generally superior

2,3-$(CH_3O)_2C_6H_3$—CHO + $CH_2(CO_2H)_2$ $\xrightarrow[\text{pyridine, reflux}]{\text{piperidine}}$ $\xrightarrow{H_3O^{\oplus}}$ 2,3-$(CH_3O)_2C_6H_3$—CH=CH—CO_2H (trans) (87–98%) (*Ref.* 34)

C_6H_5—CHO + CH_3—$CH(CO_2H)_2$ $\xrightarrow[\text{pyridine, 100°}]{\text{piperidine}}$ $\xrightarrow{H_3O^{\oplus}}$ C_6H_5(H)C=C(CH_3)CO_2H (96%) (*Ref.* 35)

CH_3—CH=CH—CHO + $CH_2(CO_2H)_2$ $\xrightarrow[100°]{\text{pyridine}}$ $\xrightarrow{H_3O^{\oplus}}$ CH_3—CH=CH—CH=CH—CO_2H (28–32%) (*Ref.* 36)

2-Furyl—CHO + $CH_2(CN)$—CO_2H $\xrightarrow[\text{pyridine, } C_6H_5CH_3\text{, reflux with separation of } H_2O]{NH_4OCOCH_3}$ $\xrightarrow{H_3O^{\oplus}}$ 2-Furyl—CH=CH—C≡N (75–78%) (*Ref.* 37)

(33) (a) E. J. Corey, *J. Am. Chem. Soc.*, **74**, 5897 (1952); (b) E. J. Corey, *ibid.*, **75**, 1163 (1953); (c) E. J. Corey and G. Fraenkel, *ibid.*, **75**, 1168 (1953).

(34) (a) J. Koo, M. S. Fish, G. N. Walker, and J. Blake, *Org. Syn.*, **Coll. Vol. 4,** 327 (1963); see also (b) S. Rajagopalan and P. V. A. Raman, *Org. Syn.*, **Coll. Vol. 3**, 425 (1955); (c) R. H. Wiley and N. R. Smith, *Org. Syn.*, **Coll. Vol. 4**, 731 (1963).

(35) W. J. Gensler and E. Berman, *J. Am. Chem. Soc.*, **80**, 4949 (1958).

(36) C. F. H. Allen and J. VanAllan, *Org. Syn.*, **Coll. Vol. 3,** 783 (1955).

(37) J. M. Patterson, *Org. Syn.*, **40**, 46 (1960).

$$n\text{-}C_6H_{13}\text{—CHO} + CH_2(CO_2H)_2 \xrightarrow[100°]{\text{pyridine}} \xrightarrow{H_3O^{\oplus}} n\text{-}C_6H_{13}\text{—CH=CH—}CO_2H$$

(75–85%; contains about 5% of β,γ-unsaturated isomer) (*Ref.* 22)

to the subsequently discussed Perkin reaction because it is applicable to aliphatic aldehydes that would be polymerized by more vigorous reaction conditions and because it usually results in better yields for aromatic aldehyde reactions. An investigation[33] of the decarboxylation that accompanies this condensation indicates that decarboxylation must either precede or occur concurrently with the introduction of the carbon-carbon double bond in condensations involving aliphatic aldehydes. The reaction is believed to proceed by the decarboxylative elimination outlined below. Although the same sequence may be applicable to reactions

$$\text{R—CHO} + CH_2(CO_2H)_2 \xrightarrow[\text{pyridine}]{\text{piperidine}} \text{R–CH(OH)–CH(}CO_2H\text{)–C(=O)–}O^{\ominus} \text{ or R–CH(}\overset{\oplus}{\text{N}}\text{H}C_5H_{10}\text{)–CH(}CO_2H\text{)–C(=O)–}O^{\ominus}$$

$$\longrightarrow \text{R—CH=CH—}CO_2H$$

involving aromatic aldehydes, an alternative addition-elimination process has been demonstrated for arylidenemalonic acid derivatives (e.g., **[25]**).

$$\underset{[25]}{C_6H_5\text{—CH=C(}CO_2H\text{)(}CO_2C_2H_5\text{)}} \xrightarrow[111°]{\text{pyridine}} C_6H_5\text{–CH(}\overset{\oplus}{\text{N}}C_5H_5\text{)–CH(}CO_2C_2H_5\text{)–C(=O)–}O^{\ominus} \xrightarrow{-CO_2}$$

$$C_6H_5\text{(H)C=C(H)}CO_2C_2H_5$$

(77%) (*Ref.* 33c)

The Mannich Reaction

The aldol condensation of active methylene compounds (e.g., [**26**]) with formaldehyde (Tollen's condensation) occurs readily,

$$\underset{[26]}{CH_3—NO_2} + \underset{\text{(introduced as the trimer)}}{CH_2O} \xrightarrow[\substack{CH_3OH \\ CH_3NO_2 \\ 25\text{–}35°}]{KOH} \xrightarrow{H_2SO_4} \underset{(46\text{–}49\%)}{HO—CH_2—CH_2—NO_2} \qquad (Ref.\ 38)$$

but the reaction is often difficult to control in a routine laboratory preparation, and polycondensation results. A further complication is the fact that formaldehyde may reduce other carbonyl groups present (the Cannizzaro reaction[39]). Examples of the reaction of carbonyl compounds with excess formaldehyde are provided in the following equations.

$$CH_3—CHO + \underset{\text{(excess introduced as the trimer)}}{CH_2O} \xrightarrow[\substack{H_2O \\ 50\text{–}55°}]{Ca(OH)_2} \left[(HOCH_2)_3C—CHO\right] \xrightarrow[OH^{\ominus}]{CH_2O} \underset{(55\text{–}57\%)}{C(CH_2OH)_4} \qquad (Ref.\ 40)$$

$$\text{cyclohexanone} + \underset{\text{(excess introduced as the trimer)}}{CH_2O} \xrightarrow[\substack{H_2O \\ 35\text{–}40°}]{Ca(OH)_2} \underset{(73\text{–}85\%)}{\text{2,2,6,6-}(HOCH_2)_4\text{-cyclohexanol (H, OH)}} \qquad (Ref.\ 41)$$

A more satisfactory method for the introduction of a single carbon atom is the reaction of an active methylene compound with formaldehyde and an amine to form a β-aminocarbonyl compound. This reaction, known as the Mannich reaction,[42] is usually run in water, methanol, ethanol, or acetic acid. The formaldehyde is introduced as an aqueous solution (20 to 40 per cent formaldehyde by weight), as the solid trimer (trioxymethylene), or as the solid polymer (polyoxymethylene); the latter two reagents are converted to formaldehyde by acid present in the reaction mixture. The amine is normally introduced as its hydrochloride,

(38) W. E. Noland, *Org. Syn.*, **41**, 67 (1961).

(39) T. A. Geissman, *Org. Reactions*, **2**, 94 (1944).

(40) H. B. J. Schurink, *Org. Syn.*, **Coll. Vol. 1**, 425 (1944).

(41) H. Wittcoff, *Org. Syn.*, **Coll. Vol. 4**, 907 (1963).

(42) (a) F. F. Blicke, *Org. Reactions*, **1**, 303 (1942); (b) B. Reichert, *Die Mannich Reaktion*, Springer Verlag, Berlin, 1959; (c) H. Hellmann and G. Opitz, *Angew Chem.*, **68**, 265 (1956).

and several drops of hydrochloric acid are frequently added to ensure that the reaction mixture is not basic. Usually a secondary amine (e.g., dimethylamine, diethylamine, piperidine, morpholine, pyrrolidine) is employed to avoid side reactions, such as might occur between the initially formed Mannich base and additional formaldehyde and active methylene compound if a primary amine or ammonia were used. Typical examples of the Mannich are provided in the following equations.

$$C_6H_5—CO—CH_3 + (CH_2O)_3 + (CH_3)_2NH_2^{\oplus}Cl^{\ominus} \xrightarrow[\text{reflux}]{HCl,\ C_2H_5OH} C_6H_5—CO—CH_2—CH_2—NH^{\oplus}(CH_3)_2Cl^{\ominus}$$

(68–72%) (*Ref. 43*)

$$CH_3—CO—CH_3 + (CH_2O)_3 + (C_2H_5)_2NH_2^{\oplus}Cl^{\ominus} \xrightarrow[CH_3OH,\ CH_3COCH_3,\ \text{reflux}]{HCl} \xrightarrow[H_2O]{NaOH} CH_3—CO—CH_2—CH_2—N(C_2H_5)_2$$

(62–70%) (*Ref. 44*)

Under the usual slightly acidic reaction conditions, the mechanism of the Mannich reaction is believed[42c,45] to involve electrophilic attack by an imminium salt (e.g., **[27]**) on the enol (e.g., **[28]**) of the active methylene compound. A consequence of this mechanistic

$$(CH_3)_2NH + CH_2O \overset{H^{\oplus}}{\rightleftharpoons} (CH_3)_2\overset{\oplus}{N}{=}CH_2\ \textbf{[27]} + \text{1-hydroxycyclohexene}\ \textbf{[28]} \longrightarrow$$

$$(CH_3)_2N—CH_2\text{-(protonated cyclohexanone, }\overset{\oplus}{O}H) \xrightarrow{-H^{\oplus}} (CH_3)_2N—CH_2\text{-(cyclohexanone)}$$

(43) C. E. Maxwell, *Org. Syn.*, **Coll. Vol. 3,** 305 (1955).

(44) A. L. Wilds, R. M. Nowak, and K. E. McCaleb, *Org. Syn.*, **Coll. Vol. 4,** 281 (1963).

(45) T. F. Cummings and J. R. Shelton, *J. Org. Chem.*, **25**, 419 (1960).

scheme is the expectation that unsymmetrical ketones will react predominantly at the more highly substituted alpha position, corresponding to the more stable enol (see Chapters 6 and 7). Although early studies[46] provided examples that appeared contrary to this expectation, reinvestigation[47] has shown the Mannich reaction products from ketones **[29]**, **[30]**, and **[31]** to be predominantly those that result from attack at the more highly substituted position.

$$CH_3{-}CO{-}CH(CH_3)_2 + (CH_2O)_3 + (CH_3)_2NH_2^{\oplus}Cl^{\ominus} \xrightarrow[C_2H_5OH,\ reflux]{HCl} \xrightarrow{OH^{\ominus}}$$

[29]

$$CH_3{-}CO{-}C(CH_3)_2{-}CH_2{-}N(CH_3)_2$$

(39%) *(Ref. 47a)*

$$\text{[30] (2-methylcyclopentanone)} + (CH_2O)_3 + (CH_3)_2NH_2^{\oplus}Br^{\ominus} \xrightarrow[reflux]{C_2H_5OH} \xrightarrow{OH^{\ominus}}$$

[30]

$$\text{2-}CH_3\text{-2-}[CH_2{-}N(CH_3)_2]\text{cyclopentanone} \xrightarrow{CH_3I} \text{2-}CH_3\text{-2-}[CH_2{-}N^{\oplus}(CH_3)_3]\text{cyclopentanone}\ I^{\ominus}$$

(89%) *(Ref. 47b)*

$$\text{[31] (2-methylcyclohexanone)} + (CH_2O)_3 + (CH_3)_2NH_2^{\oplus}Cl^{\ominus} \xrightarrow[reflux]{H_2O} \text{2-}CH_3\text{-2-}[CH_2{-}N(CH_3)_2]\text{cyclohexanone} + \text{2-}[(CH_3)_2N{-}CH_2]\text{-6-}CH_3\text{-cyclohexanone}$$

[31]

(ca. 67% of mixture) (ca. 33% of mixture)

(59%)

Although the use of primary amines in the Mannich reaction is undesirable when a monocondensation product is required, a number of cyclic products have been prepared via double Mannich

(46) (a) E. C. duFeu, F. J. McQuillin, and R. Robinson, *J. Chem. Soc.*, **1937,** 53; (b) R. Jaquier, M. Mousseron, and S. Boyer, *Bull. Soc. Chim. France*, **1956,** 1653.

(47) (a) M. Brown and W. S. Johnson, *J. Org. Chem.*, **27**, 4706 (1962); (b) H. O. House and B. M. Trost, *ibid.*, **29**, 1339 (1964).

condensations with primary amines. The second of the two examples cited below also illustrates the use of an aldehyde other than formaldehyde in the Mannich reaction.

CH_3O_2C (cyclohexanone with CO_2CH_3 groups) $+ CH_2O + CH_3NH_2 \xrightarrow[CH_3OH,\ 25^\circ]{H_2O}$ CH_3O_2C, CO_2CH_3, $N{-}CH_3$ (80%) (*Ref. 48*)

CHO / $(CH_2)_3$ / CHO $+ CH_3NH_2 +$ $CH_2{-}CO_2H$ / CO / $CH_2{-}CO_2H$ $\xrightarrow[pH\ 2.5\text{–}4.5,\ 25^\circ]{H_2O} \xrightarrow[100^\circ,\ -CO_2]{H_3O^\oplus} \xrightarrow{NaOH}$ $CH_3{-}N$, O (58–68%) (*Ref. 49*)

Apart from the applicability of the Mannich reaction to ketones and other active methylene compounds,[42] the intermediate imminium salt [**27**] is a sufficiently reactive electrophilic agent to attack such relatively reactive aromatic nuclei as phenol and indole ([**32**]).

[**32**] (N–H) $+ CH_2O + (C_2H_5)_2NH \xrightarrow[CH_3CO_2H]{H_2O}$ $CH_2{-}N(C_2H_5)_2$ (N–H) (95%) (*Ref. 42b*)

Mannich bases are used primarily as synthetic intermediates, in which the amino function is subsequently replaced by some other group.[42,50] The most common reactions of this type involve elimination of the amine function from a β-aminoketone (e.g., [**33**]) or from the corresponding quaternary ammonium salt (e.g., [**34**]) to produce an α,β-unsaturated ketone (e.g., [**35**]). If the unsaturated ketone is formed in the presence of a nucleophilic reagent (e.g., an enolate anion or cyanide anion), conjugate addition of the

(48) (a) F. F. Blicke and F. J. McCarty, *J. Org. Chem.*, **24**, 1379 (1959); (b) W. Schneider and H. Götz, *Arch. Pharm.*, **294**, 506 (1961); (c) H. O. House and H. C. Müller, *J. Org. Chem.*, **27**, 4436 (1962).

(49) A. C. Cope, H. L. Dryden, Jr., and C. F. Howell, *Org. Syn.*, **Coll. Vol. 4,** 816 (1963).

(50) J. H. Brewster and E. L. Eliel, *Org. Reactions*, **7**, 99 (1953).

$$C_6H_5{-}CO{-}CH_2CH_2CH_3 + (CH_2O)_3 + (CH_3)_2{}^{\oplus}NH_2Cl^{\ominus} \xrightarrow[\text{reflux}]{C_2H_5OH} C_6H_5{-}CO{-}CH(C_2H_5){-}CH_2{-}{}^{\oplus}NH(CH_3)_2Cl^{\ominus}$$

[33] (60%)

$$\textbf{[33]} \xrightarrow{\text{steam distillation}} C_6H_5{-}CO{-}C(=CH_2){-}C_2H_5 \ \textbf{[35]}$$

$$\textbf{[33]} \xrightarrow{1.\ Na_2CO_3,\ H_2O;\ 2.\ CH_3I} C_6H_5{-}CO{-}CH(C_2H_5){-}CH_2{-}N^{\oplus}(CH_3)_3I^{\ominus}$$

(*Ref. 51*)

[34] (63% over-all)

$$\textbf{[34]} \xrightarrow[CH_3OH,\ -2^\circ]{NaOH,\ H_2O} \textbf{[35]}$$

nucleophile to the unsaturated system occurs in the reaction mixture. Several examples are cited in the Chapter 7 discussion of the Michael reaction; another is given below, along with an illustration of the use of a Mannich base derived from an aromatic system. As indicated, the latter reaction occurs[51c] by the same type of elimination-addition sequence that is operative with β-amino ketones.

$$C_6H_5{-}CO{-}CH_2CH_2{-}{}^{\oplus}NH(CH_3)_2{}^{\ominus}Cl \xrightarrow[H_2O,\ \text{reflux}]{KCN} [C_6H_5{-}CO{-}CH{=}CH_2] \xrightarrow{HCN} C_6H_5{-}CO{-}CH_2{-}CH_2{-}C{\equiv}N$$

(67%) (*Ref. 50*)

$$\text{3-}(CH_2{-}N(CH_3)_2)\text{indole} \xrightarrow[C_6H_5CH_3,\ \text{reflux}]{NaOH,\ CH_3CONHCH(CO_2C_2H_5)_2} [\text{3-methyleneindolenine}] \xrightarrow{CH_3CONH^{\ominus}C(CO_2C_2H_5)_2} \text{3-}(CH_2{-}C(NHCOCH_3)(CO_2C_2H_5)_2)\text{indole}$$

(90%) (*Refs. 50, 51c*)

Condensation in which Equilibrium Is Favored by Ring Closure Involving the Intermediate Aldol Product: The Perkin, Stobbe, and Darzens Reactions

These modifications of the aldol condensation have as a common feature the presence of a functional group that can react intramolecularly with the alkoxide anion (analogous to **[3]**) initially

(51) (a) J. H. Burckhalter and R. C. Fuson, *J. Am. Chem. Soc.*, **70**, 4184 (1948); (b) H. O. House, D. J. Reif, and R. L. Wasson, *ibid.*, **79**, 2490 (1957); (c) for demonstration of an analogous reaction with the Mannich bases derived from indole, see J. D. Albright and H. R. Snyder, *ibid.*, **81**, 2239 (1959).

formed, thus favoring the formation of the condensation product. The Perkin reaction,[22] which is normally applicable only to aromatic aldehydes, is usually effected by heating a mixture of the aldehyde, an acid anhydride (the active methylene component), and a weak base (such as the sodium or potassium salt of the acid or triethylamine) to relatively high temperatures (150–200°), as illustrated in the accompanying equations. Note from the second

$$\text{2-furyl-CHO} + (CH_3CO)_2O \xrightarrow[150^\circ]{KOCOCH_3} \xrightarrow{H_2O} \text{2-furyl}(H)C{=}C(H)CO_2H \quad (65\text{–}70\%)$$

(Ref. 52)

$$C_6H_5\text{—}CHO + C_6H_5\text{—}CH_2\text{—}CO_2H \xrightarrow[(CH_3CO)_2O]{(C_2H_5)_3N} [C_6H_5\text{—}CH_2\text{—}CO\text{—}O\text{—}CO\text{—}CH_3]$$

$$\xrightarrow{C_6H_5\text{—}CHO} (C_6H_5)(H)C{=}C(C_6H_5)(CO_2H) \quad (83\%)$$

(Refs. 10b, 53)

equation that acids and anhydrides present in the reaction mixture are rapidly equilibrated.

The Perkin reaction is believed to proceed by formation of an enolate anion (e.g., [**36**]) from the acid anhydride and subsequent reaction with the aldehyde to form an alkoxide (e.g., [**37**]). The ensuing intramolecular acylation affords a β-acyloxy derivative (e.g., [**38**]), which can either undergo elimination to form a cinnamic acid or decarboxylative elimination (e.g., [**39**]) to form an olefin. As in previously discussed condensations, the kinetically favored stereoisomer is the one with the carboxyl group *trans* to the larger group at the beta carbon atom.[10b] Decarboxylative elimination (e.g., [**39**]) to form an olefin is usually minor in the Perkin reaction; however, higher temperatures may cause this

(52) (a) J. R. Johnson, *Org. Syn.*, **Coll. Vol. 3,** 426 (1955); see also (b) F. K. Thayer, *Org. Syn.*, **Coll. Vol. 1,** 398 (1944).

(53) (a) L. F. Fieser, *Experiments in Organic Chemistry,* 3d ed., Heath, Boston, 1955, pp. 182–185; (b) R. E. Buckles and K. Bremer, *Org. Syn.*, **Coll. Vol. 4,** 777 (1963); see also D. F. DeTar, *ibid.*, **Coll. Vol. 4,** 730 (1963).

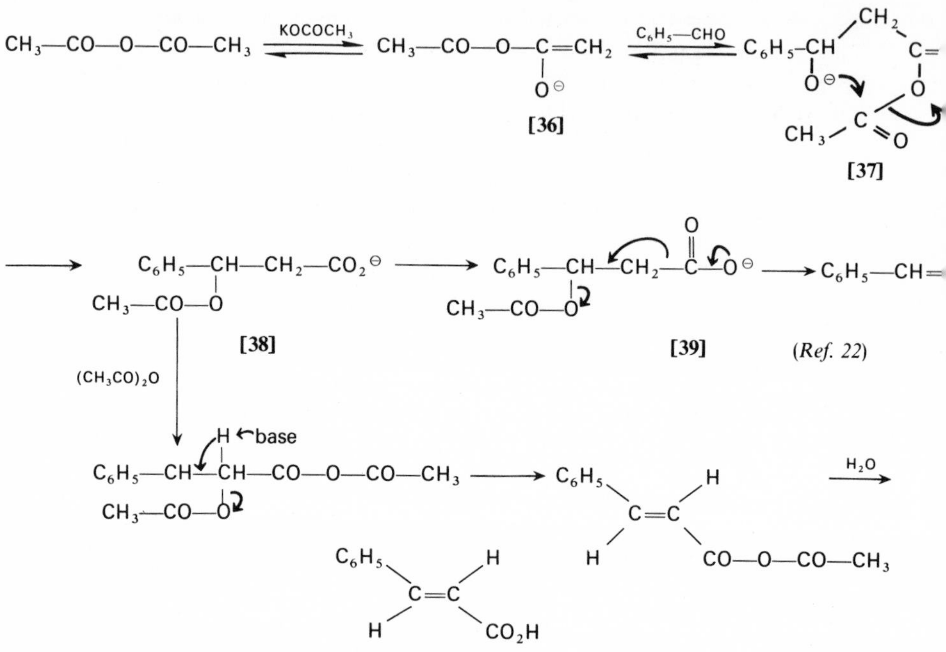

$$CH_3—CO—O—CO—CH_3 \underset{}{\overset{KOCOCH_3}{\rightleftharpoons}} CH_3—CO—O—\underset{O^{\ominus}}{C}=CH_2 \;[36] \underset{}{\overset{C_6H_5—CHO}{\rightleftharpoons}} [37]$$

$$\longrightarrow \underset{CH_3—CO—O}{C_6H_5—CH}—CH_2—CO_2^{\ominus} \;[38] \longrightarrow \underset{CH_3—CO—O}{C_6H_5—CH}—CH_2—\overset{O}{\overset{\|}{C}}—O^{\ominus} \;[39] \longrightarrow C_6H_5—CH=$$

(*Ref. 22*)

$$[38] \xrightarrow{(CH_3CO)_2O} \underset{CH_3—CO—O}{C_6H_5—CH}—\overset{H \leftarrow base}{CH}—CO—O—CO—CH_3 \longrightarrow (C_6H_5)(H)C=C(H)(CO—O—CO—CH_3) \xrightarrow{H_2O} (C_6H_5)(H)C=C(H)(CO_2H)$$

(55–60%)

process to become the major reaction, as the following equations demonstrate.

$$C_6H_5—CH=CH—CHO + C_6H_5—CH_2—CO_2H \xrightarrow[(CH_3CO)_2O \text{ reflux}]{PbO} C_6H_5—CH=CH—CH=CH—C_6H_5$$

(27–29%)

(*Ref. 54*)

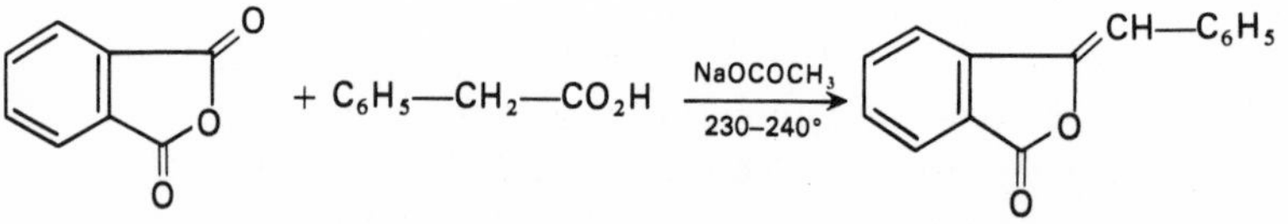

$$\text{phthalic anhydride} + C_6H_5—CH_2—CO_2H \xrightarrow[230–240°]{NaOCOCH_3} \text{3-benzylidenephthalide } (=CH—C_6H_5)$$

(71–74%)

(*Ref. 55*)

The use of α-acylamido acids in the Perkin reaction leads to the formation of arylidene derivatives of oxazolone called azlactones.[56] These substances, whose preparations are illustrated by

(54) B. B. Corson, *Org. Syn.*, **Coll. Vol. 2,** 229 (1943).

(55) R. Weiss, *ibid.*, **Coll. Vol. 2,** 61 (1943).

(56) (a) H. E. Carter, *Org. Reactions,* **3**, 198 (1946); (b) for a related condensation, see R. Filler, E. J. Piasek, and H. A. Leipold, *Org. Syn.* **43**, 3 (1963).

$$C_6H_5{-}CHO + CH_2(NH{-}CO{-}CH_3){-}CO_2H \xrightarrow[\text{reflux}]{NaOCOCH_3,\ (CH_3CO)_2O} \left[\text{2-methyl-5-oxazolone}\right] \xrightarrow{C_6H_5{-}CHO} C_6H_5{-}CH{=}C\text{(oxazolone, 2-}CH_3\text{)}$$

(74–77%)

(*Ref.* 57)

$$3,4\text{-}(CH_3O)_2C_6H_3{-}CHO + CH_2(NH{-}CO{-}C_6H_5){-}CO_2H \xrightarrow[(CH_3CO)_2O,\ 100^\circ]{NaOCOCH_3} 3,4\text{-}(CH_3O)_2C_6H_3{-}CH{=}C\text{(CO{-}O{-}C(}C_6H_5\text{){=}N)}$$

(69–73%)

(*Ref.* 58)

the accompanying equations, serve as useful intermediates for the synthesis of α-amino acids (e.g., **[40]**) and α-keto acids (e.g., **[41]**).

$$C_6H_5{-}CH{=}C\text{(oxazolone, 2-}CH_3\text{)} \xrightarrow[\text{acetone, reflux}]{H_2O} C_6H_5{-}CH{=}C(NH{-}CO{-}CH_3){-}CO_2H \xrightarrow[CH_3CO_2H,\ 25^\circ]{H_2(2\text{–}3\text{ atm}),\ Pt(\text{from }PtO_2)}$$

(80–90%)

(*Refs.* 57, 59)

$$C_6H_5{-}CH_2{-}CH(NH{-}CO{-}CH_3){-}CO_2H \xrightarrow[H_2O]{HCl} \xrightarrow{\text{neutralize}} C_6H_5{-}CH_2{-}CH(\oplus NH_3){-}CO_2^{\ominus}$$

[40] (85–86%)

$$C_6H_5{-}CH{=}C(NH{-}CO{-}CH_3){-}CO_2H \xrightarrow[H_2O,\ \text{reflux}]{HCl} C_6H_5{-}CH_2{-}CO{-}CO_2H$$

[41] (88–94%) (*Ref.* 60)

Ketones or aldehydes react with diethyl succinate in the presence of a strong base such as sodium hydride or potassium *t*-butoxide to form monoesters of an α-alkylidene- (or arylidene) succinic acid. The reaction, known as the Stobbe condensation,[61] is thought to

(57) R. M. Herbst and D. Shemin, *Org. Syn.*, **Coll. Vol. 2,** 1 (1943).
(58) J. S. Buck and W. S. Ide, *ibid.*, **Coll. Vol. 2,** 55 (1943).
(59) (a) R. M. Herbst and D. Shemin, *ibid.*, **Coll. Vol. 2,** 491 (1943); see also (b) H. B. Gillespie and H. R. Snyder, *ibid.*, **Coll. Vol. 2,** 489 (1943).
(60) (a) R. M. Herbst and D. Shemin, *ibid.*, **Coll. Vol. 2,** 519 (1943); (b) for a related synthetic procedure, see Ref. 24b.
(61) W. S. Johnson and G. H. Daub, *Org. Reactions*, **6,** 1 (1951).

proceed by initial aldol condensation and subsequent intramolecular lactone formation (i.e., **[42]**); ensuing base-catalyzed elimination (e.g., **[43]**) yields the product. Because the last step

$$(C_6H_5)_2C{=}O + \begin{matrix} CH_2{-}CO_2C_2H_5 \\ | \\ CH_2{-}CO_2C_2H_5 \end{matrix} \xrightarrow[\text{(CH}_3)_3\text{COH, reflux}]{\text{KOC(CH}_3)_3} (C_6H_5)_2C(O^{\ominus}){-}CH(CO_2C_2H_5){-}CH_2{-}C({=}O)OC_2H_5 \; [42] \longrightarrow$$

$$[43] \xrightarrow{\text{base}} (C_6H_5)_2C{=}C(CO_2C_2H_5){-}CH_2{-}CO_2^{\ominus} \; [44] \xrightarrow{H_3O^{\oplus}} (C_6H_5)_2C{=}C(CO_2C_2H_5){-}CH_2{-}CO_2H \; (90\text{–}94\%)$$

(*Ref. 62*)

in this sequence, that forming the carboxylate ion (e.g., **[44]**), is essentially irreversible, this condensation may be applied successfully even to relatively hindered ketones, where other types of aldol condensation fail. Additional Stobbe reactions are outlined in the following equations. It will be noted that the

$$C_6H_5{-}CO{-}CH_3 + \begin{matrix} CH_2{-}CO_2C_2H_5 \\ | \\ CH_2{-}CO_2C_2H_5 \end{matrix} \xrightarrow[C_6H_6,\ 40^\circ]{\text{NaH (cat. amt.) } C_2H_5OH} \xrightarrow[2.\ H_2O]{1.\ CH_3CO_2H}$$

(*Ref. 61*)

$$(C_6H_5)(CH_3)C{=}C(CO_2C_2H_5)(CH_2{-}CO_2H) + (C_6H_5)(CH_3)C{=}C(CH_2{-}CO_2H)(CO_2{-}C_2H_5)$$

(92–93% of mixture)

$$n\text{-}C_{11}H_{23}{-}CHO + \begin{matrix} CH_2{-}CO_2C_2H_5 \\ | \\ CH_2{-}CO_2C_2H_5 \end{matrix} \xrightarrow[\text{(CH}_3)_3\text{COH, reflux}]{\text{KOC(CH}_3)_3} \xrightarrow{H_3O^{\oplus}} n\text{-}C_{11}H_{23}{-}CH{=}C(CO_2C_2H_5){-}CH_2{-}CO_2H$$

$$\xrightarrow[C_2H_5OH,\ 25^\circ]{HCl} n\text{-}C_{11}H_{23}{-}CH{=}C(CO_2C_2H_5){-}CH_2{-}CO_2C_2H_5 \; (58\%)$$

(*Ref. 63*)

(62) W. S. Johnson and W. P. Schneider, *Org. Syn.*, **Coll. Vol. 4,** 132 (1963).

(63) C. G. Overberger and C. W. Roberts, *J. Am. Chem. Soc.*, **71**, 3618 (1949).

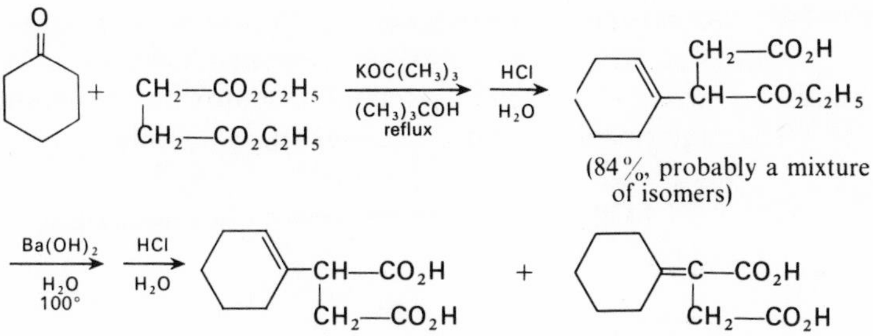

Cyclohexanone + $CH_2—CO_2C_2H_5$ / $CH_2—CO_2C_2H_5$ $\xrightarrow[(CH_3)_3COH \text{ reflux}]{KOC(CH_3)_3}$ $\xrightarrow[H_2O]{HCl}$ cyclohexenyl–$CH(CO_2C_2H_5)—CH_2—CO_2H$

(84%, probably a mixture of isomers)

$\xrightarrow[H_2O,\ 100°]{Ba(OH)_2}$ $\xrightarrow[H_2O]{HCl}$ cyclohexenyl–$CH(CO_2H)—CH_2—CO_2H$ + cyclohexylidene$=C(CO_2H)—CH_2—CO_2H$ (*Ref. 64*)

unsaturated product may consist of mixtures, both of stereoisomers and of structural isomers in which the double bond can occupy several positions.

The prime synthetic utility of the Stobbe condensation arises from the fact that the initial condensation product (e.g., **[45]**) may be decarboxylated as illustrated below. The propionic acid derivatives formed by this reaction sequence serve as intermediates for

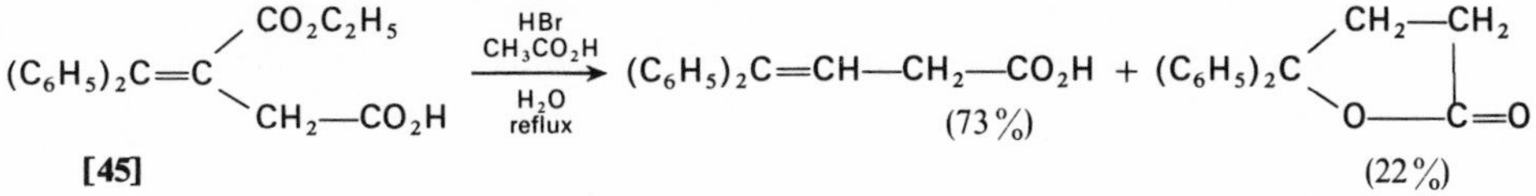

$(C_6H_5)_2C{=}C(CO_2C_2H_5)—CH_2—CO_2H$ **[45]** $\xrightarrow[H_2O \text{ reflux}]{HBr,\ CH_3CO_2H}$ $(C_6H_5)_2C{=}CH—CH_2—CO_2H$ (73%) + $(C_6H_5)_2C<$ lactone ($CH_2—CH_2$, $O—C{=}O$) (22%)

(*Ref. 65*)

the preparation of cyclic ketones, as shown in the following examples.

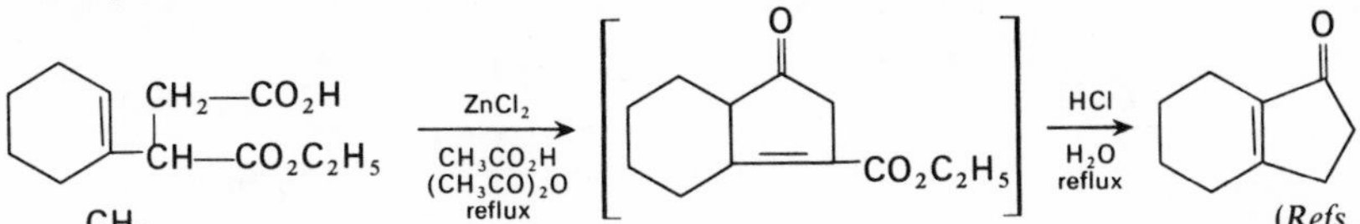

cyclohexenyl–$CH(CO_2C_2H_5)—CH_2—CO_2H$ $\xrightarrow[CH_3CO_2H,\ (CH_3CO)_2O,\ \text{reflux}]{ZnCl_2}$ [bicyclic enone–$CO_2C_2H_5$] $\xrightarrow[H_2O \text{ reflux}]{HCl}$ bicyclic enone

(*Refs. 64, 66*)

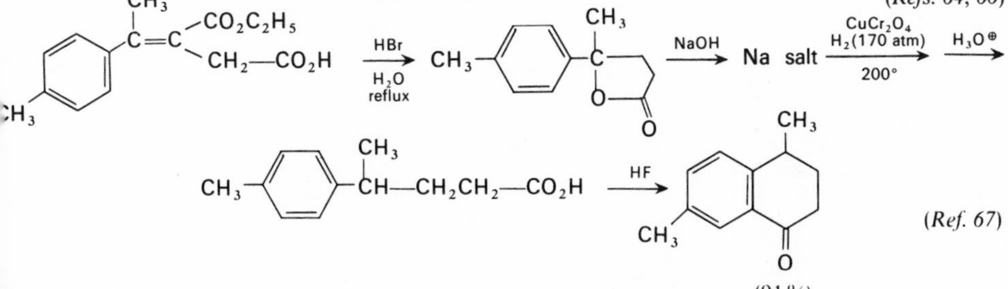

p-$CH_3C_6H_4—C(CH_3){=}C(CO_2C_2H_5)—CH_2—CO_2H$ $\xrightarrow[H_2O \text{ reflux}]{HBr}$ CH_3–C_6H_4–lactone (CH_3) $\xrightarrow{NaOH}$ Na salt $\xrightarrow[200°]{CuCr_2O_4,\ H_2(170 \text{ atm})}$ $\xrightarrow{H_3O^{\oplus}}$

$CH_3—C_6H_4—CH(CH_3)—CH_2CH_2—CO_2H$ $\xrightarrow{HF}$ 4,7-dimethyl-1-tetralone (91%) (*Ref. 67*)

(64) W. S. Johnson, C. E. Davis, R. H. Hunt, and G. Stork, *ibid.*, **70**, 3021 (1948).
(65) W. S. Johnson, J. W. Petersen, and W. P. Schneider, *ibid.*, **69**, 74 (1947).
(66) D. W. Mathieson, *J. Chem. Soc.*, **1953**, 3248.
(67) W. S. Johnson and A. R. Jones, *J. Am. Chem. Soc.*, **69**, 792 (1947).

The Darzens glycidic ester condensation[68] involves the reaction of an α-halo ester with a ketone or an aromatic aldehyde in the presence of a strong base such as potassium *t*-butoxide or sodium amide. The intermediate aldol condensation product (e.g., [**46**])[10c,68,69] undergoes intramolecular ring closure to form an α,β-epoxy ester (e.g., [**47**]) called a glycidic ester. The predominant

$$\text{cyclohexanone} + Cl{-}CH_2{-}CO_2C_2H_5 \xrightarrow[\text{: }(CH_3)_3COH,\ 10\text{–}15^\circ]{KOC(CH_3)_3\ \text{(solution added dropwise)}} [46] \longrightarrow [47]\ (83\text{–}95\%)$$

(*Ref. 70*)

stereoisomer produced in this condensation is frequently the one in which the ester function is *trans* to the larger group at the beta carbon atom, a result that has been attributed to assistance by the carboalkoxyl function in the ring-closure step (e.g., [**48**]).[10c,69c] This assistance in the displacement reaction is sterically unfavorable when the carboalkoxyl function and a large beta substituent are *cis* to one another. Other Darzens condensations, including

$$C_6H_5{-}CHO + C_6H_5{-}CHCl{-}CO_2C_2H_5 \underset{(CH_3)_3COH}{\overset{KOC(CH_3)_3}{\rightleftharpoons}} \longrightarrow [48] \longrightarrow \text{epoxide}\ (75\%)$$

(*Ref. 10c*)

(68) (a) M. S. Newman and B. J. Magerlein, *Org. Reactions*, **5**, 413 (1949); (b) M. Ballester, *Chem. Rev.*, **55**, 283 (1955).

(69) (a) M. Ballester and P. D. Bartlett, *J. Am. Chem. Soc.*, **75**, 2042 (1953); (b) M. Ballester and D. Perez-Blanco, *J. Org. Chem.*, **23**, 652 (1958); (c) C. C. Tung, A. J. Speziale, and H. W. Frazier, *ibid.*, **28**, 1514 (1963).

(70) R. H. Hunt, L. J. Chinn, and W. S. Johnson, *Org. Syn.*, **Coll. Vol. 4,** 459 (1963).

that with an α-haloketone (e.g., [**49**]), are described by the accompanying equations.

$$C_6H_5\text{—CHO} + C_6H_5\text{—CO—CH}_2\text{—Cl} \xrightarrow[H_2O,\ \text{dioxane},\ 0°]{\text{NaOH}} \text{[epoxide: } C_6H_5,\ H \text{ on one C; } H,\ CO\text{—}C_6H_5 \text{ on other C]}$$

[**49**] (95%) (*Ref. 69a*)

$$C_6H_5\text{—CO—CH}_3 + Cl\text{—CH}_2\text{—CO}_2C_2H_5 \xrightarrow[(CH_3)_3COH,\ 10\text{–}15°]{KOC(CH_3)_3} \text{[epoxide: } C_6H_5,\ CH_3;\ H,\ CO_2C_2H_5] + \text{[epoxide: } CH_3,\ C_6H_5;\ H,\ CO_2C_2H_5]$$

(82% of mixture) (*Ref. 71*)

$$\text{cyclohexanone} + n\text{-}C_5H_{11}\text{—CH(Br)—CO}_2C_2H_5 \xrightarrow[\text{xylene}]{NaOC_2H_5} \xrightarrow[H_2O]{CH_3CO_2H} \text{[spiro-epoxide: cyclohexane—C(O)—C(}n\text{-}C_5H_{11})\text{—CO}_2C_2H_5]$$

(45%) (*Ref. 72*)

$$(CH_3)_2C{=}CH\text{—CO—CH}_3 + Cl\text{—CH}_2\text{—CO}_2C(CH_3)_3 \xrightarrow[(CH_3)_3COH,\ 10\text{–}15°]{KOC(CH_3)_3}$$

$$(CH_3)_2C{=}CH\text{—C(CH}_3)\text{—CH—CO}_2C(CH_3)_3 \ \text{[epoxide O bridging the two C]}$$

(82%) (*Ref. 73*)

Careful saponification and subsequent acidification of glycidic esters (e.g., [**50**]) produce glycidic acids (e.g., [**51**]) that are thermally unstable, decomposing to the enols of aldehydes (e.g., [**52**]) or ketones when warmed. Other examples of the preparation and

(71) (a) W. S. Johnson, J. S. Belew, L. J. Chinn, and R. H. Hunt, *J. Am. Chem. Soc.*, **75**, 4995 (1953); (b) H. O. House and J. W. Blaker, *ibid.*, **80**, 6389 (1958); see also (c) C. F. H. Allen and J. VanAllan, *Org. Syn.*, **Coll. Vol. 3,** 727 (1955).

(72) H. H. Morris and M. L. Lusth, *J. Am. Chem. Soc.*, **76**, 1237 (1954).

(73) E. P. Blanchard, Jr. and G. Büchi, *ibid.*, **85**, 955 (1963).

$$C_6H_5-\underset{\underset{O}{\diagdown\,\diagup}}{\overset{CH_3}{\overset{|}{C}}}-CH-CO_2C_2H_5 \xrightarrow[C_2H_5OH]{NaOC_2H_5\ (1.3\ equiv.)\ H_2O} C_6H_5-\underset{\underset{O}{\diagdown\,\diagup}}{\overset{CH_3}{\overset{|}{C}}}-CH-CO_2Na \xrightarrow[H_2O,\ 100^\circ]{HCl}$$

[50] (80–85%)

(*Refs.* 71b, 74)

$$[51] \xrightarrow{-CO_2} C_6H_5-\overset{CH_3}{\overset{|}{C}}=\underset{OH}{\underset{|}{CH}}\ [52] \longrightarrow C_6H_5-\overset{CH_3}{\overset{|}{CH}}-CHO$$

(65–70%)

decomposion of glycidic acids, including the pyrolytic decomposition of a *t*-butyl ester, are outlined below.

$$\text{(cyclohexane spiro-epoxide)}-\overset{n\text{-}C_5H_{11}}{\overset{|}{C}}-CO_2C_2H_5 \xrightarrow[\text{diethylene glycol, reflux}]{NaOH} \xrightarrow{H_3O^{\oplus}} \text{(cyclohexane spiro-epoxide)}-\overset{n\text{-}C_5H_{11}}{\overset{|}{C}}-CO_2H \xrightarrow[-CO_2]{heat}$$

(*Ref.* 72)

$$\text{(cyclohexyl)}-CO-C_5H_{11}\text{-}n$$

(37%)

$$(CH_3)_2CH-\underset{\underset{CH_2}{\|}}{C}-CH_2-CH_2-\underset{\underset{O}{\diagdown\,\diagup}}{\overset{CH_3}{\overset{|}{C}}}-CH-CO_2C(CH_3)_3$$

$$\xrightarrow[\text{hot tube packed with Pyrex helices}]{350\text{–}360^\circ} (CH_3)_2CH-\underset{\underset{CH_2}{\|}}{C}-CH_2-CH_2-\overset{CH_3}{\overset{|}{CH}}-CHO$$

(56%) (*Ref.* 73)

The Reformatsky Reaction

An alternative method for forcing an aldol condensation to completion utilizes a base sufficiently strong to convert an active methylene compound completely to its enolate anion. A case in point is the condensation of ethyl acetate with benzophenone described in the accompanying equation. An ester enolate anion may also be generated in high yield by reaction of an α-halo ester (usually an α-bromo ester) with zinc in an inert solvent such as benzene or ether. The formation of such an enolate anion in the presence of an aldehyde or ketone, a process known as the

(74) (a) C. F. H. Allen and J. VanAllan, *Org. Syn.*, **Coll. Vol. 3,** 733 (1955); (b) V. J. Shiner, Jr., and B. Martin, *J. Am. Chem. Soc.*, **84**, 4824 (1962).

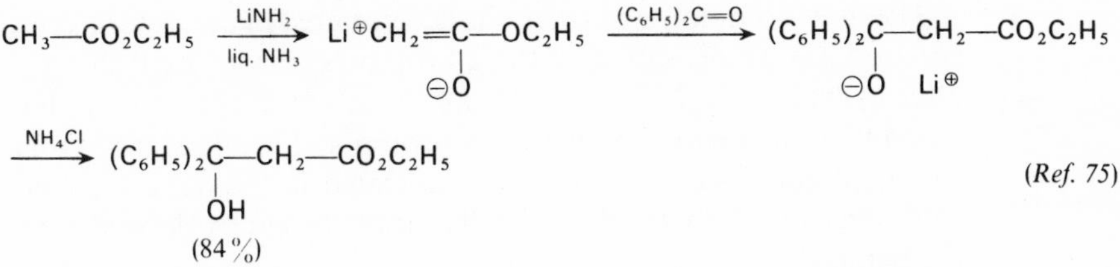

$$CH_3—CO_2C_2H_5 \xrightarrow[\text{liq. } NH_3]{LiNH_2} Li^{\oplus}CH_2=C(O^{\ominus})—OC_2H_5 \xrightarrow{(C_6H_5)_2C=O} (C_6H_5)_2C(O^{\ominus}\ Li^{\oplus})—CH_2—CO_2C_2H_5$$

$$\xrightarrow{NH_4Cl} (C_6H_5)_2C(OH)—CH_2—CO_2C_2H_5 \quad (84\%)$$

(*Ref.* 75)

Reformatsky reaction,[76] provides a useful preparative route to β-hydroxy esters, as shown below. This type of reaction is unique

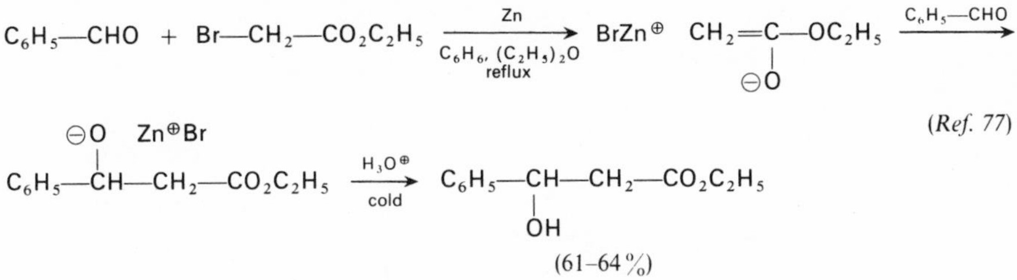

$$C_6H_5—CHO + Br—CH_2—CO_2C_2H_5 \xrightarrow[\substack{C_6H_6,\ (C_2H_5)_2O \\ \text{reflux}}]{Zn} BrZn^{\oplus}\ CH_2=C(O^{\ominus})—OC_2H_5 \xrightarrow{C_6H_5—CHO}$$

$$C_6H_5—CH(O^{\ominus}\ Zn^{\oplus}Br)—CH_2—CO_2C_2H_5 \xrightarrow[\text{cold}]{H_3O^{\oplus}} C_6H_5—CH(OH)—CH_2—CO_2C_2H_5 \quad (61–64\%)$$

(*Ref.* 77)

among the aldol condensations in that it permits the isolation of the initial aldol product, even when relatively hindered ketones (e.g., **[53]**) are employed. As illustrated, the β-hydroxy ester can be subsequently dehydrated.

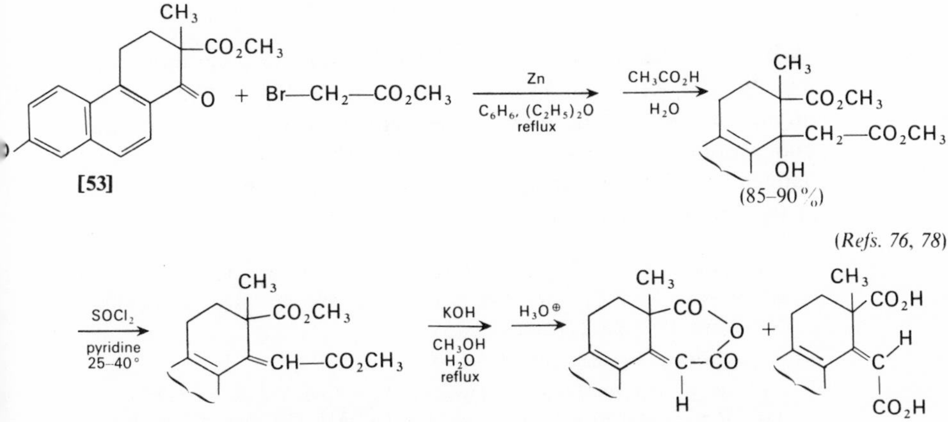

$$\textbf{[53]} + Br—CH_2—CO_2CH_3 \xrightarrow[\substack{C_6H_6,\ (C_2H_5)_2O \\ \text{reflux}}]{Zn} \xrightarrow[H_2O]{CH_3CO_2H} \text{(hydroxy diester: } CH_3,\ CO_2CH_3,\ CH_2—CO_2CH_3,\ OH) \quad (85–90\%)$$

(*Refs.* 76, 78)

$$\xrightarrow[\substack{\text{pyridine} \\ 25–40°}]{SOCl_2} (CH_3,\ CO_2CH_3,\ =CH—CO_2CH_3) \xrightarrow[\substack{CH_3OH \\ H_2O \\ \text{reflux}}]{KOH} \xrightarrow{H_3O^{\oplus}} (\text{anhydride: } CH_3,\ CO—O—CO,\ C—H) + (CH_3,\ CO_2H,\ =C(H)CO_2H)$$

(75) (a) W. R. Dunnavant and C. R. Hauser, *J. Org. Chem.*, **25**, 503 (1960); (b) C. R. Hauser and W. R. Dunnavant, *ibid.*, **25**, 1296 (1960); (c) β-hydroxy esters and/or α,β-unsaturated esters are also available from the reaction of ketones with the lithium derivative of ethoxyacetylene and subsequent reactions of the resultant acetylenic ethers with dilute aqueous acid: see

The most common side reactions encountered in the Reformatsky reaction are condensation of the α-bromo ester with itself to form, after hydrolysis, a β-keto ester[79]; and reaction of the ester enolate anion with the ketone to abstract a proton and produce the ketone enolate anion. The latter process, illustrated in the accompanying equation, may lead to aldol condensation products derived from the ketone.[76,80]

C_6H_5 + CH_3CH_2—CH(Br)—$CO_2C_2H_5$ $\xrightarrow[C_6H_6,\ reflux]{Zn}$ $BrZn^{\oplus}$ $O^{\ominus}$ CH(C_2H_5)—$CO_2C_2H_5$, C_6H_5 +

$CH_3CH_2CH_2CO_2C_2H_5$ + $O^{\ominus}$ $ZnBr^{\oplus}$ C_6H_5 $\xrightarrow[2.\ KOH,\ C_2H_5OH,\ reflux]{1.\ H_3O^{\oplus}}$ CH(C_2H_5)—CO_2H, C_6H_5 (28%) +

O, C_6H_5; (48%)

(*Ref. 80*)

γ-Bromocrotonic esters have been found to give moderate yields in the Reformatsky reaction. As indicated in the accompanying equations, an interesting change in the nature of the condensation product was observed when the reaction solvent was changed from benzene or 1,2-dimethoxyethane to ether. The reason for the change in product structure is not known.

J. F. Arens in R. A. Raphael, E. C. Taylor, and H. Wynberg (eds.), *Advances in Organic Chemistry; Methods and Results,* Vol. 2, Wiley-Interscience, New York, 1960, pp. 117–212.

(76) R. L. Shriner, *Org. Reactions,* **1,** 1 (1942).

(77) (a) C. R. Hauser and D. S. Breslow, *Org. Syn.,* **Coll. Vol. 3,** 408 (1955); see also (b) K. L. Rinehart, Jr. and E. G. Perkins, *ibid.,* **Coll. Vol. 4,** 444 (1963).

(78) W. E. Bachmann, W. Cole, and A. L. Wilds, *J. Am. Chem. Soc.,* **62,** 824 (1940).

(79) A. S. Hussey and M. S. Newman, *ibid.,* **70,** 3024 (1948).

(80) (a) M. S. Newman, *ibid.,* **62,** 870 (1940); (b) M. S. Newman, *ibid.,* **64,** 2131 (1942).

$$\text{cyclohexanone} + Br{-}CH_2{-}CH{=}CH{-}CO_2CH_3 \xrightarrow[\text{1,2-dimethoxyethane (or } C_6H_6\text{), reflux}]{Zn} \xrightarrow{H_2O} \text{1-hydroxy-1-}(CH_2{-}CH{=}CH{-}CO_2CH_3)\text{cyclohexane} \ (30\text{–}39\%)$$

(*Ref. 81*)

$$\text{cyclohexanone} + Br{-}CH_2{-}CH{=}CH{-}CO_2CH_3 \xrightarrow[(C_2H_5)_2O,\ \text{reflux}]{Zn} \xrightarrow{H_2O} \text{1-hydroxy-1-}[CH(CH{=}CH_2){-}CO_2CH_3]\text{cyclohexane} \ (60\%)$$

The Wittig Reaction

The reaction of a tertiary phosphine (usually triphenylphosphine) with an alkyl halide yields a phosphonium salt (e.g., [**54**]) in which the alpha C—H bonds are sufficiently acidic to be removed by a strong base (e.g., an organolithium compound, sodium hydride, or sodium amide). The ylid (e.g., [**55**]) that results from reaction with base is believed to be stabilized by overlap between the *p* orbital at carbon and one of the *d* orbitals of the phosphorus atom.[82] Subsequent reaction of these ylids (e.g., [**55**]) with aldehydes or ketones offers the very useful synthesis for olefins known as the Wittig reaction.[83] The initial nucleophilic attack by the ylid on the

$$(C_6H_5)_3P + CH_3Br \xrightarrow[25^\circ]{C_6H_6} \underset{[\mathbf{54}]}{(C_6H_5)_3P^{\oplus}{-}CH_3 \quad Br^{\ominus}} \xrightarrow[(C_2H_5)_2O,\ 25^\circ]{n\text{-}C_4H_9Li}$$

$$\underset{[\mathbf{55a}]}{(C_6H_5)_3P^{\oplus}{-}CH_2^{\ominus}} \longleftrightarrow \underset{[\mathbf{55b}]}{(C_6H_5)_3P{=}CH_2} \xrightarrow[(C_2H_5)_2O,\ \text{reflux}]{\text{cyclohexanone}} \underset{[\mathbf{56}]}{\text{1-}(^{\ominus}O)\text{-1-}[CH_2{-}P^{\oplus}(C_6H_5)_3]\text{cyclohexane}}$$

(*Ref. 84*)

$$\longrightarrow [\text{cyclohexane}{-}CH_2 \cdots P(C_6H_5)_3 \cdots O] \longrightarrow \text{cyclohexane}{=}CH_2 + (C_6H_5)_3P{=}O \quad (35\text{–}40\%)$$

(81) A. S. Dreiding and R. J. Pratt, *ibid.*, **75**, 3717 (1953).

(82) (a) W. von E. Doering and A. K. Hoffmann, *J. Am. Chem. Soc.*, **77**, 521 (1955); (b) for a discussion of the mechanism of proton removal, see D. Seyferth, J. K. Heeren, and W. B. Hughes, Jr., *ibid.*, **84**, 1764 (1962).

(83) (a) G. Wittig and U. Schöllkopf, *Chem. Ber.*, **87**, 1318 (1954); (b) G. Wittig and W. Haag, *ibid.*, **88**, 1654 (1955); (c) G. Wittig, H. D. Weigmann, and M. Schlosser, *ibid.*, **94**, 676 (1961); (d) U. Schöllkopf, *Angew Chem.*, **71**, 260

carbonyl function forms a betaine intermediate (e.g., **[56]**). This attack is accelerated by the presence of electron-withdrawing groups in the component containing the carbonyl function, by the presence of alkyl groups rather than phenyl groups bonded to the phosphorus atom of the ylid, and by the use of polar reaction solvents.[83,85] The formation of the betaine appears to be reversible in most, if not all, cases.[85a,d] Subsequent decomposition of the betaine intermediate (e.g., **[56]**) to produce an olefin and a tertiary phosphine oxide is believed to occur by the indicated cyclic four-center transition state.[83] Depending on the structures of the carbonyl compound and the ylid, either the formation of the betaine or its subsequent decomposition may be the rate-limiting step.[83,85] The acidity of the alpha C—H bonds of phosphonium salts is enhanced by the presence of an alpha substituent (e.g., $—CO_2C_2H_5$, $—CO—C_6H_5$, $—C{\equiv}N$, $—C_6H_5$, $—CH{=}CH_2$), which aids the stabilization of a negative charge at carbon.[83,85,86] From a comparison of the pK_a values cited for the formulas below[85a,d] with the acidities of other active methylene compounds (Chapter 7), one may conclude that a triphenylphosphonium substituent will

$$(C_6H_5)_3P^{\oplus}—CH_2—CO—C_6H_5 \quad \text{p}K_a\ 6.0 \qquad (C_6H_5)_3P^{\oplus}—CH_2—C{\equiv}N \quad \text{p}K_a\ 7.5 \qquad (C_6H_5)_3P^{\oplus}—CH_2—CO_2C_2H_5 \quad \text{p}K_a\ 9.0\text{–}9.2$$

stabilize an adjacent carbanion to a slightly greater extent than will an adjacent carbonyl function. As a result, the various ylids that have an additional stabilizing substituent may be prepared by

---

(1959); (e) S. Trippett in R. A. Raphael, E. C. Taylor, and H. Wynberg (eds.), *Advances in Organic Chemistry; Methods and Results*, Vol. 1, Wiley-Interscience, New York, 1960, pp. 83–102; (f) S. Trippett, *Quart. Rev. (London)*, **17**, 406 (1963); (g) L. D. Bergelson and M. M. Shemyakin, *Angew. Chem., Intern. Ed. Engl.*, **3**, 250 (1964); (h) A. Maercker, *Org. Reactions*, **14**, 270 (1965).

(84) G. Wittig and U. Schöllkopf, *Org. Syn.*, **40**, 66 (1960).

(85) (a) S. Fliszar, R. F. Hudson, and G. Salvadori, *Helv. Chim. Acta*, **46**, 1580 (1963); (b) H. Goetz, F. Nerdel, and H. Michaelis, *Naturwissenschaften*, **50**, 496 (1963); (c) A. W. Johnson and R. B. LaCount, *Tetrahedron*, **9**, 130 (1960); (d) A. J. Speziale and K. W. Ratts, *J. Am. Chem. Soc.*, **85**, 2790 (1963); (e) A. J. Speziale and D. E. Bissing, *ibid.*, **85**, 1888, 3878 (1963); (f) R. Greenwald, M. Chaykovsky, and E. J. Corey, *J. Org. Chem.*, **28**, 1128 (1963); (g) C. Rüchart, S. Eickler, and P. Panse, *Angew. Chem., Intern. Ed. Engl.*, **2**, 619 (1963); (h) S. Fliszar, R. F. Hudson, and G. Salvadori, *Helv. Chim. Acta*, **47**, 159 (1964).

(86) (a) F. Ramirez and S. Dershowitz, *J. Org. Chem.*, **22**, 41 (1957); (b) S. Trippett and D. M. Walker, *J. Chem. Soc.*, **1961,** 1266.

reaction of the corresponding phosphonium salts with relatively weak bases such as metal alkoxides, metal hydroxides, and, in some cases, even metal carbonates. The ylids stabilized by an adjacent carbonyl function are readily isolated stable crystalline solids, as illustrated by the following examples.

$$C_6H_5—CO—CH_2—Br + (C_6H_5)_3P \xrightarrow{CHCl_3} C_6H_5—CO—CH_2—P^{\oplus}(C_6H_5)_3\ Br^{\ominus} \xrightarrow[H_2O]{Na_2CO_3}$$

(79%)

$$C_6H_5—\overset{\overset{\displaystyle O}{\|}}{C}—CH{=}P(C_6H_5)_3 \longleftrightarrow C_6H_5—\overset{\overset{\displaystyle O^{\ominus}}{|}}{C}{=}CH—P^{\oplus}(C_6H_5)_3$$

(96%; m.p. 178–180°) *(Ref. 86a)*

$$CH_3—\underset{\underset{\displaystyle Br}{|}}{CH}—CO_2CH_3 + (C_6H_5)_3P \xrightarrow[70°]{C_6H_6} (C_6H_5)_3P^{\oplus}—\overset{\overset{\displaystyle CH_3}{|}}{CH}—CO_2CH_3\ Br^{\ominus} \xrightarrow[H_2O]{NaOH}$$

$$(C_6H_5)_3P{=}\overset{\overset{\displaystyle CH_3}{|}}{C}—CO_2CH_3$$

(44%; m.p. 152–154.5°) *(Ref. 87)*

The ylids that do not contain stabilizing alpha substituents react rapidly with oxygen[88], a condition requiring their preparation and use in an inert atmosphere. Ylids having stabilizing alpha carbonyl substituents are not readily attacked by molecular oxygen but may be oxidized by peracids.[89] All ylids are hydrolyzed by reaction with water, though the stabilized ylids require rather vigorous conditions. The probable course of this hydrolysis[90] is outlined below. It will be noted that the ease of cleaving groups

$$(C_6H_5)_3P^{\oplus}—CH_3\ \ Br^{\ominus} \xrightarrow[H_2O]{Ag_2O} (C_6H_5)_3P^{\oplus}—CH_3\ \ OH^{\ominus} \overset{140°}{\rightleftharpoons} C_6H_5—\overset{\overset{\displaystyle CH_3}{|}}{\underset{\underset{\displaystyle O—H}{|}}{P}}(C_6H_5)_2 \longrightarrow$$

$$(C_6H_5)_2\overset{\overset{\displaystyle CH_3}{|}}{P}{=}O + C_6H_5^{\ominus} \xrightarrow{H_2O} C_6H_6$$

(67%) *(Ref. 83a)*

(87) (a) O. Isler, H. Gutmann, M. Montavon, R. Rüegg, G. Ryser, and P. Zeller, *Helv. Chim. Acta*, **40**, 1242 (1957); (b) H. O. House and G. Rasmusson, *J. Org. Chem.*, **26**, 4278 (1961).

(88) (a) H. J. Bestmann and O. Kratzer, *Angew. Chem., Intern. Ed. Engl.*, **1**, 512 (1962); (b) H. J. Bestmann and O. Kratzer, *Chem. Ber.*, **96**, 1899 (1963).

(89) (a) D. B. Denney, L. C. Smith, J. Song, C. J. Rossi, and C. D. Hall, *J. Org. Chem.*, **28**, 778 (1963); (b) H. O. House and H. Babad, *ibid.*, **28**, 90 (1963).

$$\text{2-(triphenylphosphoranylidene)cyclopentanone} \xrightarrow[\text{180°, 3 days}]{H_2O} (C_6H_5)_3P{=}O \ (92\%) + \text{cyclopentanone} \ (93\%, \text{isolated as 2,4-dinitrophenylhydrazone})$$

(*Ref. 89b*)

from the phosphorus atom (i.e., $—CH_2—CO—R < —C_6H_5 <$ alkyl) is directly related to the stability of the carbanion lost in the hydrolysis. A more satisfactory method for the cleavage of α-keto-alkyl groups from phosphonium salts (e.g., **[57]**) is reduction with zinc and acetic acid, a reaction that has been discussed previously (Chapter 3).

$$\underset{[57]}{(C_6H_5)_3P^{\oplus}—CH_2—CO—C_6H_5 \ Br^{\ominus}} \xrightarrow[\text{CHCl}_3,\ CH_3CO_2H,\ \text{reflux}]{Zn} \underset{(56\%)}{(C_6H_5)_3P} + \underset{(95\%, \text{ isolated as 2,4-dinitrophenylhydrazone})}{C_6H_5—CO—CH_3}$$

(*Ref. 86b*)

Although ylids that do not contain good stabilizing substituents in the alpha position are slowly cleaved by reaction with alcohols, it is none the less possible to generate these ylids with metal alkoxides in alcohol solution. The ylid (e.g., **[58]**), which is apparently in equilibrium with the phosphonium alkoxide (e.g., **[59]**)[83] under such conditions, will react with a carbonyl compound present in the reaction mixture.

$$C_6H_5—CH{=}CH—CH_2—Cl + (C_6H_5)_3P \xrightarrow[\text{reflux}]{\text{xylene}} \underset{(91–93\%)}{C_6H_5—CH{=}CH—CH_2—P^{\oplus}(C_6H_5)_3 \ Cl^{\ominus}}$$

(*Ref. 91*)

$$\xrightarrow[C_2H_5OH,\ 25°]{LiOC_2H_5} \underset{[58]}{C_6H_5—CH{=}CH—CH{=}P(C_6H_5)_3} \xrightarrow{C_6H_5CHO} \underset{(60–67\%)}{C_6H_5—CH{=}CH—CH{=}CH—C_6H_5}$$

$$[58] \underset{}{\overset{C_2H_5OH}{\rightleftharpoons}} \underset{[59]}{C_6H_5—CH{=}CH—CH_2—P^{\oplus}(C_6H_5)_3 \ {}^{\ominus}OC_2H_5}$$

The prime utility of the Wittig reaction lies in the ease with which the reaction occurs under mild conditions and in the fact that no ambiguity exists concerning the location of the double

(90) (a) R. F. Hudson and B. A. Chopard, *Helv. Chim. Acta,* **45**, 1137 (1962); (b) R. F. Hudson and M. Green, *Angew. Chem., Intern. Ed. Engl.,* **2**, 11 (1963).

(91) (a) R. N. McDonald and T. W. Campbell, *Org. Syn.,* **40**, 36 (1960); see also (b) T. W. Campbell and R. N. McDonald, *ibid.,* **40**, 85 (1960).

bond in the product. The following equations provide additional examples of its use for the preparation of olefins. The ylids that

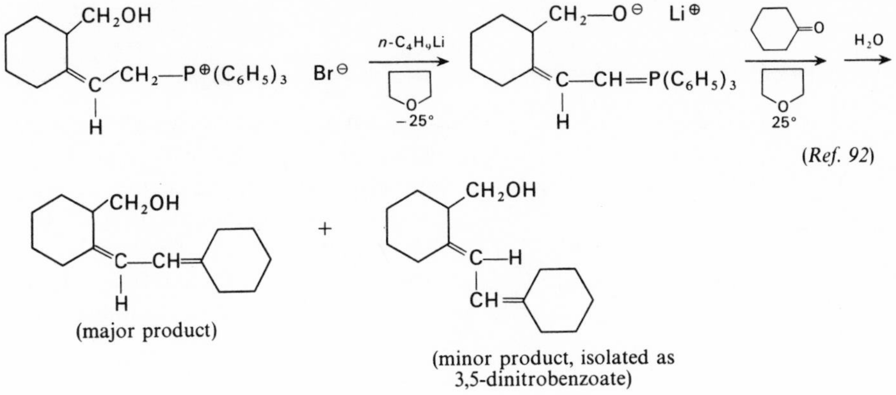

CH_2OH ... CH_2—$P^{\oplus}(C_6H_5)_3$ $Br^{\ominus}$ $\xrightarrow[\text{THF}, -25°]{n\text{-}C_4H_9Li}$ CH_2—$O^{\ominus}$ $Li^{\oplus}$ ... C—CH=$P(C_6H_5)_3$ $\xrightarrow[\text{THF}, 25°]{\text{cyclohexanone}}$ $\xrightarrow{H_2O}$

(Ref. 92)

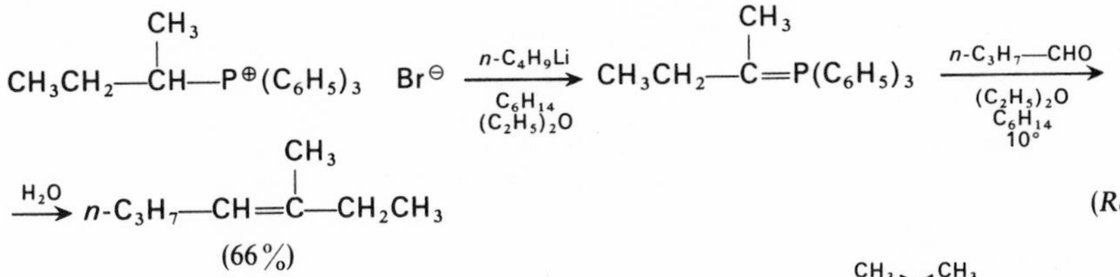

CH_2OH ... C—CH= (major product) + CH_2OH ... C—H, CH= (minor product, isolated as 3,5-dinitrobenzoate)

$$CH_3CH_2\text{—}CH(CH_3)\text{—}P^{\oplus}(C_6H_5)_3\ Br^{\ominus} \xrightarrow[C_6H_{14},\ (C_2H_5)_2O]{n\text{-}C_4H_9Li} CH_3CH_2\text{—}C(CH_3){=}P(C_6H_5)_3 \xrightarrow[(C_2H_5)_2O,\ C_6H_{14},\ 10°]{n\text{-}C_3H_7\text{—}CHO}$$

$$\xrightarrow{H_2O} n\text{-}C_3H_7\text{—}CH{=}C(CH_3)\text{—}CH_2CH_3 \quad (66\%)$$

(Ref. 93)

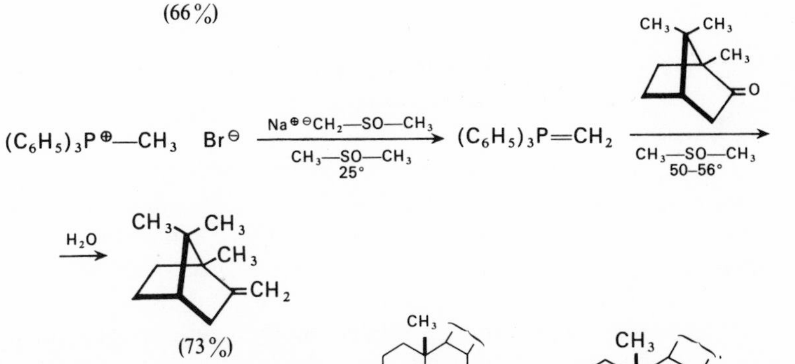

$$(C_6H_5)_3P^{\oplus}\text{—}CH_3\ Br^{\ominus} \xrightarrow[CH_3\text{—}SO\text{—}CH_3,\ 25°]{Na^{\oplus}\ {}^{\ominus}CH_2\text{—}SO\text{—}CH_3} (C_6H_5)_3P{=}CH_2 \xrightarrow[CH_3\text{—}SO\text{—}CH_3,\ 50\text{–}56°]{\text{fenchone}}$$

(Ref. 85f)

$\xrightarrow{H_2O}$ CH_3, CH_3, CH_3, $=CH_2$ (73%)

$$(C_6H_5)_3P^{\oplus}\text{—}CH_3\ Br^{\ominus} \xrightarrow[(C_2H_5)_2O]{n\text{-}C_4H_9Li} \xrightarrow[(C_2H_5)_2O,\ \text{THF, reflux}]{\text{enone } (CH_3)} CH_2{=} \ldots (80\%)$$

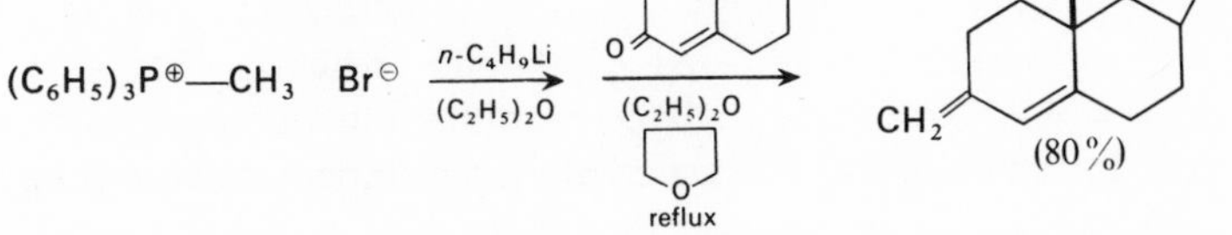

(Ref. 94)

(92) I. T. Harrison and B. Lythgoe, *J. Chem. Soc.*, **1958**, 843.

(93) C. F. Hauser, T. W. Brooks, M. L. Miles, M. A. Raymond, and G. B. Butler, *J. Org. Chem.*, **28**, 372 (1963).

(94) F. Sondheimer and R. Mechoulam, *J. Am. Chem. Soc.*, **79**, 5029 (1957).

$$(C_6H_5)_3P{=}C(CH_3){-}CO_2CH_3 + CH_2{=}CH{-}CHO \xrightarrow[\text{reflux}]{CH_2Cl_2} CH_2{=}CH(H)C{=}C(CH_3)CO_2CH_3 \quad (60\%)$$

(*Ref.* 87*b*)

are stabilized by the presence of an alpha carbonyl substituent are sufficiently less reactive than other ylids that it is difficult to effect their successful reaction with ketones, especially in the absence of benzoic acid as a catalyst.[85g,85h] A modification of the Wittig reaction, utilizing a phosphonate ylid (e.g., **[60]**) with the carbonyl compound,[95] has proved of value in such cases. This modification also circumvents the problems often encountered in

$$(C_2H_5O)_2P(=O){-}CH_2{-}CO_2C_2H_5 \xrightarrow[\substack{CH_3OCH_2CH_2OCH_3 \\ \text{reflux}}]{NaH} (C_2H_5O)_2P(O^{\ominus}){=}CH{-}CO_2C_2H_5 \; Na^{\oplus} \; \textbf{[60a]} \leftrightarrow$$

$$(C_2H_5O)_2P(=O){-}CH^{\ominus}{-}CO_2C_2H_5 \; Na^{\oplus} \; \textbf{[60b]} \xrightarrow[\substack{CH_3OCH_2CH_2OCH_3 \\ 30^{\circ}}]{\text{cyclohexanone}}$$

(*Ref.* 95*a*)

$$\text{[cyclohexyl adduct: } C(O^{\ominus}){-}CH{-}CO_2C_2H_5 \text{ with } P(=O)(OC_2H_5)_2, \; Na^{\oplus}] \longrightarrow \text{cyclohexylidene}{=}CH{-}CO_2C_2H_5 \; (70\%) + (C_2H_5O)_2P(=O)O^{\ominus} \; Na^{\oplus}$$

separating the product from the triphenylphosphine oxide in the usual Wittig procedure.

The reaction between phosphorus ylids and carboxylic acid derivatives is mechanistically related to the acylation of enolate anions (Chapter 9).[86,96] This reaction provides an alternative preparative route to stabilized ylids and, when accompanied by cleavage of the resulting acylated phosphonium salts, constitutes a synthesis for ketones, as illustrated in the accompanying equations.

(95) (a) W. S. Wadsworth and W. D. Emmons, *ibid.*, **83**, 1733 (1961); (b) A. K. Bose and R. T. Dahill, Jr., *Tetrahedron Letters*, **No. 15**, 959 (1963).

(96) (a) H. J. Bestmann and B. Arnason, *Chem. Ber.*, **95**, 1513 (1962); (b) A. J. Speziale and K. W. Ratts, *J. Org. Chem.*, **28**, 465 (1963); (c) G. Märkl, *Tetrahedron Letters*, **No. 22**, 1027 (1962).

$$(C_6H_5)_3P{=}CH_2 \xrightarrow[C_6H_6\ \text{reflux}]{C_6H_5{-}CO{-}Cl} [(C_6H_5)_3P^{\oplus}{-}CH_2{-}CO{-}C_6H_5]\ Cl^{\ominus} \xrightarrow{(C_6H_5)_3P{=}CH_2}$$

$$\underset{(71\%)}{(C_6H_5)_3P{=}CH{-}CO{-}C_6H_5} + (C_6H_5)_3P^{\oplus}{-}CH_3\quad Cl^{\ominus}$$ (*Ref. 96a*)

$$(C_6H_5)_3P{=}CH{-}CH_3 + C_6H_5{-}CH{=}CH{-}CO{-}S{-}C_2H_5 \xrightarrow[\text{reflux}]{C_6H_5CH_3}$$

$$(C_6H_5)_3P^{\oplus}{-}CH(CH_3){-}CO{-}CH{=}CH{-}C_6H_5\quad S^{\ominus}{-}C_2H_5$$ (*Ref. 96a*)

$$\xrightarrow[\text{reflux}]{-C_2H_5SH} \underset{(70\%)}{(C_6H_5)_3P{=}C(CH_3){-}CO{-}CH{=}CH{-}C_6H_5} \xrightarrow[CH_3OH\ \text{reflux}]{NaOH\ H_2O} \underset{(74\%)}{C_6H_5{-}CH{=}CH{-}CO{-}CH_2CH_3}$$

There is a sufficient difference between the reaction rates of Wittig reagents with ketones and with esters to make possible the selective reaction of an ylid with a keto ester (e.g., [**61**]) only at its ketone function. The presence of an ester function in the phosphonium

$$\underset{[\mathbf{61}]}{CH_3O{-}C_6H_4{-}CO{-}CH_2CH_2{-}CO_2CH_3} + (C_6H_5)_3P{=}CH_2 \xrightarrow[25^\circ]{CH_3{-}SO{-}CH_3}$$

$$\underset{(81\%)}{CH_3O{-}C_6H_4{-}C({=}CH_2){-}CH_2CH_2{-}CO_2CH_3}$$ (*Ref. 85f*)

salt at a position other than alpha or beta to the phosphorus atom (e.g., [**62**]) may also result in either intramolecular or intermolecular acylation upon generation of the ylid; however, this acylation

$$\underset{I^{\ominus}\quad [\mathbf{62}]}{(C_6H_5)_3P^{\oplus}{-}CH_2{-}(CH_2)_3{-}CO_2C_2H_5} \xrightarrow[(CH_3)_3COH\ \text{reflux}]{KOC(CH_3)_3} (C_6H_5)_3P{=}CH{-}(CH_2)_3{-}CO_2C_2H_5$$

$$\xrightarrow[2.\ KOC(CH_3)_3]{1.\ \text{cyclization}} \underset{(84\%)}{\text{2-(triphenylphosphoranylidene)cyclopentanone, } (C_6H_5)_3P{=}C_5H_6O}$$ (*Ref. 89b*)

is apparently slow enough to permit the use of ylids containing ester functions in a normal Wittig reaction provided that the very favorable intramolecular acylation to form a five- or six-membered ring is not possible.[83g,97] The alkylation of phosphorus ylids with alkyl halides has also been observed.[86a,98]

(97) (a) L. D. Bergel'son, V. A. Vaver, V. Yu. Kovtun, L. B. Senyavina, and M. M. Shemyakin, *Zh. Obshch. Khim.*, **32**, 1802 (1962); *CA*, **58**, 4415 (1963); (b)

The phosphonium salts derived from α-halo ethers (e.g., **[63]**) have been used in the Wittig reaction to form vinyl ethers and, after hydrolysis, aldehydes.[99] Other modifications of the Wittig

$$CH_3-C_6H_4-O-CH_2-Cl \xrightarrow[(C_6H_5)_2O \text{ reflux}]{(C_6H_5)_3P} CH_3-C_6H_4-O-CH_2-P^{\oplus}(C_6H_5)_3\ Cl^{\ominus} \xrightarrow[(C_2H_5)_2O]{C_6H_5Li}$$

[63] (96%)

$$CH_3-C_6H_4-O-CH{=}P(C_6H_5)_3 \xrightarrow[(C_2H_5)_2O]{(C_2H_5)_2CO} CH_3-C_6H_4-O-CH{=}C(C_2H_5)_2$$

(72%)

$$\xrightarrow[(C_2H_5)_2O \text{ reflux}]{HClO_4,\ H_2O} (C_2H_5)_2CH-CHO$$

(80%. isolated as 2,4-dinitrophenylhydrazone) (*Ref. 99b*)

reaction include addition of phosphorus ylids to conjugated double bonds, a process analogous to the Michael reaction (Chapter 7)[95a,100]; and preparation of chloroölefins by reaction of carbonyl compounds with phosphorus ylids that have one or two halogen substituents at the alpha carbon atom.[101]

The reaction of α-halocarbonyl compounds with triphenylphosphine to form phosphonium salts that may be used to generate α-keto ylids is sometimes complicated by the formation of enol phosphonium salts (e.g., **[64]**), which react with alcohol, water, or other protonic solvents to yield a dehalogenated ketone.[102] This complication appears to result from a nucleophilic attack (e.g., **[65]**) by the triphenylphosphine at the halogen atom[102e]; it becomes

L. D. Bergel'son, V. A. Vaver, A. A. Bezzubov, and M. M. Shemyakin, *Zh. Obshch. Khim.*, **32**, 1807 (1962); *CA*, **58**, 4416 (1963).

(98) (a) H. J. Bestmann and H. Schulz, *Tetrahedron Letters*, **No. 4**, 5 (1960); (b) H. J. Bestmann and H. Häberlein, *Z. Naturforsch.*, **17B**, 787 (1962).

(99) (a) S. G. Levine, *J. Am. Chem. Soc.*, **80**, 6150 (1958); (b) G. Wittig, W. Böll, and K. H. Krück, *Chem. Ber.*, **95**, 2514 (1962).

(100) (a) R. Mechoulam and F. Sondheimer, *J. Am. Chem. Soc.*, **80**, 4386 (1958); (b) S. Trippett, *J. Chem. Soc.*, **1962**, 4733; (c) H. J. Bestmann and F. Seng, *Angew. Chem., Intern. Ed. Engl.*, **1**, 116 (1962).

(101) (a) D. Seyferth, S. O. Grim, and T. O. Read, *J. Am. Chem. Soc.*, **83**, 1617 (1961); (b) A. J. Speziale and K. W. Ratts, *ibid.*, **84**, 854 (1962).

(102) (a) J. I. G. Cadogan, *Quart. Rev. (London)*, **16**, 208 (1962); (b) S. Trippett, *J. Chem. Soc.*, **1962**, 2337; (c) H. Hoffmann and H. J. Diehr, *Tetrahedron Letters*, **No. 13**, 583 (1962); (d) I. J. Borowitz and L. I. Grossman, *Tetrahedron Letters*, **No. 11**, 471 (1962); (e) I. J. Borowitz and R. Virkhaus, *J.*

$$(CH_3)_2CH\text{—}CH(Br)\text{—}CO\text{—}CH_2\text{—}CH(CH_3)_2 \xrightarrow[C_6H_6,\ \text{reflux}]{(C_6H_5)_3P} (CH_3)_2CH\text{—}CH{=}C(O\text{—}P^{\oplus}(C_6H_5)_3)\text{—}CH_2\text{—}CH(CH_3)_2\ \ Br^{\ominus}\ \ \textbf{[64]}$$

(*Ref. 102b*)

$$\xrightarrow{C_2H_5OH} (CH_3)_2CH\text{—}CH_2\text{—}CO\text{—}CH_2\text{—}CH(CH_3)_2 + C_2H_5Br + (C_6H_5)_3P{=}O$$

(85%) (82%) (96%)

either a serious side reaction or the major reaction with α-bromoketones in which the bromine is bonded to a secondary or tertiary carbon atom.

[65] 2-bromocyclohexanone + $P(C_6H_5)_3$ $\xrightarrow[CH_3OH,\ \text{reflux}]{C_6H_6}$ cyclohexenolate $O^{\ominus}$ + $Br\text{—}P^{\oplus}(C_6H_5)_3$ ⟶ cyclohexenyl $O\text{—}P^{\oplus}(C_6H_5)_3$ $Br^{\ominus}$

enolate $\xrightarrow{CH_3OH}$ cyclohexanone (62%)

cyclohexenyl $O\text{—}P^{\oplus}(C_6H_5)_3$ $\xrightarrow{CH_3OH}$ (*Ref. 102d*) [$O\text{—}P(C_6H_5)_3$ attacked by $H\text{—}O^{\oplus}\text{—}CH_3$, $Br^{\ominus}$] ⟶ cyclohexanone

Although the position of the carbon–carbon double bond in an olefin formed by a Wittig reaction may be predicted with certainty, the stereochemistry of the olefin product is less predictable. The following examples illustrate the fact that stereoisomer mixtures are usually produced when reactive ylids (i.e., ylids not stabilized by an adjacent carbonyl function) are employed. However, reactions employing stabilized ylids frequently yield as the predominant product the stereoisomer in which the carbonyl

$$(C_6H_5)_3P^{\oplus}\text{—}CH_2C_6H_5\ \ Cl^{\ominus} + C_6H_5\text{—}CHO \xrightarrow[C_2H_5OH,\ 25°]{NaOC_2H_5}$$

trans-$C_6H_5CH{=}CHC_6H_5$ (35%) + cis-$C_6H_5CH{=}CHC_6H_5$ (41%) (*Ref. 83b*)

Am. Chem. Soc., **85**, 2183 (1963); (f) H. Hoffmann and H. Förster, *Tetrahedron Letters*, **No. 23**, 1547 (1963); (g) for a comparable reaction of α-halo ketones with triethylphosphite, see H. Machleidt and G. W. Strehlke, *Angew. Chem., Intern. Ed. Engl.*, **3**, 443 (1964).

$$(C_6H_5)_3P^{\oplus}—CH_2—CH_3 \quad Br^{\ominus} \xrightarrow[(C_2H_5)_2O]{n\text{-}C_4H_9Li} \xrightarrow[(C_2H_5)_2O,\ 65°]{CH_3—CO—CH(CH_3)_2}$$

$$(CH_3)(H)C{=}C(CH_3)(CH(CH_3)_2) \text{ (90\% of product)} + (H)(CH_3)C{=}C(CH_3)(CH(CH_3)_2) \text{ (10\% of product)}$$

(*Ref. 103*)

function is *trans* to the larger group at the beta carbon atom, a circumstance reminiscent of the stereoselectivity observed in the aldol condensation. This selectivity, illustrated in the equations below, is believed to result, at least in part, from the more rapid decomposition of the betaine (e.g., **[66]**) in which there is less steric interference with overlap between the pi orbital of the carbonyl function and the pi orbital of the developing double bond. The degree of stereoselectivity observed may be influenced by

$$CH_3—CHO + CH_3—C(CO_2CH_3){=}P(C_6H_5)_3 \xrightarrow[\text{reflux}]{CH_2Cl_2} [66] \longrightarrow (CH_3)(H)C{=}C(CH_3)(CO_2CH_3)$$

[66] (96% of product) (*Ref. 87b*)

$$O_2N{-}C_6H_4{-}CHO + (C_6H_5)_3P{=}C(Cl)—CO—C_6H_5 \xrightarrow[\text{reflux}]{CHCl_3} (O_2N{-}C_6H_4)(H)C{=}C(Cl)(CO—C_6H_5)$$

(57%)

(*Ref. 96b*)

the nature of the substituents both on the ylid and on the carbonyl component, as indicated in the accompanying examples.[85,104] That the nature of the reaction medium has also been found

(103) J. P. Dusza, *J. Org. Chem.*, **25**, 93 (1960).

(104) (a) R. Ketcham, D. Jambotkar, and L. Martinelli, *J. Org. Chem.*, **27**, 4666 (1962); (b) H. J. Bestmann and O. Kratzer, *Chem. Ber.*, **95**, 1894 (1962); (c) H. Heitman, U. K. Pandit, and H. O. Huisman, *Tetrahedron Letters*, **No. 14**, 915 (1963); (d) H. O. House, V. K. Jones, and G. Frank, *J. Org. Chem.*, **29**, 3327 (1964).

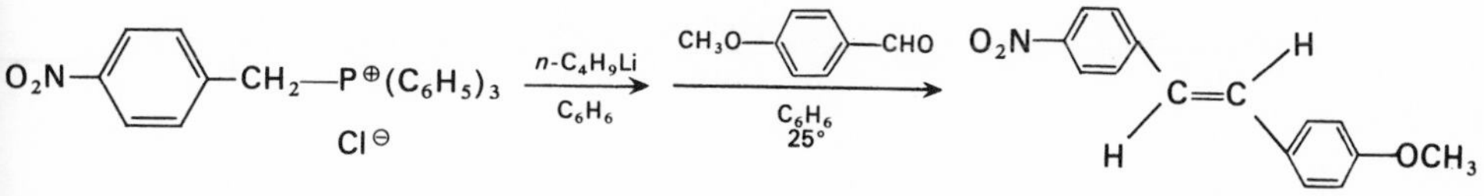

$$O_2N\text{-}C_6H_4\text{-}CH_2\text{-}P^{\oplus}(C_6H_5)_3\ Cl^{\ominus} \xrightarrow[C_6H_6]{n\text{-}C_4H_9Li} \xrightarrow[C_6H_6,\ 25^\circ]{CH_3O\text{-}C_6H_4\text{-}CHO} O_2N\text{-}C_6H_4\text{-}CH{=}CH\text{-}C_6H_4\text{-}OCH_3\ (trans)$$

(89%)

(*Ref. 104a*)

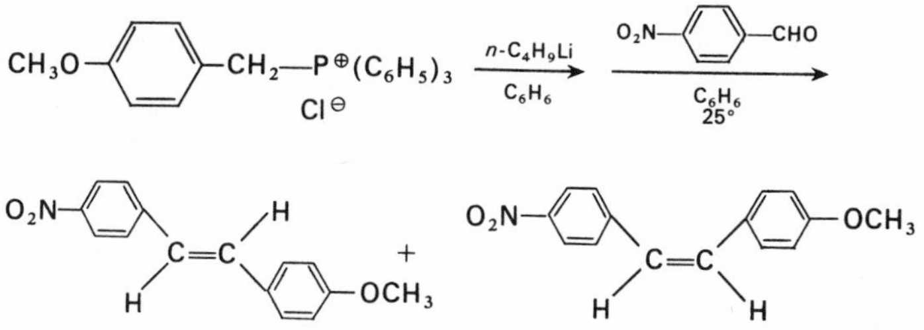

$$CH_3O\text{-}C_6H_4\text{-}CH_2\text{-}P^{\oplus}(C_6H_5)_3\ Cl^{\ominus} \xrightarrow[C_6H_6]{n\text{-}C_4H_9Li} \xrightarrow[C_6H_6,\ 25^\circ]{O_2N\text{-}C_6H_4\text{-}CHO}$$

$$O_2N\text{-}C_6H_4\text{-}CH{=}CH\text{-}C_6H_4\text{-}OCH_3\ (trans) + O_2N\text{-}C_6H_4\text{-}CH{=}CH\text{-}C_6H_4\text{-}OCH_3\ (cis)$$

(46%) (43%)

$$X\text{—}CH_2\text{—}CHO + (C_6H_5)_3P{=}CH\text{—}CO_2CH_3 \xrightarrow{CH_2Cl_2} X\text{—}CH_2\text{—}CH{=}CH\text{—}CO_2CH_3$$

(*Ref. 104d*)
(X = H: 96% *trans* isomer in product)
(X = Cl: 71% *trans* isomer in product)

to influence the proportions of stereoisomers[83b,104d,105] is illustrated below. In general, the percentage of *cis* isomer in the product mixture increases as the reactivity of the carbonyl function in the reactant increases; its predominance is also favored by a reaction medium consisting of a lithium salt *in solution* or, preferably, of a protonic solvent. Recent kinetic studies[85a,b,d] have disproved, at least for stabilized ylids, the theory[105] that the added-salt effect is

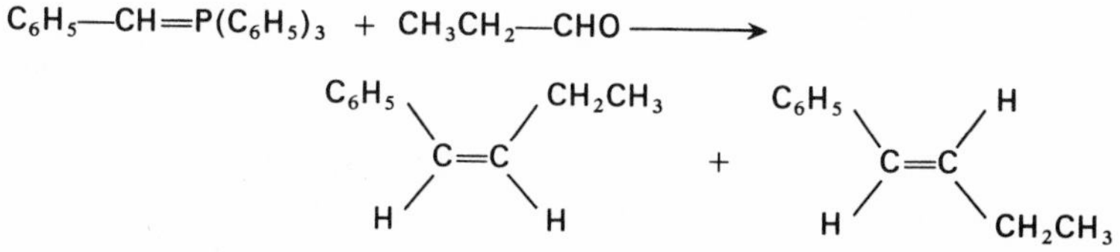

$$C_6H_5\text{—}CH{=}P(C_6H_5)_3 + CH_3CH_2\text{—}CHO \longrightarrow$$

$$\underset{cis}{C_6H_5(H)C{=}C(H)CH_2CH_3} + \underset{trans}{C_6H_5(H)C{=}C(CH_2CH_3)H}$$

(*Ref. 105*)

Reaction medium	% of product	% of product
C_6H_6	26	74
C_2H_5OH	47	53

(105) (a) L. D. Bergel'son and M. M. Shemyakin, *Tetrahedron*, **19**, 149 (1963); (b) G. Drefahl, D. Lorenz, and G. Schnitt, *J. prakt. Chem.*, **[4] 23**, 143 (1964); (c) L. D. Bergel'son, V. A. Vaver, L. I. Barsukov, and M. M. Shemyakin, *Tetrahedron Letters*, **No. 38**, 2669 (1964).

$$CH_3{-}CHO + (C_6H_5)_3P{=}CH{-}CO_2CH_3 \xrightarrow[25°]{}$$

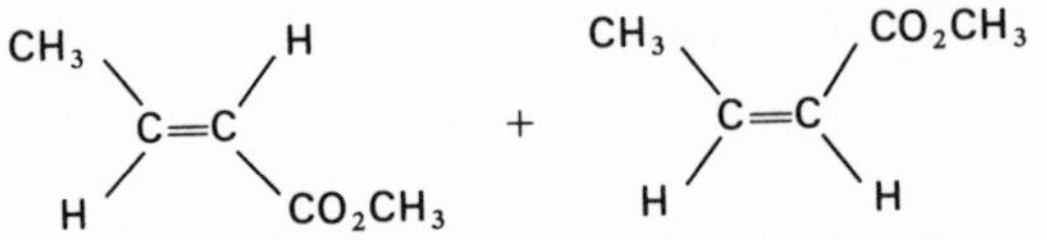

$$\underset{\text{trans}}{(CH_3)HC{=}CH(CO_2CH_3)} + \underset{\text{cis}}{(CH_3)HC{=}CH(CO_2CH_3)}$$

(*Ref. 104d*)

reaction medium	% of *trans* product	% of *cis* product
$(CH_3)_2N{-}CHO$	97	3
$(CH_3)_2N{-}CHO$, $Li^{\oplus}X^{\ominus}$ ($X = Br, Cl, ClO_4, NO_3$)	80	20
CH_3OH	62	38

based on an electrophilic attack by the phosphorus atom of the ylid at the oxygen atom of the carbonyl function. Both the catalysis of the reaction by protonic solvents and the increased proportion of *cis* isomer formed are believed to be attributable to coordination of the carbonyl oxygen atom with the protonic solvent (or lithium cation) as illustrated in structure **[67]**.[85h,104d] This coordination, and consequent delocalization of negative charge, is expected to increase the proportion of *cis* isomer both by retarding the reversal of the initial addition step (to form **[67]**) and by favoring the formation of the solvated betaine **[68]** (the precursor of a *cis* olefin) rather than **[69]** (the precursor of a *trans* olefin).

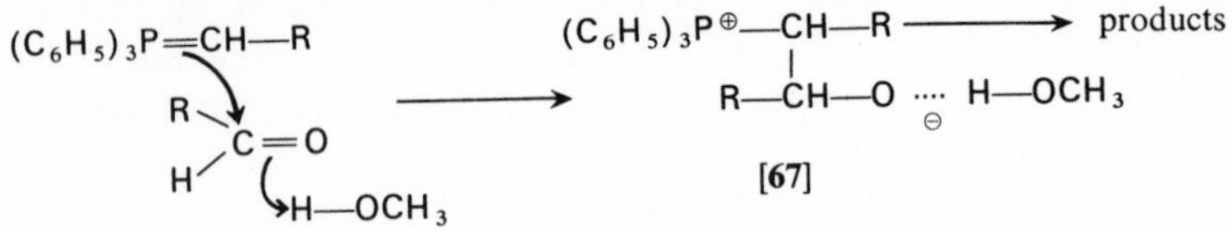

$$(C_6H_5)_3P{=}CH{-}R + R(H)C{=}O \cdots H{-}OCH_3 \longrightarrow (C_6H_5)_3P^{\oplus}{-}CH(R){-}CH(R){-}O^{\ominus} \cdots H{-}OCH_3 \longrightarrow \text{products}$$

[67]

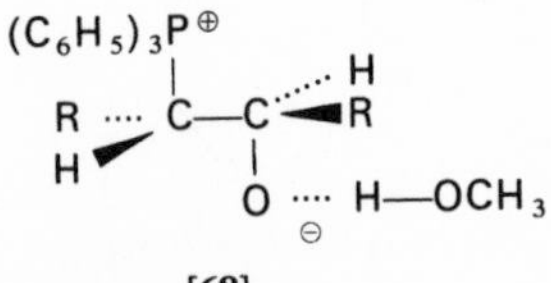

$$(C_6H_5)_3P^{\oplus}{-}C(R)(H){-}C(H)(R){-}O^{\ominus} \cdots H{-}OCH_3$$

[68]

$$R(H)C(P^{\oplus}(C_6H_5)_3){-}C(H)(R)O^{\ominus}$$

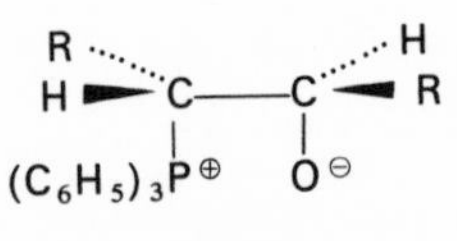

[69]

9

· ACYLATION AT CARBON

REACTIONS THAT RESULT IN THE INTRODUCTION of acyl groups at carbon include the base-catalyzed acylation of active methylene compounds; the acid-catalyzed acylation of active methylene compounds, olefins, and aromatic systems[1]; and the acylation of certain organometallic compounds.[2] The commonly employed acylating agents are the following carboxylic acid derivatives, listed in order of increasing reactivity: $R—CO—NR_2 < R—CO—OH < R—CO—OC_2H_5 < R—CO—OC_6H_5 < R—CO—O—CO—R < R—CO—Cl$ and R—CH═C═O.

Nitriles may also serve as acylating agents since the intermediate imines formed by the addition of a nucleophile to the nitrile function may be hydrolyzed to carbonyl functions. The discussion in this chapter will be restricted to the acylations of active methylene compounds, olefins, and aromatic systems.

(1) D. P. N. Satchell, *Quart. Rev.* (*London*), **17**, 160 (1963).

(2) (a) D. A. Shirley, *Org. Reactions*, **8**, 28 (1954); (b) J. Cason, *Chem.Rev.*, **40**, 15 (1947); (c) M. S. Kharasch and O. Reinmuth, *Grignard Reactions of Nonmetallic Substances*, Prentice-Hall, Englewoods Cliffs, N.J., 1954.

Acylation of Active Methylene Compounds

The principles involved in the acylation of an active methylene compound with an ester may be illustrated by the condensation of ethyl acetate [**1**], a reaction usually called the acetoacetic ester condensation.[3] When the condensation is catalyzed by relatively

$$\underset{[\mathbf{1}]}{CH_3{-}CO_2C_2H_5} \xrightarrow[\substack{CH_3CO_2C_2H_5 \\ \text{reflux}}]{\substack{Na \\ \text{cat. amt. } C_2H_5OH}} CH_3{-}CO_2C_2H_5 + NaOC_2H_5 \rightleftharpoons \underset{[\mathbf{3}]}{\overset{Na^{\oplus}}{CH_2^{\ominus}{-}CO_2C_2H_5}} + C_2H_5OH$$

$$CH_3{-}\overset{\overset{O}{\|}}{\underset{\underset{OC_2H_5}{|}}{C}}\;\; \overset{\ominus}{C}H_2{-}CO_2C_2H_5 \; Na^{\oplus} \rightleftharpoons CH_3{-}\overset{O^{\ominus}}{\underset{OC_2H_5}{C}}{-}CH_2{-}CO_2C_2H_5$$

$$\rightleftharpoons CH_3{-}CO{-}CH_2{-}CO_2C_2H_5 + C_2H_5O^{\ominus} \rightleftharpoons$$

$$\underset{[\mathbf{2}]}{CH_3{-}\underset{\underset{O}{\|}}{C}{-}CH^{\ominus}{-}CO_2C_2H_5} + C_2H_5OH \xrightarrow[H_2O]{CH_3CO_2H}$$

$$\underset{(28\text{–}29\%)}{CH_3{-}CO{-}CH_2{-}CO_2C_2H_5} \qquad (Ref.\ 4)$$

weak bases such as sodium ethoxide or sodium methoxide,[5] each of the steps leading to the enolate anion [**2**] of the β-keto ester is reversible and the initial equilibrium to form the ester enolate anion [**3**] is not favored. In such cases the success of the condensation reaction is attributable to the final formation of the very stable enolate anion [**2**], which displaces previous unfavorable equilibria. In cases (e.g., [**4**]) where a very stable β-keto ester enolate anion cannot be formed, the condensation does not occur with bases such as sodium ethoxide but can be effected with

(3) C. R. Hauser and B. E. Hudson, Jr., *Org. Reactions,* **1**, 266 (1942).

(4) J. K. H. Inglis and K. C. Roberts, *Org. Syn.*, **Coll. Vol. 1**, 235 (1944).

(5) (a) E. E. Royals, *J. Am. Chem. Soc.*, **70**, 489 (1948); (b) E. E. Royals, J. C. Hoppe, A. D. Jordan, Jr., and A. G. Robinson, III, *ibid.*, **73**, 5857 (1951); (c) E. E. Royals and D. G. Turpin, *ibid.*, **76**, 5452 (1954).

strong bases (see Chapter 7) such as sodium triphenylmethyl.

$$\underset{[\mathbf{4}]}{(CH_3)_2CH{-}CO_2C_2H_5} + (C_6H_5)_3C^{\ominus}Na^{\oplus} \xrightarrow[25^{\circ}]{(C_2H_5)_2O} \underset{[\mathbf{5}]}{(CH_3)_2\overset{Na^{\oplus}}{C^{\ominus}}{-}CO_2C_2H_5} \xrightarrow{(CH_3)_2CHCO_2C_2H_5}$$

$$\underset{[\mathbf{6}]}{(CH_3)_2CH{-}CO{-}C(CH_3)_2{-}CO_2C_2H_5} \xrightarrow[\text{(or [5])}]{(C_6H_5)_3C^{\ominus}Na^{\oplus}} \underset{[\mathbf{7}]}{(CH_3)_2\overset{Na^{\oplus}}{C^{\ominus}}{-}CO{-}C(CH_3)_2{-}CO_2C_2H_5}$$

$$\xrightarrow[H_2O]{CH_3CO_2H} \underset{(35\%)}{(CH_3)_2CH{-}CO{-}C(CH_3)_2{-}CO_2C_2H_5} \qquad \textit{(Ref. 6)}$$

The success of this procedure results from the quantitative conversion of the starting ester [**4**] to its enolate anion [**5**]. Condensation then leads to the formation of ethoxide ion, which is a weaker base than the enolate anion [**5**] derived from the ester. Although the β-keto ester [**6**] formed here is converted to the enolate anion [**7**], the latter step is not essential to the success of the condensation.[6b]

Even in cases where sodium ethoxide is successful as a catalyst for acetoacetic ester condensations, better yields have been obtained under forcing conditions, the ethanol being continuously removed from the reaction mixture to force the reaction to completion.[3,5] Alternatively, the yields obtained from acetoacetic ester condensations have been improved by the use of strong bases such as sodium amide,[7] diisopropylaminomagnesium bromide,[5,8] or sodium hydride.[5,9] Sodium hydride accompanied by a catalytic amount of alcohol, appears to be the catalyst of choice because it reacts irreversibly with the alcohol liberated during the reaction to form sodium alkoxide and hydrogen and force the reaction to completion. It is probable that the catalyst actually effecting

(6) (a) C. R. Hauser and W. B. Renfrow, Jr., *J. Am. Chem. Soc.*, **59**, 1823 (1937); (b) B. E. Hudson, Jr., and C. R. Hauser, *ibid.*, **63**, 3156 (1941).

(7) J. C. Shivers, M. L. Dillon, and C. R. Hauser, *ibid.*, **69**, 119 (1947).

(8) F. C. Frostick, Jr., and C. R. Hauser, *ibid.*, **71**, 1350 (1949).

(9) (a) F. W. Swamer and C. R. Hauser, *ibid.*, **72**, 1352 (1950); (b) N. Green and F. B. LaForge, *ibid.*, **70**, 2287 (1948).

condensation in most of these cases is not sodium hydride but rather the sodium alkoxide it generates.

For the synthesis of simple β-keto acid derivatives, a method often superior to the acetoacetic ester condensation of esters is the preparation and subsequent dimerization of ketenes.[10] The following equations illustrate the formation and hydrolysis of a ketene dimer [**8**] to produce a symmetrical ketone. Reactions

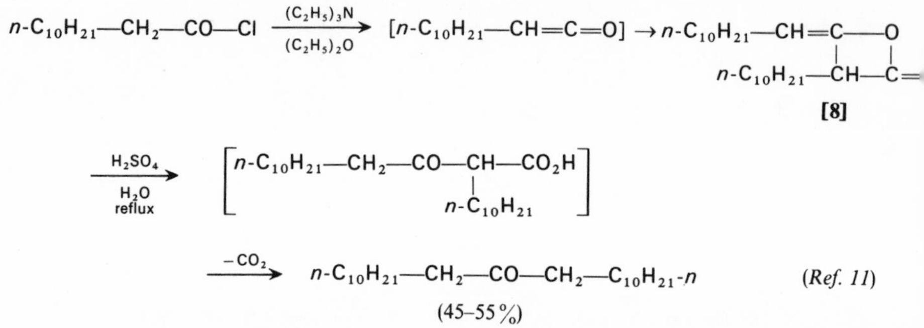

$$n\text{-}C_{10}H_{21}\text{—}CH_2\text{—}CO\text{—}Cl \xrightarrow[(C_2H_5)_2O]{(C_2H_5)_3N} [n\text{-}C_{10}H_{21}\text{—}CH{=}C{=}O] \rightarrow \begin{matrix} n\text{-}C_{10}H_{21}\text{—}CH{=}C\text{—}O \\ n\text{-}C_{10}H_{21}\text{—}CH\text{—}C{=}O \end{matrix}$$

[8]

$$\xrightarrow[\substack{H_2O \\ \text{reflux}}]{H_2SO_4} \left[\begin{matrix} n\text{-}C_{10}H_{21}\text{—}CH_2\text{—}CO\text{—}CH\text{—}CO_2H \\ n\text{-}C_{10}H_{21} \end{matrix} \right]$$

$$\xrightarrow{-CO_2} n\text{-}C_{10}H_{21}\text{—}CH_2\text{—}CO\text{—}CH_2\text{—}C_{10}H_{21}\text{-}n \quad (45\text{–}55\%) \qquad (\textit{Ref. 11})$$

of ketene dimers with alcohols or amines lead to the corresponding esters or amides of the β-keto acids as shown below. Another alternative procedure for the preparation of symmetrical ketones,

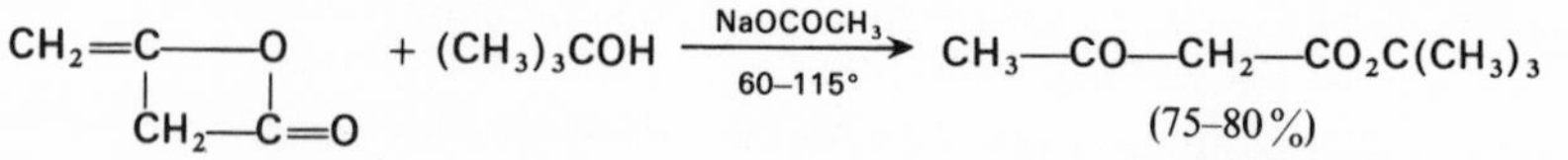

$$\begin{matrix} CH_2{=}C\text{—}O \\ CH_2\text{—}C{=}O \end{matrix} + (CH_3)_3COH \xrightarrow[60\text{–}115°]{NaOCOCH_3} CH_3\text{—}CO\text{—}CH_2\text{—}CO_2C(CH_3)_3 \quad (75\text{–}80\%) \qquad (\textit{Ref. 12})$$

$$\begin{matrix} CH_2{=}C\text{—}O \\ CH_2\text{—}C{=}O \end{matrix} + C_6H_5\text{—}NH_2 \xrightarrow[\text{reflux}]{C_6H_6} CH_3\text{—}CO\text{—}CH_2\text{—}CO\text{—}NH\text{—}C_6H_5 \quad (74\%) \qquad (\textit{Ref. 13})$$

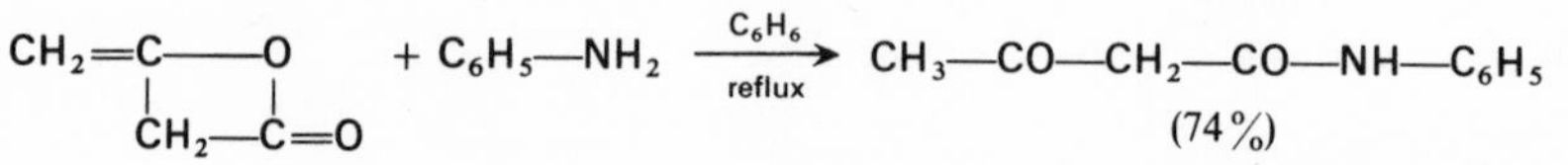

again often superior to acetoacetic ester condensations and subsequent hydrolysis, involves pyrolysis of the salt (e.g., [**9**]) of a carboxylic acid. Although the formation of an intermediate β-keto

(10) (a) W. E. Hanford and J. C. Sauer, *Org. Reactions*, **3**, 108 (1946); (b) R. N. Lacey in R. Raphael, E. C. Taylor, and H. Wynberg (eds.), *Advances in Organic Chemistry; Methods and Results*, Vol. 2, Wiley-Interscience, New York, 1960, pp. 213–263; (c) G. Quadbeck in W. Foerst (ed.), *Newer Methods of Preparative Organic Chemistry*, Vol. 2, Academic, New York, 1963, pp. 133–161.

(11) J. C. Sauer, *Org. Syn.*, **Coll. Vol. 4**, 560 (1963).

(12) S. O. Lawesson, S. Gronwall, and R. Sandberg, *Org. Syn.*, **42**, 28 (1962).

(13) J. W. Williams and J. A. Krynitsky, *Org. Syn.*, **Coll. Vol. 3**, 10 (1955).

$$n\text{-}C_{17}H_{35}\text{—}CO_2H + MgO \xrightarrow[335\text{–}340^\circ]{} (n\text{-}C_{17}H_{35}\text{—}CO\text{—}O)_2Mg \; \textbf{[9]} \xrightarrow{-CO_2}$$

$$n\text{-}C_{17}H_{35}\text{—}CO\text{—}C_{17}H_{35}\text{-}n \quad (81\text{–}87\%) \qquad (Ref.\ 14)$$

acid derivative, has been postulated, the mechanism of this reaction is uncertain at the present time.

Esters of dicarboxylic acids may undergo an intramolecular acetoacetic ester condensation, called the Dieckmann condensation,[3] leading to cyclic β-keto esters. The reversibility of this reaction normally restricts its use to diesters (e.g., **[10]**) that can

$$C_2H_5O\text{—}CO\text{—}(CH_2)_4\text{—}CO_2C_2H_5 \; \textbf{[10]} \xrightarrow[C_6H_5CH_3,\ 100\text{–}115^\circ]{Na,\ \text{cat. amt. } C_2H_5OH} \textbf{[11]} \; (\text{sodium enolate of 2-carbethoxycyclopentanone}, O^\ominus\ Na^\oplus)$$

$$\xrightarrow[H_2O]{CH_3CO_2H} \text{2-carbethoxycyclopentanone } (CO_2C_2H_5) \; (74\text{–}81\%) \qquad (Ref.\ 15)$$

yield five- and six-membered ring products; however, it has occasionally been successful for the preparation of larger rings.[16] Metallic sodium, accompanied by a catalytic amount of ethanol or methanol is often employed to effect both the Dieckmann condensations[15a,17] and intermolecular acetoacetic ester condensation.[4] Although the use of these materials serves to displace the various equilibria in favor of the final β-keto ester enolate anion (e.g., **[2]** and **[11]**), it may lead to complications from a competing acyloin condensation (see Chapter 3),[5c] especially if an insufficient amount of alcohol is present in the original reaction mixture. For this reason sodium hydride, accompanied

(14) A. G. Dobson and H. H. Hatt, *Org. Syn.*, **Coll. Vol. 4**, 854 (1963); also (b) J. F. Thorpe and G. A. R. Kon, *Org. Syn.*, **Coll. Vol. 1**, 192 (1944); (c) R. M. Herbst and R. H. Manske, *Org. Syn.*, **Coll. Vol. 2**, 389 (1943).

(15) (a) P. S. Pinkney, *ibid.*, **Coll. Vol. 2,** 116 (1943); (b) R. Mayer in W. Foerst (ed.), *Newer Methods of Preparative Organic Chemistry*, Vol. 2, Academic, New York, 1963, pp. 101–131.

(16) (a) N. J. Leonard and R. C. Sentz, *J. Am. Chem. Soc.*, **74**, 1704 (1952); (b) W. S. Johnson, A. R. Jones, and W. P. Schneider, *ibid.*, **72**, 2395 (1950).

(17) J. Dutta and R. N. Biswas, *J. Chem. Soc.*, **1963**, 2387.

by a catalytic amount of alcohol, as a condensing agent (e.g., with **[12]**), appears to be more desirable particularly in view of its previously discussed advantages.

[12]

$\xrightarrow[\text{THF, reflux}]{NaH} \xrightarrow{H_3O^{\oplus}}$ (90%) (*Ref. 18*)

The application of the acetoacetic ester condensation to a mixture of two esters, each of which possesses two alpha hydrogen atoms, is usually not a satisfactory synthetic procedure because a mixture of all four possible products is obtained. However, such mixed-ester condensations are of value when one of the two has no alpha hydrogen atoms; commonly employed esters of this type include those of aromatic acids such as benzoic and furoic, as well as ethyl formate, diethyl carbonate, and diethyl oxalate. Whereas either forcing conditions (removal of the alcohol as it is formed) or strong bases are normally required for successful condensations with aromatic esters and with diethyl carbonate, ethyl formate and diethyl oxalate are sufficiently reactive that

$$C_6H_5{-}CO_2CH_3 + CH_3CH_2{-}CO_2CH_3 \xrightarrow[C_6H_6,\ \text{reflux}]{NaH} C_6H_5{-}CO{-}\overset{CH_3}{\underset{\ominus\ Na^{\oplus}}{C}}{-}CO_2CH_3$$

$$\xrightarrow{H_3O^{\oplus}} C_6H_5{-}CO{-}\overset{CH_3}{CH}{-}CO_2CH_3 \quad (56\%) \qquad (\textit{Ref. 5c})$$

$$C_6H_5{-}CH_2{-}CO_2C_2H_5 + (C_2H_5O)_2CO \xrightarrow[\substack{(C_2H_5O)_2CO \\ \text{reflux with continuous removal of } C_2H_5OH}]{NaOC_2H_5}$$

$$C_6H_5{-}\overset{Na^{\oplus}}{C^{\ominus}}(CO_2C_2H_5)_2 \xrightarrow{H_3O^{\oplus}} C_6H_5{-}CH(CO_2C_2H_5)_2 \quad (86\%) \qquad (\textit{Ref. 19})$$

(18) J. D. Hobson, J. Raines, and R. J. Whiteoak, *ibid.*, **1963**, 3495.

(19) (a) V. H. Wallingford, A. H. Homeyer, and D. M. Jones, *J. Am. Chem. Soc.*, **63**, 2056, 2252 (1941); (b) V. H. Wallingford, D. M. Jones, and A. H. Homeyer, *ibid.*, **64**, 576 (1942); (c) see also Ref. 9.

$$\text{3,4-(CH}_3\text{O)}_2\text{C}_6\text{H}_3\text{—CH}_2\text{CH}_2\text{—CH}_2\text{—CO}_2\text{C}_2\text{H}_5 \xrightarrow[\substack{(C_2H_5)_2O \\ -10 \text{ to } 25°}]{\substack{NaOC_2H_5 \\ HCO_2C_2H_5}} \xrightarrow{H_3O^{\oplus}}$$

(Ref. 20)

$$\text{3,4-(CH}_3\text{O)}_2\text{C}_6\text{H}_3\text{—CH}_2\text{CH}_2\text{—CH(CHO)—CO}_2\text{C}_2\text{H}_5 \xrightarrow[\substack{H_2SO_4 \\ 0 \text{ to } 10°}]{H_3PO_4} \text{6,7-dimethoxy-3,4-dihydronaphthalene-2-CO}_2\text{C}_2\text{H}_5$$

(40–43%, isolated after saponification)

$$CH_3\text{—}CH_2\text{—}CO_2C_2H_5 + C_2H_5O\text{—}CO\text{—}CO\text{—}OC_2H_5 \xrightarrow[(C_2H_5)_2O]{NaOC_2H_5} \xrightarrow{H_3O^{\oplus}}$$

$$\underset{(60\text{–}70\%)}{CH_3\text{—}CH(CO\text{—}CO_2C_2H_5)\text{—}CO_2C_2H_5} \xrightarrow[130\text{–}150°]{-CO} \underset{(97\%)}{CH_3\text{—}CH(CO_2C_2H_5)_2}$$

(Ref. 21)

$$\begin{matrix} CH_2\text{—}CO_2C_2H_5 \\ | \\ CH_2\text{—}CO_2C_2H_5 \end{matrix} + C_2H_5O\text{—}CO\text{—}CO\text{—}OC_2H_5 \xrightarrow[\substack{(C_2H_5)_2O \\ 25°}]{\substack{KOC_2H_5 \\ C_2H_5OH}} \begin{matrix} CO\text{—}CO_2C_2H_5 \\ | \\ CH\text{—}CO_2C_2H_5 \\ | \\ CH_2\text{—}CO_2C_2H_5 \end{matrix}$$

(82–83%)

$$\xrightarrow[\substack{H_2O \\ \text{reflux}}]{HCl} \underset{(92\text{–}93\%)}{HO_2C\text{—}CH_2\text{—}CH_2\text{—}CO\text{—}CO_2H}$$

(Ref. 22)

neither provision may be necessary. Examples of mixed-ester condensations are provided in the accompanying equations. It will be noted that these examples also illustrate the use of condensation products from ethyl oxalate as precursors for the synthesis of α-keto and malonic acids. The thermal decarbonylation of systems of the type $\text{—CO—CH}_2\text{—CO—CO}_2C_2H_5$ to form products of the type $\text{—CO—CH}_2\text{—CO}_2C_2H_5$ is a general reaction provided that the beta carbonyl function is acyclic or is part of a six-membered or larger ring. Although the mechanisms of certain

(20) H. L. Holmes and L. W. Trevoy, *Org. Syn.*, **Coll. Vol. 3**, 300 (1955).

(21) (a) R. F. B. Cox and S. M. McElvain, *Org. Syn.*, **Coll. Vol. 2**, 272, 279 (1943); see also (b) P. A. Levene and G. M. Meyer, *ibid.*, **Coll. Vol. 2**, 288 (1943); (c) D. E. Floyd and S. E. Miller, *Org. Syn.*, **Coll. Vol. 4**, 141 (1963).

(22) L. Friedman and E. Kosower, *Org. Syn.*, **Coll. Vol. 3**, 510 (1955).

decarbonylation reactions have been investigated,[23] the reaction path followed in those described here remains to be established.

The foregoing principles are also applicable to the acylation of ketones[9,19a,24] and nitriles[19b,25] by condensation with esters. As the accompanying examples show, sodium ethoxide is an adequate base to promote condensations with the very reactive esters, ethyl formate and diethyl oxalate. However, strong bases such as sodium amide, the sodium salt of dimethyl sulfoxide, or sodium hydride are often more satisfactory for condensations involving less reactive esters. From several of the foregoing

$$\text{cyclohexanone} + C_2H_5O\text{—CO—CO—}OC_2H_5 \xrightarrow[C_2H_5OH,\ 10^\circ]{NaOC_2H_5} \xrightarrow{H_3O^{\oplus}} \text{2-}(CO\text{—}CO_2C_2H_5)\text{cyclohexanone}\ (63\text{–}67\%)$$

$$\xrightarrow[165\text{–}175^\circ]{\text{powdered glass, Fe powder}} \text{2-}(CO_2C_2H_5)\text{cyclohexanone}\ (59\text{–}62\%\ \text{overall})$$

(*Ref.* 26)

$$C_6H_5\text{—}CH_2\text{—}CN + C_2H_5O\text{—CO—CO—}OC_2H_5 \xrightarrow[C_2H_5OH,\ 25^\circ]{NaOC_2H_5} \xrightarrow{H_3O^{\oplus}} C_6H_5\text{—}CH(CN)\text{—}CO\text{—}CO_2C_2H_5\ (69\text{–}75\%)$$

(*Ref.* 27)

(23) (a) M. Calvin and R. M. Lemmon, *J. Am. Chem. Soc.*, **69**, 1232 (1947); (b) J. D. Roberts, D. R. Smith, and C. C. Lee, *ibid.*, **73**, 618 (1951).

(24) (a) C. R. Hauser, F. W. Swamer, and J. T. Adams, *Org. Reactions*, **8**, 59 (1954); (b) R. Levine, J. A. Conroy, J. T. Adams, and C. R. Hauser, *J. Am. Chem. Soc.*, **67**, 1510 (1945); (c) J. J. Bloomfield, *J. Org. Chem.*, **27**, 2742 (1962); (d) S. D. Work and C. R. Hauser, *ibid.*, **28**, 725 (1963).

(25) (a) B. Abramovitch and C. R. Hauser, *J. Am. Chem. Soc.*, **64**, 2720 (1942); (b) R. Levine and C. R. Hauser, *ibid.*, **68**, 760 (1946); (c) R. S. Long, *ibid.*, **69**, 990 (1947); (d) C. J. Eby and C. R. Hauser, *ibid.*, **79**, 723 (1957).

(26) (a) H. R. Snyder, L. A. Brooks, and S. H. Shapiro, *Org. Syn.*, **Coll. Vol. 2**, 531 (1943); see also (b) C. S. Marvel and E. E. Dreger, *Org. Syn.*, **Coll. Vol. 1**, 238 (1944); (c) E. R. Riegel and F. Zwilgmeyer, *Org. Syn.*, **Coll. Vol. 2**, 126 (1943); (d) for an example involving the condensation of ethyl oxalate at the methyl group of o-nitrotoluene, see W. E. Noland and F. J. Baude, *Org. Syn.*, **43**, 40 (1963).

(27) R. Adams and H. O. Calvery, *Org. Syn.*, **Coll. Vol. 2**, 287 (1943).

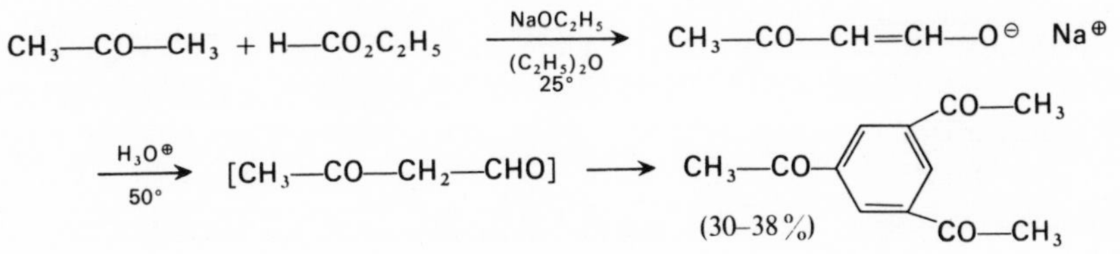

$$CH_3—CO—CH_3 + H—CO_2C_2H_5 \xrightarrow[(C_2H_5)_2O,\ 25°]{NaOC_2H_5} CH_3—CO—CH{=}CH—O^{\ominus}\ Na^{\oplus}$$

$$\xrightarrow[50°]{H_3O^{\oplus}} [CH_3—CO—CH_2—CHO] \longrightarrow 1,3,5\text{-}(CH_3—CO)_3C_6H_3$$

(30–38%)

(*Ref. 28*)

$$\text{cyclohexanone} + H—CO_2C_2H_5 \xrightarrow[(C_2H_5)_2O]{NaH,\ \text{cat. amt. } C_2H_5OH} \xrightarrow{H_3O^{\oplus}} \text{2-formylcyclohexanone (2-CHO)}$$

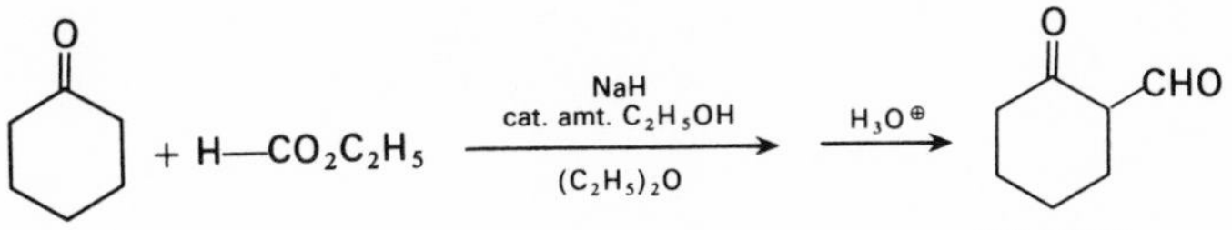

(70–74%)

(*Ref. 29*)

$$C_6H_5—CH_2—CN + (C_2H_5O)_2CO \xrightarrow[(C_2H_5O)_2CO,\ C_6H_5CH_3]{NaOC_2H_5} \xrightarrow[H_2O]{CH_3CO_2H} C_6H_5—CH(CN)—CO_2C_2H_5$$

reflux with continuous separation of C_2H_5OH

(70–78%)

(*Ref. 30*)

$$CH_3—CH{=}CH—CH_2CH_2—CO—CH_3 + (C_2H_5O)_2CO \xrightarrow[(C_2H_5)_2O,\ 25°]{NaH} \xrightarrow[H_2O]{CH_3CO_2H}$$

$$CH_3—CH{=}CH—CH_2CH_2—CO—CH_2—CO_2C_2H_5$$

(85%)

(*Ref. 9b*)

$$C_6H_5—CO_2C_2H_5 + C_6H_5—CO—CH_3 \xrightarrow[150\text{–}160°]{NaOC_2H_5} \xrightarrow{H_3O^{\oplus}}$$

continuous separation of C_2H_5OH as it is formed

$$C_6H_5—CO—CH_2—CO—C_6H_5$$

(62–71%)

(*Ref. 31*)

(28) (a) R. L. Frank and R. H. Varland, *Org. Syn.*, **Coll. Vol. 3**, 829 (1955); see also (b) R. P. Mariella, *Org. Syn.*, **Coll. Vol. 4**, 210 (1963); (c) W. Franke and R. Kraft in W. Foerst (ed.), *Newer Methods of Preparative Organic Chemistry*, Vol. 2, Academic, New York, 1963, pp. 1–30.

(29) C. Ainsworth, *Org. Syn.*, **Coll. Vol. 4**, 536 (1963).

(30) E. C. Horning and A. F. Finelli, *ibid.*, **Coll. Vol. 4**, 461 (1963).

(31) A. Magnani and S. M. McElvain, *Org. Syn.*, **Coll. Vol. 3**, 251 (1955).

$$(CH_3)_2CH{-}CH_2{-}CO{-}CH_3 + (CH_3)_2CH{-}CH_2{-}CO_2C_2H_5 \xrightarrow[(C_2H_5)_2O,\ \text{reflux}]{NaNH_2} \xrightarrow{H_3O^{\oplus}}$$

$$(CH_3)_2CH{-}CH_2{-}CO{-}CH_2{-}CO{-}CH_2{-}CH(CH_3)_2 \quad (\textit{Ref. 32})$$

(69–79%, isolated as the copper complex)

$$\text{3-cyclohexenyl}{-}CO{-}CH_3 + \text{3-cyclohexenyl}{-}CO_2CH_3 \xrightarrow[CH_3{-}SO{-}CH_3,\ 60°]{Na^{\oplus}\ {}^{\ominus}CH_2{-}SO{-}CH_3\ (\text{from } NaH + CH_3SOCH_3)} \xrightarrow{H_3O^{\oplus}}$$

$$\text{3-cyclohexenyl}{-}CO{-}CH_2{-}CO{-}\text{3-cyclohexenyl} \quad (\textit{Ref. 24c})$$

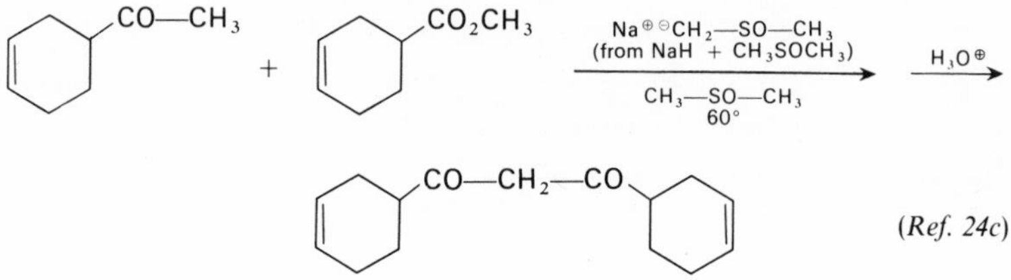

(83%, isolated as the copper complex

$$Cl{-}C_6H_4{-}CH_2{-}CN + C_6H_5{-}CH_2{-}CO_2C_2H_5 \xrightarrow[C_2H_5OH,\ \text{reflux}]{NaOC_2H_5} \xrightarrow{H_3O^{\oplus}}$$

$$Cl{-}C_6H_4{-}CH(CN){-}CO{-}CH_2{-}C_6H_5 \ (74\text{–}82\%) \xrightarrow[H_2O,\ \text{reflux}]{H_2SO_4} Cl{-}C_6H_4{-}CH_2{-}CO{-}CH_2{-}C_6H_5 \ (66\text{–}75\%) \quad (\textit{Ref. 33})$$

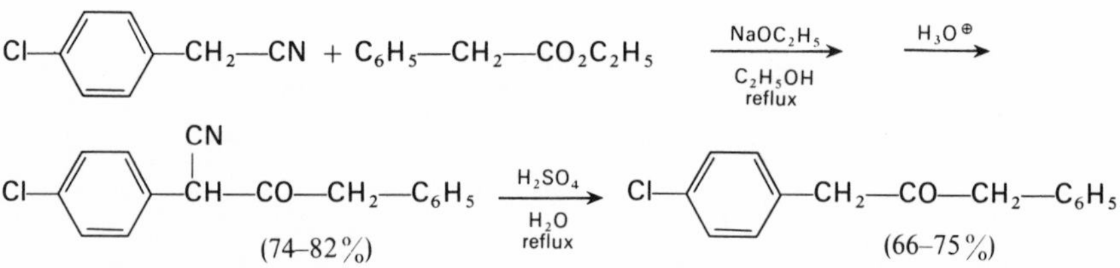

examples, as well as from the acylation of the ketone **[13]** shown below, it will be seen that methyl alkyl ketones are acylated

$$\underset{[13]}{CH_3{-}CH_2{-}CO{-}CH_3} + CH_3{-}CH_2{-}CO_2C_2H_5 \xrightarrow[(C_2H_5)_2O,\ 40\text{–}55°]{NaH}$$

$$\underset{[14]}{CH_3{-}CH_2{-}C(O^{\ominus}\ Na^{\oplus}){=}CH{-}C({=}O){-}CH_2{-}CH_3} + \underset{[15]}{CH_3{-}CH_2{-}C(O^{\ominus}\ Na^{\oplus}){=}C(CH_3){-}C({=}O){-}CH_3} \xrightarrow{H_3O^{\oplus}} \quad (\textit{Ref. 9a})$$

$$\underset{(51\%)}{CH_3{-}CH_2{-}CO{-}CH_2{-}CO{-}CH_2{-}CH_3} + \underset{(9\%)}{CH_3{-}CH_2{-}CO{-}CH(CH_3){-}CO{-}CH_3}$$

(32) C. R. Hauser, J. T. Adams, and R. Levine, *ibid.*, **Coll. Vol. 3,** 291 (1955).

(33) (a) S. B. Coan and E. I. Becker, *Org. Syn.*, **Coll. Vol. 4**, 174, 176 (1963); see also (b) P. L. Julian, J. J. Oliver, R. H. Kimball, A. B. Pike, and G. D. Jefferson, *Org. Syn.*, **Coll. Vol. 2**, 487 (1943).

predominantly at the methyl group by this procedure. Since the reactions leading to the structurally isomeric enolate anions **[14]** and **[15]** are reversible, this preferential acylation reflects the previously noted (Chapter 7) fact that the stability of enolate anions derived from 1,3-dicarbonyl compounds is diminished by alkyl substitution (i.e., **[15]** is less stable than **[14]**). The condensation of 3-ketosteroids (e.g., **[16]**) and other *β*-decalone derivatives with esters has been found to yield predominantly the 2-formyl derivative, irrespective of whether the A-B ring fusion is *cis* or *trans* (cf. Chapter 6).[34] To account for this, it has been suggested[34a,c] that the acylation is a thermodynamically controlled reaction leading to the more stable 2-acyl derivative in which steric interactions are minimized. The intramolecular acylation of ketones

CH_3 ... O ... H — $HCO_2C_2H_5$, $NaOCH_3$ / C_6H_6 → $H_3O^{\oplus}$ → OHC ... CH_3 ... O ... H (*Ref. 34a*)

[16] (86%, isolated as one of the enol tautomers)

provides a useful synthesis for cyclic compounds provided the condensation can lead to five- or six-membered rings as in the equations below.

CH_3, $CO_2C_2H_5$, H, CH_2–CO–CH_3 — NaH, cat. amt. C_2H_5OH / C_6H_6, reflux → CH_3 O ... O ... H (*Ref. 35*)

(86%, isolated as one of the isomeric enols)

$$CH_3—CO—CH_2—CH_3 + C_2H_5O—CO—CO—OC_2H_5 \xrightarrow[C_2H_5OH]{NaOC_2H_5} \xrightarrow{H_3O^{\oplus}}$$

CH_3 ... O ... CO—$CO_2C_2H_5$ ... O ... O (*Ref. 24a*)

(35–38%)

(34) (a) R. O. Clinton, R. L. Clarke, F. W. Stonner, A. J. Manson, K. F. Jennings,

$$o\text{-}(C_6H_5CO\text{—}O)C_6H_4\text{—}CO\text{—}CH_3 \xrightarrow[C_5H_5N,\ 50^\circ]{KOH} o\text{-}(C_6H_5\text{—}C(=O)\text{—}O)C_6H_4\text{—}CO\text{—}CH_2^{\ominus} \longrightarrow o\text{-}(O^{\ominus})C_6H_4\text{—}CO\text{—}CH_2\text{—}CO\text{—}C_6H_5$$

$$\xrightarrow[H_2O]{CH_3CO_2H} \underset{(80\text{–}85\%)}{o\text{-}(OH)C_6H_4\text{—}CO\text{—}CH_2\text{—}CO\text{—}C_6H_5} \xrightarrow[CH_3CO_2H,\ 100^\circ]{H_2SO_4} \underset{(94\text{–}97\%)}{\text{2-}C_6H_5\text{-chromone}} \qquad (Ref.\ 36)$$

All the foregoing acylations suffer from the fact that the step resulting in introduction of the acyl group is reversible, requiring the use of one of the previously discussed methods to force the reaction to completion. The acylation step may normally be made irreversible by allowing an enolate anion to react with an acid chloride or an acid anhydride in an inert solvent. This procedure has been most frequently applied to the acylations of enolate anions derived from malonic esters or β-keto esters, as illustrated in the accompanying equations. The use of an inert solvent rather

$$CH_2(CO_2C_2H_5)_2 \xrightarrow[C_2H_5OH]{Mg,\ \text{cat. amt. } CCl_4} C_2H_5O\text{—}Mg^{\oplus}\,{}^{\ominus}CH(CO_2C_2H_5)_2 \xrightarrow[(C_2H_5)_2O]{Cl\text{—}CO_2C_2H_5}$$

$$Cl\text{—}Mg^{\oplus}\,{}^{\ominus}C(CO_2C_2H_5)_3 \xrightarrow[H_2O]{CH_3CO_2H} \underset{(88\text{–}93\%)}{CH(CO_2C_2H_5)_3} \qquad (Ref.\ 37)$$

$$CH_2(CO_2C_2H_5)_2 \xrightarrow[C_2H_5OH]{Mg,\ \text{cat. amt. } CCl_4} C_2H_5O\text{—}Mg^{\oplus}\,{}^{\ominus}CH(CO_2C_2H_5)_2 \xrightarrow[(C_2H_5)_2O]{o\text{-}NO_2C_6H_4\text{—}CO\text{—}Cl}$$

$$o\text{-}NO_2C_6H_4\text{—}CO\text{—}CH(CO_2C_2H_5)_2 \xrightarrow[H_2O,\ CH_3CO_2H,\ \text{reflux}]{H_2SO_4} \underset{(82\text{–}83\%)}{o\text{-}NO_2C_6H_4\text{—}COCH_3} \qquad (Ref.\ 38)$$

---

and D. K. Phillips, *J. Org. Chem.*, **27**, 2800 (1962); (b) P. J. Palmer, *J. Chem. Soc.*, **1963**, 3901; (c) G. Stork and R. K. Hill, *J. Am. Chem. Soc.*, **79**, 495 (1957).

(35) H. Conroy, *ibid.*, **74**, 3046 (1952).

(36) (a) T. S. Wheeler, *Org. Syn.*, **Coll. Vol. 4**, 478 (1963); see also (b) R. Mozingo, *Org. Syn.*, **Coll. Vol. 3**, 387 (1955).

(37) (a) H. Lund and A. Voigt, *Org. Syn.*, **Coll. Vol. 2**, 594 (1943); see also (b) B. B. Corson and J. L. Sayre, *ibid.*, **Coll. Vol. 2,** 596 (1943).

(38) (a) G. A. Reynolds and C. R. Hauser, *Org. Syn.*, **Coll. Vol. 4**, 708 (1963); see also (b) K. Meyer and H. S. Bloch, *Org. Syn.*, **Coll. Vol. 3**, 637 (1955).

$$CH_3\text{—}CO\text{—}CH_2\text{—}CO_2C_2H_5 + CH_3\text{—}CO\text{—}Cl \xrightarrow[C_6H_6,\ \text{reflux}]{Mg} \xrightarrow[Cu(OCOCH_3)_2]{H_2O}$$

$$\text{copper complex} \xrightarrow[H_2O]{H_2SO_4} (CH_3\text{—}CO)_2CH\text{—}CO_2C_2H_5 \quad (46\text{–}52\%) \qquad (Ref.\ 39)$$

$$C_6H_5\text{—}CO_2H + Cl\text{—}CO_2C_2H_5 \xrightarrow[C_6H_5CH_3,\ 0°]{(C_2H_5)_3N} C_6H_5\text{—}CO\text{—}O\text{—}CO_2C_2H_5$$

$$\xrightarrow[(C_2H_5)_2O,\ C_6H_5CH_3]{C_2H_5O\text{—}Mg^{\oplus}CH^{\ominus}(CO_2C_2H_5)_2} C_6H_5\text{—}CO\text{—}CH(CO_2C_2H_5)_2 \quad (68\text{–}75\%) \qquad (Ref.\ 40)$$

$$C_6H_5\text{—}CH_2\text{—}CH(CO_2C_4H_9\text{-}t)_2 \xrightarrow[C_6H_6]{NaH} C_6H_5\text{—}CH_2\text{—}C^{\ominus}(CO_2C_4H_9\text{-}t)_2\ Na^{\oplus} \xrightarrow[C_6H_6]{C_6H_5\text{—}CO\text{—}Cl} \qquad (Ref.\ 41)$$

$$C_6H_5\text{—}CO\text{—}C(CH_2\text{—}C_6H_5)(CO_2C_4H_9\text{-}t)_2 \xrightarrow[CH_3CO_2H,\ \text{reflux}]{p\text{-}CH_3\text{—}C_6H_4\text{—}SO_3H} C_6H_5\text{—}CO\text{—}CH_2\text{—}CH_2\text{—}C_6H_5\ (80\%) + (CH_3)_2C{=}CH_2 + CO_2$$

than an alcohol is necessary to prevent reaction of the acid chloride or anhydride with the solvent. The ethoxymagnesium cation employed in several of the examples offers the advantage of forming enolate salts that are soluble in inert solvents such as benzene or ether. However, the same solubility advantage may be gained by reaction of malonic esters or β-keto esters with sodium hydride in 1,2-dimethoxyethane to produce solutions of the sodium enolates.

An alternative procedure for the acylation of active methylene compounds utilizes the ability of the magnesium cation to form stable chelate structures with the enolate anions of β-keto acids and related compounds.[42] The introduction of a carboxyl function

$$Mg(OCH_3)_2 + CO_2 \underset{}{\overset{(CH_3)_2N\text{—}CHO}{\rightleftharpoons}} CH_3\text{—}O\text{—}Mg\text{—}O\text{—}CO\text{—}O\text{—}CH_3 \qquad (Ref.\ 42c)$$

[17]

(39) A. Spassow, *ibid.,* **Coll. Vol. 3,** 390 (1955).

(40) (a) J. A. Price and D. S. Tarbell, *Org. Syn.,* **Coll. Vol. 4,** 285 (1963); (b) D. S. Tarbell and J. A. Price, *J. Org. Chem.,* **22,** 245 (1957).

(41) G. S. Fonken and W. S. Johnson, *J. Am. Chem. Soc.,* **74,** 831 (1952).

(42) (a) M. Stiles and H. L. Finkbeiner, *J. Am. Chem. Soc.,* **81,** 505 (1959); (b) M. Stiles, *ibid.,* **81,** 2598 (1959); (c) H. L. Finkbeiner and M. Stiles, *ibid.,* **85,** 616 (1963); (d) R. E. Ireland and J. A. Marshall, *ibid.,* **81,** 2907 (1959).

$$C_6H_5{-}CO{-}CH_3 + \underset{[\mathbf{17}]}{CH_3{-}O{-}Mg{-}O{-}CO{-}O{-}CH_3} \xrightarrow[110\text{–}120^\circ]{(CH_3)_2N{-}CHO} \text{magnesium chelate} \xrightarrow{H_3O^{\oplus}} \underset{(68\%)}{C_6H_5{-}CO{-}CH_2{-}CO_2H} \quad (Ref.\ 42b)$$

$$\text{magnesium chelate} \xrightarrow{1.\ CH_3I;\ 2.\ H_3O^{\oplus},\ -CO_2} \underset{(74\%)}{C_6H_5{-}CO{-}CH(CH_3)_2}$$

at a methyl or methylene group alpha to a carbonyl or nitro group has been achieved by reaction of the active methylene compound with the reagent [**17**], called by the authors methyl magnesium carbonate, in dimethylformamide solution. As indicated in the scheme outlined above, the resulting solution of the magnesium chelate can be either hydrolyzed or alkylated (cf. Chapter 7) and then hydrolyzed and decarboxylated. A related procedure, employed for the synthesis of β-keto esters, utilizes the acylation of an intermediate magnesium chelate as shown.

$$CH_3{-}CH(CO_2H){-}CO_2C_2H_5 \xrightarrow[\text{THF}]{2\text{ equiv. }(CH_3)_2CH{-}MgBr} \text{magnesium chelate} \xrightarrow[\text{THF},\ 0^\circ]{CH_3{-}CO{-}Cl} \quad (Ref.\ 42d)$$

$$\left[CH_3{-}C(CO_2C_2H_5)(CO{-}CH_3){-}CO_2^{\ominus}\ \ \overset{\oplus}{MgCl} \right] \xrightarrow{-CO_2} \text{chelate with } Mg^{\oplus}Cl \xrightarrow{H_3O^{\oplus}} \underset{(62\%)}{CH_3{-}CO{-}CH(CH_3){-}CO_2C_2H_5}$$

The products of β-keto ester acylations are readily cleaved by reaction with base, especially if there is no acidic proton at the alpha carbon atom. As illustrated in the accompanying equations, the cleavage normally occurs preferentially at the most reactive carbonyl function to produce the anion of the strongest acid (i.e., the most stable anion). Therefore, a corresponding cleavage of α-acylmalonic esters removes the acyl group; nonhydrolytic conditions (see Chapter 7 and subsequent discussion) are required

$$CH_3{-}CO{-}CH_2{-}CO_2C_2H_5 \xrightarrow[C_6H_6]{Na} CH_3{-}CO{-}\overset{Na^{\oplus}}{^{\ominus}CH}{-}CO_2C_2H_5 \xrightarrow[C_6H_6]{C_6H_5{-}CO{-}Cl}$$

$$\underset{(63\text{–}75\%)}{C_6H_5{-}CO{-}\underset{\underset{CH_3{-}CO}{|}}{CH}{-}CO_2C_2H_5} \xrightarrow[H_2O,\ 42^{\circ}]{NH_4OH,\ NH_4Cl} \underset{(77\text{–}78\%)}{C_6H_5{-}CO{-}CH_2{-}CO_2C_2H_5} + CH_3CO_2{}^{\ominus}NH_4{}^{\oplus}$$ (*Ref. 43a*)

$$CH_3{-}CO{-}CH_2{-}CO_2C_2H_5 \xrightarrow[(C_2H_5)_2O]{Na} CH_3{-}CO{-}\overset{Na^{\oplus}}{^{\ominus}CH}{-}CO_2C_2H_5 \xrightarrow[(C_2H_5)_2O]{Cl{-}CO{-}(CH_2)_3{-}CO_2C_2H_5}$$

$$\underset{(61\text{–}66\%)}{CH_3{-}CO{-}\underset{\underset{CO_2C_2H_5}{|}}{CH}{-}CO{-}(CH_2)_3{-}CO_2C_2H_5} \xrightarrow[(C_2H_5)_2O]{NH_3}$$ (*Ref. 43b*)

$$\underset{\textbf{[18]}\ (50\text{–}59\%)}{C_2H_5{-}O{-}CO{-}CH_2{-}CO{-}(CH_2)_3{-}CO_2C_2H_5} + CH_3{-}CO{-}NH_2$$

for the synthetically useful cleavage of these substances to give ketones. The cleavage of α-acyl-β-keto esters outlined above provides a good synthetic route to β-keto esters (e.g., **[18]**) of the type that would be obtained as one of a mixture of products from an acetoacetic ester condensation involving two different esters. The acid-catalyzed cleavage of α-acylmalonic esters provides a second such synthetic route, as the following equations demonstrate.

$$CH_2(CO_2C_2H_5)_2 \xrightarrow[C_2H_5OH,\ 25^{\circ}]{KOH} \underset{\underset{CO_2C_2H_5}{|}}{CH_2}{-}CO_2{}^{\ominus}\ K^{\oplus} \xrightarrow{H_3O^{\oplus}} \xrightarrow[100\text{–}110^{\circ}]{C_6H_4(CO{-}Cl)_2\ (o\text{-phthaloyl chloride})} \underset{\underset{CO_2C_2H_5}{|}}{CH_2}{-}CO{-}Cl$$

$$\xrightarrow[C_6H_5N(CH_3)_2,\ (C_2H_5)_2O,\ reflux]{(CH_3)_3COH} \underset{\underset{CO_2C_2H_5}{|}}{CH_2}{-}CO_2C(CH_3)_3 \xrightarrow[C_2H_5OH,\ (C_2H_5)_2O,\ reflux]{Mg,\ cat.\ amt.\ CCl_4} C_2H_5OMg^{\oplus}\ {}^{\ominus}\underset{\underset{CO_2C_2H_5}{|}}{CH}{-}CO_2{-}C(CH_3)_3$$

$$\xrightarrow[(C_2H_5)_2O]{C_6H_5{-}CH_2{-}CO{-}Cl} C_6H_5{-}CH_2{-}CO{-}\underset{\underset{CO_2C_2H_5}{|}}{CH}{-}CO_2C(CH_3)_3 \xrightarrow[C_6H_6,\ reflux]{p\text{-}CH_3{-}C_6H_4{-}SO_3H}$$

$$\underset{(47\%)}{C_6H_5{-}CH_2{-}CO{-}CH_2{-}CO_2C_2H_5} + CO_2 + (CH_3)_2C{=}CH_2$$ (*Ref. 44*)

(43) (a) R. L. Shriner, A. G. Schmidt, and L. J. Roll, *Org. Syn.*, **Coll. Vol. 2**, 266 (1943); see also J. M. Straley and A. C. Adams, *Org. Syn.*, **Coll. Vol. 4**, 415 (1963); (b) M. Guha and D. Nasipuri, *Org. Syn.*, **42**, 41 (1962).

(44) (a) D. S. Breslow, E. Baumgarten, and C. R. Hauser, *J. Am. Chem. Soc.*, **66**, 1286 (1944); (b) W. H. Miller, A. M. Dessert, and G. W. Anderson, *ibid.*, **70**, 500 (1948).

$$C_2H_5OMg^{\oplus}\ {}^{\ominus}CH(CO_2C_2H_5)_2 \xrightarrow[(C_2H_5)_2O,\ \text{reflux}]{CH_3{-}CH_2{-}CO{-}Cl} \xrightarrow{H_3O^{\oplus}} CH_3{-}CH_2{-}CO{-}CH(CO_2C_2H_5)_2$$

$$\xrightarrow[200^\circ]{\text{2-naphthalenesulfonic acid } (C_{10}H_7SO_3H)} CH_3{-}CH_2{-}CO{-}CH_2{-}CO_2C_2H_5 \quad (57\%)$$

(*Ref. 45*)

Acid chlorides and anhydrides may also be used to acylate enolate anions derived from simple esters (e.g., **[19]**) and from ketones (e.g., **[20]** and **[21]**). In order to obtain good yields for the

$$\underset{[19]}{(CH_3)_2CH{-}CO_2C_2H_5} \xrightarrow[(C_2H_5)_2O]{(C_6H_5)_3C^{\ominus}Na^{\oplus}} (CH_3)_2C^{\ominus}{-}CO_2C_2H_5\ Na^{\oplus} \xrightarrow[(C_2H_5)_2O]{C_6H_5{-}CO{-}Cl} C_6H_5{-}CO{-}C(CH_3)_2{-}CO_2C_2H_5 \quad (50\text{–}55\%)$$

(*Ref. 46*)

$$\underset{[20]}{(CH_3)_3C{-}CO{-}CH_3} \xrightarrow[(C_2H_5)_2O]{NaNH_2} \underset{(3\ \text{equiv.})}{(CH_3)_3C{-}CO{-}{}^{\ominus}CH_2\ Na^{\oplus}} \xrightarrow[(C_2H_5)_2O,\ 0^\circ]{1\ \text{equiv.}\ (CH_3)_3C{-}CO{-}Cl}$$

$$(CH_3)_3C{-}CO{-}CH^{\ominus}{-}CO{-}C(CH_3)_3\ Na^{\oplus} \xrightarrow{H_3O^{\oplus}} (CH_3)_3C{-}CO{-}CH_2{-}CO{-}C(CH_3)_3 \quad (58\%)$$

(*Ref. 47a*)

$$\underset{[21]}{\text{cyclohexanone}} \xrightarrow[(C_2H_5)_2O]{NaNH_2} \underset{(3\ \text{equiv.})}{\text{sodium cyclohexenolate } (O^{\ominus}\ Na^{\oplus})} \xrightarrow[(C_2H_5)_2O,\ -30\ \text{to}\ -40^\circ]{1\ \text{equiv.}\ C_2H_5O{-}CO{-}CH_2CH_2{-}CO{-}Cl}$$

$$\text{2-oxocyclohexyl carbanion}{-}CO{-}CH_2CH_2{-}CO_2C_2H_5\ Na^{\oplus} \xrightarrow{H_3O^{\oplus}} \text{2-oxocyclohexyl}{-}CO{-}CH_2CH_2{-}CO_2C_2H_5 \quad (44\%)$$

(*Ref. 47b*)

(45) (a) B. Riegel and W. M. Lilienfeld, *ibid.*, **67**, 1273 (1945); (b) acylmalonates have also been cleaved in boiling water to form β-keto esters: see B. R. Baker, R. E. Schaub, and J. H. Williams, *J. Org. Chem.*, **17**, 116 (1952).

(46) (a) C. R. Hauser and W. B. Renfrew, Jr., *Org. Syn.*, **Coll. Vol. 2**, 268 (1943); (b) D. F. Thompson, P. L. Bayless, and C. R. Hauser, *J. Org. Chem.*, **19**, 1490 (1954).

(47) (a) B. O. Linn and C. R. Hauser, *J. Am. Chem. Soc.*, **78**, 6066 (1956); (b) C. R. Hauser and B. O. Linn, *ibid.*, **79**, 731 (1957).

acylation of ketones by this procedure, it is normally necessary to employ an excess of the enolate anion (usually two or three equivalents per equivalent of the acid chloride or anhydride). In cases where the product is an enolizable 1,3-dicarbonyl compound, a second equivalent of the original enolate is consumed in the conversion of the 1,3-dicarbonyl compound to its enolate anion in the reaction mixture. When enolate anions of ketones (e.g., **[22]**) and of aldehydes (e.g., **[23]**) are treated with excess acid chloride or acid anhydride, the acyl group is introduced predominantly at oxygen rather than at carbon (cf. Chapter 7). It is probable that this initial O-acylation is the first step in the aforementioned C-acylation reactions. However, when excess enolate

[22] $\xrightarrow[CH_3O{-}CH_2CH_2{-}OCH_3]{(C_6H_5)_3C^{\ominus}K^{\oplus}}$ (enolate $O^{\ominus}$ $K^{\oplus}$, CH_3) + (enolate $O^{\ominus}$ $K^{\oplus}$, CH_3)

$\xrightarrow{\text{excess }(CH_3CO)_2O}$ $O{-}CO{-}CH_3$, CH_3 (ca. 35% of mixture) $O{-}CO{-}CH_3$, CH_3 (ca. 65% of mixture) (81%) (*Ref. 48*)

$$(C_6H_5)_2CH{-}CHO \xrightarrow[(C_2H_5)_2O]{NaH} (C_6H_5)_2C{=}CH{-}O^{\ominus}\ Na^{\oplus} \xrightarrow{1.7\text{ equiv. } C_6H_5{-}CO{-}Cl}$$

[23] (1 equiv.)

$$(C_6H_5)_2C{=}CH{-}O{-}CO{-}C_6H_5$$ (39%) (*Ref. 49*)

anion is present, its gradual reaction with the O-acyl derivative leads to the observed C-acylated product, as illustrated in the following equations. In certain cases involving hindered ketones[47] or β-keto esters,[48b] the O-acylated compound has been isolated either as a by-product or as a major product from the reaction of

(48) (a) H. O. House and V. Kramar, *J. Org. Chem.*, **28**, 3362 (1963); (b) acylation of cyclic β-keto esters has also been found to yield substantial amounts of the O-acylated product: see J. P. Ferris, C. E. Sullivan, and B. G. Wright, *ibid.*, **29**, 87 (1964); J. P. Ferris, B. G. Wright, and C. C. Crawford, *ibid.*, **30**, 2367 (1965).

(49) H. O. House and D. J. Reif, *J. Am. Chem. Soc.*, **77**, 6525 (1955).

$$CH_3-C(O^\ominus)=CH_2 \xrightarrow{(CH_3CO)_2O} CH_3-C(=CH_2)-O-C(=O)-CH_3 \quad CH_2=C(O^\ominus)-CH_3 \longrightarrow$$

$$CH_3-CO-CH_2-CO-CH_3 + CH_2=C(O^\ominus)-CH_3 \longrightarrow CH_3-C(O^\ominus)=CH-C(=O)-CH_3 + CH_3-CO-CH_3$$

an acid chloride with excess enolate anion. This result presumably reflects the fact that the reaction of the excess enolate anion with the O-acylated product is relatively slow.

An alternative procedure for the acylation of ketones utilizes the reaction of enamines (see Chapters 7 and 8) with acid chlorides or acid anhydrides.[50] Unlike that with alkylating agents, the reaction of enamines with acylating reagents at nitrogen (e.g., to form [**24**]) is believed to be reversible and so results in good yields of C-acylated products. It will be noted in the accompanying examples that the C-acylated product (e.g., [**25**]), a weakly basic enamine, does not absorb the acid formed during the acylation. Consequently, it is necessary to employ either two equivalents of the enamine or a mixture of one equivalent of the enamine and one equivalent

1-morpholinocyclohexene (2 equiv.) + $CH_3-(CH_2)_6-CO-Cl$ (1 equiv.) $\xrightarrow[\text{reflux}]{\text{dioxane}}$ morpholinium cyclohexylidene $Cl^\ominus$ + 2-[$CO-(CH_2)_6-CH_3$]-1-morpholinocyclohexene [**25**]

$\xrightarrow[\text{H}_2\text{O, reflux}]{\text{HCl}}$ 2-[$CO-(CH_2)_6-CH_3$]cyclohexanone (75%)

$Cl^\ominus$ N-acyl morpholinium ($\oplus$, $CO-(CH_2)_6-CH_3$) cyclohexenyl [**24**]

(*Ref. 50a*)

(50) (a) G. Stork, A. Brizzolara, H. Landesman, J. Szmuszkovicz, and R. Terrell, *ibid.*, **85**, 207 (1963); (b) J. Szmuszkovicz in R. A. Raphael, E. C. Taylor, and H. Wynberg (eds), *Advances in Organic Chemistry; Methods and Results*, Vol. 4, Wiley-Interscience, New York, 1963, pp. 1–113.

$$\text{(1-morpholino-1-cyclohexene)} + Cl{-}CO{-}(CH_2)_2{-}CO_2C_2H_5 \xrightarrow[\substack{CHCl_3 \\ 35^\circ}]{(C_2H_5)_3N} (C_2H_5)_3NH^{\oplus}\ Cl^{\ominus} +$$

$$\text{(morpholinocyclohexenyl)}{-}CO{-}(CH_2)_2{-}CO_2C_2H_5 \xrightarrow{H_3O^{\oplus}} \text{(2-oxocyclohexyl)}{-}CO{-}(CH_2)_2{-}CO_2C_2H_5$$

$$\xrightarrow[\substack{H_2O \\ 100^\circ}]{KOH} \xrightarrow{H_3O^{\oplus}} \underset{(57\%)}{HO_2C{-}(CH_2)_5{-}CO{-}(CH_2)_2{-}CO_2H} \quad (Ref.\ 51)$$

of a second tertiary amine (usually triethylamine) for each equivalent of the acid chloride in order that the hydrogen chloride liberated may be absorbed. The reactions of enamines with ethyl chloroformate **[26]**, with cyanogen chloride **[27]**, with nitrosyl chloride,[52b] or with the mixed anhydride of formic and acetic acids **[28]**, in each case followed by hydrolysis, provide useful routes to *β*-keto esters, *β*-ketonitriles, *α*-oximinoketones, or *β*-ketoaldehydes.

$$\underset{(2\ \text{equiv.})}{\text{(1-morpholino-1-cyclohexene)}} + \underset{(1\ \text{equiv.})}{Cl{-}CO_2C_2H_5} \xrightarrow[\text{reflux}]{C_6H_6}$$

[26]

$$\text{(N-cyclohexylidenemorpholinium)}\ Cl^{\ominus} + \text{(2-morpholinocyclohexenyl)}{-}CO_2C_2H_5 \xrightarrow[\substack{H_2O \\ 25^\circ}]{HCl} \underset{(62\%)}{\text{(2-oxocyclohexyl)}{-}CO_2C_2H_5}$$

(*Ref. 50a*)

(51) (a) S. Hünig and E. Lücke, *Chem. Ber.*, **92**, 652 (1959); see also (b) S. Hünig, E. Lücke, and E. Benzing, *ibid.*, **91**, 129 (1958); (c) S. Hünig and W. Lendle, *ibid.*, **93**, 909, 913 (1960); (d) S. Hünig, E. Lücke, and W. Brenninger, *Org. Syn.*, **43**, 34 (1963).

(52) (a) M. E. Kuehne, *J. Am. Chem. Soc.*, **81**, 5400 (1959); (b) H. Metzger, *Tetrahedron Letters*, **No. 4**, 203 (1964).

C_6H_5 + Cl—C≡N [27] $\xrightarrow[\text{dioxane, 3–8°}]{(C_2H_5)_3N}$ $(C_2H_5)_3NH^{\oplus}$ $Cl^{\ominus}$ + C_6H_5 … C≡N

$\xrightarrow[\text{H}_2\text{O, reflux}]{\text{HCl}}$ C_6H_5 … C≡N (67%, mixture of *cis* and *trans* isomers)

(*Ref.* 52)

+ H—CO—O—CO—CH_3 [28] $\xrightarrow[\text{dioxane, 0°}]{}$ CHO $\xrightarrow{H_2O}$ O, CHO (49%, isolated as enol form)

(*Ref.* 50*a*)

The acylation of ketones with acid anhydrides to form 1,3-dicarbonyl compounds may also be accomplished in the presence of the acid catalyst, boron trifluoride.[24a,53,54] This reaction is thought to involve electrophilic attack by the complex of the anhydride and the Lewis acid (e.g., **[29]**) on the enol derivative of the ketone (e.g., **[30]**). In the presence of a proton acid, it is probable that the enol of the ketone is first acylated at oxygen and that the resulting enol ester (e.g., **[31]**) is then attacked by the anhydride–Lewis acid complex. In any event, the resulting 1,3-dicarbonyl compound is subsequently converted to its borofluoride complex (e.g., **[32]**), which may be either isolated from the reaction mixture

(53) (a) D. Kästner in *Newer Methods of Preparative Organic Chemistry*, Wiley-Interscience, New York, 1948, pp. 249–313; (b) H. S. Booth and D. R. Martin, *Boron Trifluoride and its Derivatives*, Wiley, New York, 1949.

(54) (a) C. R. Hauser and J. T. Adams, *J. Am. Chem. Soc.*, **66**, 345 (1944); (b) J. T. Adams and C. R. Hauser, *ibid.*, **67**, 284 (1945); (c) C. R. Hauser, F. C. Frostick, Jr., and E. H. Man, *ibid.*, **74**, 3231 (1952); (d) R. M. Manyik, F. C. Frostick, Jr., J. J. Sanderson, and C. R. Hauser, *ibid.*, **75**, 5030 (1953); (e) 1,3-dicarbonyl compounds have also been prepared by reaction of the borofluoride complexes of β-keto acids with an acid anhydride at elevated temperatures: see H. Musso and K. Figge, *Ann. Chem.*, **668**, 1, 15 (1963).

$$CH_3{-}CO{-}CH_3 + (CH_3{-}CO)_2O \text{ (excess)} \xrightarrow[0^\circ]{BF_3} \underset{[29]}{CH_3{-}C({=}O^{\oplus}{-}BF_3^{\ominus}){-}O{-}C(CH_3){=}O} \leftarrow \underset{[30]}{CH_2{=}C(O^{\ominus}{-}BF_3){-}CH_3}$$

(*Ref. 55*)

$$\longrightarrow CH_3{-}C(=O){-}CH_2{-}C(=O^{\oplus}{-}BF_3^{\ominus}){-}CH_3 \xrightarrow{-HF} \underset{[32]}{CH_3{-}C{=}O \cdots BF_2{-}O{-}C(CH_3){=}CH \text{ (ring)}}$$

$$\underset{[29]}{CH_3{-}C(=O^{\oplus}{-}BF_3^{\ominus}){-}O{-}C(CH_3){=}O} \leftarrow \underset{[31]}{CH_2{=}C(O{-}CO{-}CH_3){-}CH_3} \xrightarrow{-H^{\oplus}} CH_3{-}C(=O){-}CH{=}C(O{-}CO{-}CH_3){-}CH_3 \xrightarrow[-CH_3COF]{BF_3} [32]$$

$$\underset{[32]}{\text{BF}_2 \text{ complex}} \xrightarrow[H_2O \text{ reflux}]{NaOCOCH_3} [CH_3{-}CO{-}CH_2{-}CO{-}CH_3] \xrightarrow[H_2O]{Cu(OCOCH_3)_2}$$

$$\underset{[33]}{\text{Cu(acac)}_2} \xrightarrow{H_3O^{\oplus}} \underset{(80\text{–}85\%)}{CH_3{-}CO{-}CH_2{-}CO{-}CH_3}$$

(55) C. E. Denoon, Jr., *Org. Syn.*, **Coll. Vol. 3**, 16 (1955).

or, more commonly, directly hydrolyzed to form the β-diketone. The conversion of the 1,3-dicarbonyl compound to its copper complex (e.g., [**33**]) is often employed to facilitate separation of the product from other components in the reaction mixture. The optimum conditions for these acylations require rapid saturation of the reaction mixture with boron trifluoride at low temperatures (0–10°) or, alternatively, addition of a mixture of the ketone and the anhydride to a preformed complex of boron trifluoride with the acid or with ethyl acetate,[54d] as illustrated in the following equation.

$$\text{cyclohexanone} + (CH_3\text{—}CH_2\text{—}CO)_2O \xrightarrow[0^\circ]{BF_3,\ CH_3CO_2C_2H_5} \text{(}BF_2\text{ complex of 2-(C(=O)—}CH_2\text{—}CH_3\text{)cyclohexenol)}$$

$$\xrightarrow[H_2O,\ \text{reflux}]{NaOCOCH_3} \text{2-(CO—}CH_2\text{—}CH_3\text{)cyclohexanone} \quad (79\%)$$

(*Refs. 54d, 24a*)

Since these acid-catalyzed acylation reactions involve the enol and not the enolate anion derived from the ketone, it is to be expected that the acylation of unsymmetrical ketones will occur at the more highly substituted alpha position, corresponding to the more stable enol. This selectivity is reported[24a] to be enhanced by the presence of a catalytic amount of a protonic acid (usually *p*-toluenesulfonic acid) in the reaction mixture. The accompanying equations illustrate this selectivity; it should be noted that, although the yield was low, even the preparation of a nonenolizable β-diketone (e.g., [**34**]), which could not form a borofluoride complex

$$n\text{-}C_4H_9\text{—}CH_2\text{—CO—}CH_3 + (CH_3\text{—CO})_2O \xrightarrow[\substack{p\text{-}CH_3C_6H_4SO_3H \\ \text{(cat. amt.)} \\ 0\text{–}10^\circ}]{BF_3} n\text{-}C_4H_9\text{—C}\langle(\text{C}(CH_3)\text{=O}\cdots BF_2\text{—O—C}(CH_3))$$

$$\xrightarrow[H_2O,\ \text{reflux}]{NaOCOCH_3} n\text{-}C_4H_9\text{—CH(CO—}CH_3)_2 \quad (66\text{–}74\%)$$

(*Ref. 24a*)

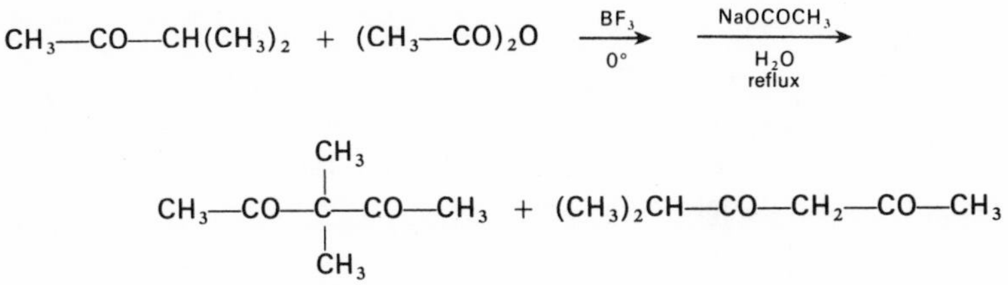

$$CH_3{-}CO{-}CH(CH_3)_2 + (CH_3{-}CO)_2O \xrightarrow[0^\circ]{BF_3} \xrightarrow[\text{H}_2\text{O, reflux}]{\text{NaOCOCH}_3}$$

$$CH_3{-}CO{-}C(CH_3)_2{-}CO{-}CH_3 + (CH_3)_2CH{-}CO{-}CH_2{-}CO{-}CH_3$$

[34] (68% of mixture) (32% of mixture)

(28%) (*Ref. 54a*)

analogous to **[32]**, was achieved. Since this procedure for the acylation of unsymmetrical ketones leads predominantly to the introduction of the acyl group at the more highly substituted position except in cases where that position is already occupied by a bulky alkyl substituent (e.g., a *t*-butyl group),[54] it supplements the methods previously described, which normally introduce the acyl group at the less highly substituted alpha position. Intramolecular acylation may also be effected with acid catalysts, as illustrated by the cyclization of the keto acid **[35]**. The β-diketone **[36]** produced in this reaction cannot form a stable enol, enolate anion, or borofluoride complex; it is presumably for this reason that

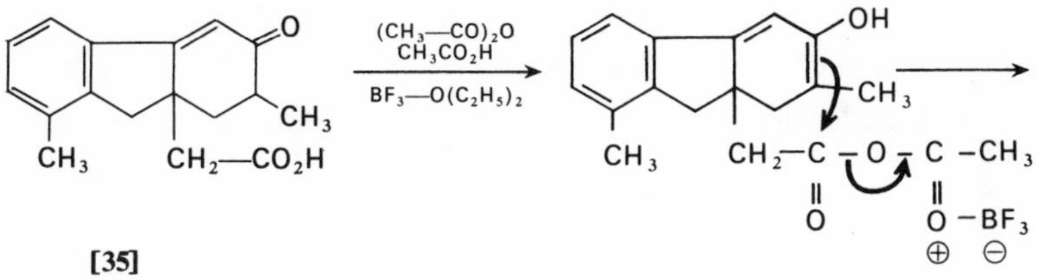

$(CH_3{-}CO)_2O$, CH_3CO_2H, $BF_3{-}O(C_2H_5)_2$

[35]

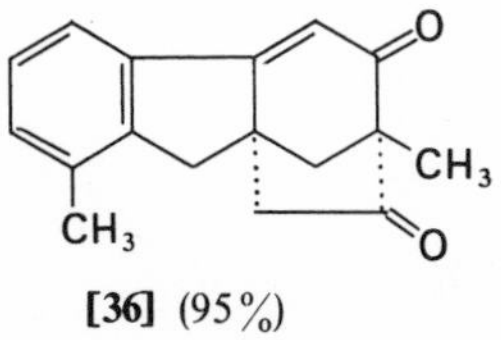

[36] (95%)

(*Ref. 56*)

attempts to effect intramolecular base-catalyzed cyclizations with the ester corresponding to the acid **[35]** failed.[56]

Enol esters (e.g., **[37]**) of ketones may be isomerized thermally or by treatment with boron trifluoride to form 1,3-dicarbonyl

(56) Y. Kos and H. J. E. Loewenthal, *J. Chem. Soc.*, **1963**, 605.

compounds.[57] The acid-catalyzed reaction is believed to involve electrophilic attack of a Lewis acid–enol ester complex (e.g., **38**]) on a second molecule of the enol ester, as shown below. This procedure appears to be particularly useful for the introduction of a benzoyl group under acidic conditions.

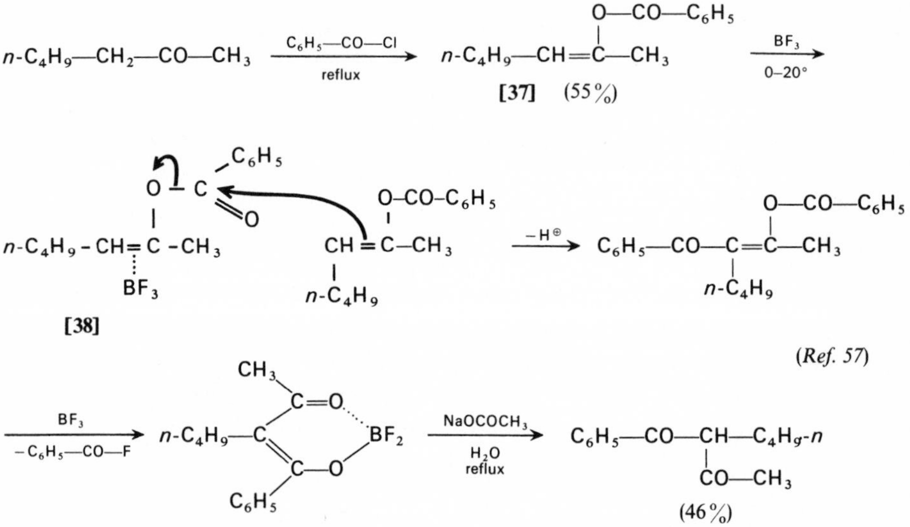

$$n\text{-}C_4H_9\text{—}CH_2\text{—}CO\text{—}CH_3 \xrightarrow[\text{reflux}]{C_6H_5\text{—}CO\text{—}Cl} n\text{-}C_4H_9\text{—}CH\text{=}C(O\text{—}CO\text{—}C_6H_5)\text{—}CH_3 \xrightarrow[0\text{–}20^\circ]{BF_3}$$

[37] (55%)

$$n\text{-}C_4H_9\text{-}CH\text{=}C(O\text{-}CO\text{-}C_6H_5)\text{-}CH_3 \cdots BF_3 + CH(n\text{-}C_4H_9)\text{=}C(O\text{-}CO\text{-}C_6H_5)\text{—}CH_3 \xrightarrow{-H^\oplus} C_6H_5\text{—}CO\text{—}C(n\text{-}C_4H_9)\text{=}C(O\text{—}CO\text{—}C_6H_5)\text{—}CH_3$$

[38]

(*Ref. 57*)

$$\xrightarrow[-C_6H_5\text{—}CO\text{—}F]{BF_3} n\text{-}C_4H_9\text{—}C[C(CH_3)\text{=}O \cdots BF_2\text{—}O\text{—}C(C_6H_5)] \xrightarrow[\substack{H_2O \\ \text{reflux}}]{NaOCOCH_3} C_6H_5\text{—}CO\text{—}CH(CO\text{—}CH_3)\text{—}C_4H_9\text{-}n$$

(46%)

The α-acylcyclohexanones and α-acylcyclopentanones obtainable from the previously described acylations (particularly from the

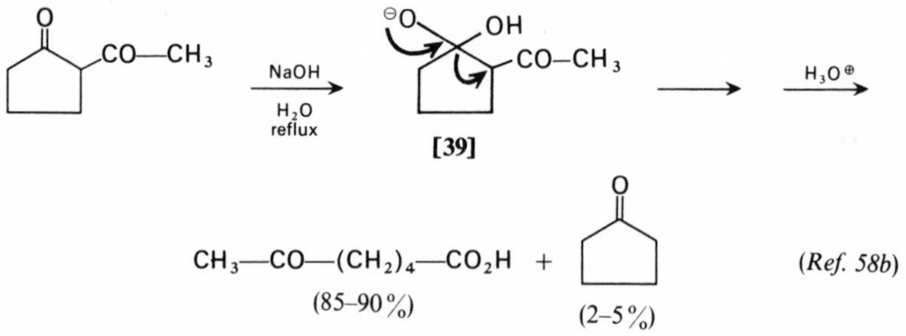

$$\text{2-acetylcyclopentanone} \xrightarrow[\substack{H_2O \\ \text{reflux}}]{NaOH} \text{[39]} \longrightarrow \xrightarrow{H_3O^\oplus} CH_3\text{—}CO\text{—}(CH_2)_4\text{—}CO_2H + \text{cyclopentanone}$$

[39]

(85–90%) (2–5%) (*Ref. 58b*)

(57) F. G. Young, F. C. Frostick, Jr., J. J. Sanderson, and C. R. Hauser, *J. Am. Chem. Soc.*, **72**, 3635 (1950).

(58) (a) C. R. Hauser, F. W. Swamer, and B. I. Ringler, *ibid.*, **70**, 4023 (1948); (b) P. J. Hamrick, Jr., C. F. Hauser, and C. R. Hauser, *J. Org. Chem.*, **24**, 583 (1959).

$$\text{2-acetylcyclohexanone} \xrightarrow[\text{H}_2\text{O, reflux}]{\text{NaOH}} \xrightarrow{\text{H}_3\text{O}^{\oplus}} \underset{(60\text{–}64\%)}{CH_3\text{—}CO\text{—}(CH_2)_5\text{—}CO_2H} + \underset{(30\text{–}32\%)}{\text{cyclohexanone}} \quad (\textit{Ref. 58b})$$

$$\text{2-acetylcycloheptanone} \xrightarrow[\text{H}_2\text{O, reflux}]{\text{NaOH}} [\text{cycloheptanone–C(HO)(O}^{\ominus}\text{)CH}_3] \longrightarrow \xrightarrow{\text{H}_3\text{O}^{\oplus}} \underset{(95\text{–}98\%)}{\text{cycloheptanone}} \quad (\textit{Ref. 58b})$$

$$\text{2-acetyl-2-methylcyclohexanone} \xrightarrow[\text{H}_2\text{O, reflux}]{\text{NaOH}} \xrightarrow{\text{H}_3\text{O}^{\oplus}} \underset{(25\%)}{CH_3\text{—}CO\text{—}CH(CH_3)\text{—}(CH_2)_4\text{—}CO_2H} + \underset{(54\%)}{\text{2-methylcyclohexanone}} \quad (\textit{Ref. 58b})$$

acylation of enamines) may be cleaved by reaction with aqueous alkali to form keto acids.[58] As illustrated in the accompanying equations, this cleavage, involving attack by hydroxide ion (e.g., **[39]**) at the cycloalkanone carbonyl function, is the predominant reaction only for α-acylcycloalkanones that have no other alpha substituent and that are derived from cyclopentanones or cyclohexanones. Subsequent reduction of the keto acids formed in this way by the Wolff-Kishner method[59] provides a useful synthetic route to long-chain carboxylic acids (e.g., **[40]**).[50a,51]

$$\text{2-[CO—(CH}_2)_7\text{—CO}_2\text{C}_2\text{H}_5\text{]cyclohexanone} \xrightarrow[\text{CH}_3\text{OH, reflux}]{\text{KOH}} \xrightarrow{\text{H}_3\text{O}^{\oplus}} \underset{(65\%)}{HO_2C\text{—}(CH_2)_5\text{—}CO\text{—}(CH_2)_7\text{—}CO_2H}$$

$$\xrightarrow[\text{HOCH}_2\text{CH}_2\text{—O—CH}_2\text{CH}_2\text{OH, 190–200°}]{\text{KOH, H}_2\text{N—NH}_2} \xrightarrow{\text{H}_3\text{O}^{\oplus}} \underset{\textbf{[40]}\ (95\%)}{HO_2C\text{—}(CH_2)_5\text{—}CH_2\text{—}(CH_2)_7\text{—}CO_2H} \quad (\textit{Ref. 50a})$$

(59) (a) D. Todd, *Org. Reactions*, **4**, 378 (1948); (b) Huang-Minlon, *J. Am. Chem. Soc.*, **68**, 2487 (1946).

Acylation of Olefins and Aromatic Systems

Acylations of olefins and aromatic systems, which may be considered examples of the Friedel-Crafts reaction,[1,60] are usually effected either with an acid chloride or anhydride in the presence of one of the Lewis acids—aluminum chloride,[61] boron trifluoride,[53] stannic chloride, or zinc chloride—or with a carboxylic acid in the presence of a protonic acid such as hydrogen fluoride,[62] sulfuric acid, or polyphosphoric acid.[63] The carboxylic acids are employed most frequently for intramolecular reactions leading to cyclic ketones.[60c,63] The Lewis acids, whose activities follow the order $AlCl_3 > BF_3 > SnCl_4 > ZnCl_2$, require anhydrous conditions since even small amounts of water markedly reduce their catalytic action; they are normally used in solvents such as carbon disulfide, methylene chloride, or nitrobenzene or in an excess of the hydrocarbon being acylated. Hydrogen fluoride is most commonly employed as an anhydrous liquid (b.p. 19.5°) in apparatus constructed of copper or polyethylene. Intramolecular acylations are usually accomplished by dissolving the acid to be cyclized in excess hydrogen fluoride and allowing the solution to stand at room temperature until the hydrogen fluoride has evaporated.[60c,62,64] Reactions catalyzed by sulfuric acid are normally performed by adding the reactant(s) to excess concentrated sulfuric acid, which then also serves as the solvent. Such reactions are run at temperatures ranging from 0 to 100°; at elevated temperatures sulfonation of aromatic systems and acid-catalyzed aldol condensation (see Chapter 8) of the ketonic products may be serious side reactions. The crude product is isolated after pouring the reaction mixture

(60) (a) P. H. Gore, *Chem. Rev.*, **55**, 229 (1955); (b) G. Baddeley, *Quart. Rev. (London)*, **8**, 355 (1954); (c) W. S. Johnson, *Org. Reactions*, **2**, 114 (1944); (d) E. Berliner, *ibid.*, **5**, 229 (1949).

(61) C. A. Thomas, *Anhydrous Aluminum Chloride in Organic Chemistry*, Reinhold, New York, 1941.

(62) K. Wiechert in *Newer Methods of Preparative Organic Chemistry*, Wiley-Interscience, New York, 1948, pp. 315–368.

(63) (a) F. Uhlig and H. R. Snyder in R. A. Raphael, E. C. Taylor, and H. Wynberg (eds.), *Advances in Organic Chemistry; Methods and Results*, Vol. 1, Wiley-Interscience, New York, 1960, pp. 35–81; (b) F. D. Popp and W. E. McEwen, *Chem. Rev.*, **58**, 321 (1958).

(64) L. F. Fieser and E. B. Hershberg, *J. Am. Chem. Soc.*, **61**, 1272 (1939); **62**, 49 (1940).

onto ice. Polyphosphoric acid,[63,65]

$$(HO)_2\overset{O}{\overset{\|}{P}}—O—(—\underset{OH}{\underset{|}{\overset{O}{\overset{\|}{P}}}}—O—)_n—\overset{O}{\overset{\|}{P}}(OH)_2,$$

which may be prepared by dissolving phosphorous pentoxide in 85 per cent aqueous phosphoric acid, is a very viscous liquid, sufficiently fluid to permit stirring, only when warmed to 40–50°. Reactions with this reagent are commonly run by adding the reactant(s) to warm polyphosphoric acid when stirring and then heating the resulting solution to 50–90° on a steam bath. The reaction mixture is poured onto ice prior to isolation of the crude product.

The acylation of olefins and acetylenes with acid chlorides in the presence of aluminum chloride is illustrated by the following equations. These reactions are believed to proceed via the indicated electrophilic attack on the olefin by a complex of the Lewis acid with the acid chloride (e.g., **[41]**); alternatively, the acylating

$$C_2H_5—CO—Cl + 1.1\text{ equiv. }AlCl_3 \xrightarrow[C_6H_5NO_2]{CH_2{=}CH_2}$$

$$CH_2{=}CH_2 \rightarrow \underset{\textbf{[41]}}{C_2H_5—\underset{Cl}{\underset{|}{C}}{=}\overset{\oplus}{O}—\overset{\ominus}{A}lCl_3} \longrightarrow \underset{\textbf{[43]}}{C_2H_5—\underset{\underset{Cl_3\overset{\ominus}{A}l}{|}}{\underset{O}{\underset{|}{\overset{Cl}{\overset{|}{C}}}}}—CH_2—CH_2^{\oplus}}$$

$$\xrightarrow{Cl^{\ominus}} \underset{\textbf{[42]}}{C_2H_5—\underset{\overset{\oplus}{O}—\overset{\ominus}{A}lCl_3}{\underset{\|}{C}}—CH_2—CH_2—Cl} \xrightarrow[H_2O]{HCl} \underset{(45\%)}{C_2H_5—CO—CH_2—CH_2—Cl}$$

$$\xrightarrow[160°]{C_6H_5N(C_2H_5)_2} \underset{(57\%)}{C_2H_5—CO—CH{=}CH_2} \qquad (\textit{Ref. 66})$$

(65) Commercially available from Victor Chemical Works, Chicago, Illinois.

(66) E. M. McMahon, J. N. Roper, Jr., W. P. Utermohlen, Jr., R. H. Hasek, R. C. Harris, and J. H. Brant, *J. Am. Chem. Soc.*, **70**, 2971 (1948).

$$(CH_3)_2CH\text{—}CH_2\text{—}CH_2\text{—}CO\text{—}Cl \xrightarrow[CCl_4,\ 0°]{HC{\equiv}CH,\ AlCl_3} \xrightarrow{H_2O}$$

$$(CH_3)_2CH\text{—}CH_2\text{—}CH_2\text{—}CO\text{—}CH{=}CH\text{—}Cl \quad (54\text{–}64\%) \qquad (Ref.\ 67)$$

agent may be formulated as an acyl cation.[60] The ketone formed in the reaction mixture is converted to its conjugate acid (e.g., **[42]**) by the aluminum chloride present. For this reason it is necessary to use at least one full equivalent of the aluminum chloride catalyst to ensure complete reaction. The conditions employed in these acylations are sufficiently vigorous that the intermediate carbonium ion (e.g., **[43]**) or the ion produced by reaction of the initially formed chloro compound with aluminum chloride may undergo further reaction, especially in cases involving more complex olefins. This possibility is demonstrated in the equations that follow.

cyclohexene + C_6H_5—CO—Cl $\xrightarrow[CS_2,\ 25°]{AlCl_3}$ $\xrightarrow{H_3O^{\oplus}}$ crude chlorine-containing product $\xrightarrow[C_2H_5OH,\ reflux]{KOH}$

Cl—(cyclohexyl)—CO—C_6H_5 + C_6H_5—CO—(cyclohexenyl) + (tetrahydrofluorenone, O) + other products

(Ref. 68)

CH_3O—(p-phenylene)—CH_2—CO—Cl $\xrightarrow[CS_2,\ 0°]{CH_2{=}CH_2,\ AlCl_3}$ [CH_3O—C_6H_4—CH_2—C(=O)—CH_2—CH_2—Cl]

$\xrightarrow{AlCl_3}$ $\xrightarrow[H_2O]{HCl}$ 6-methoxy-2-tetralone (CH_3O, =O) (56%) *(Ref. 69)*

(67) C. C. Price and J. A. Pappalardo, *Org. Syn.*, **Coll. Vol. 4**, 186 (1963).

(68) (a) R. E. Christ and R. C. Fuson, *J. Am. Chem. Soc.*, **59**, 893 (1937); (b) C. L. Stevens and E. Farkas, *ibid.*, **75**, 3306 (1953); (c) H. O. House, V. Paragamian, R. S. Ro, and D. J. Wluka, *ibid.*, **82**, 1457 (1960); (d) for other examples, see C. D. Gutsche and W. S. Johnson, *ibid.*, **68**, 2239 (1946).

(69) J. H. Burckhalter and J. R. Campbell, *J. Org. Chem.*, **26**, 4232 (1961).

Alternative procedures requiring less vigorous conditions include the acylation of olefins (e.g., [44]) with acid anhydrides in the

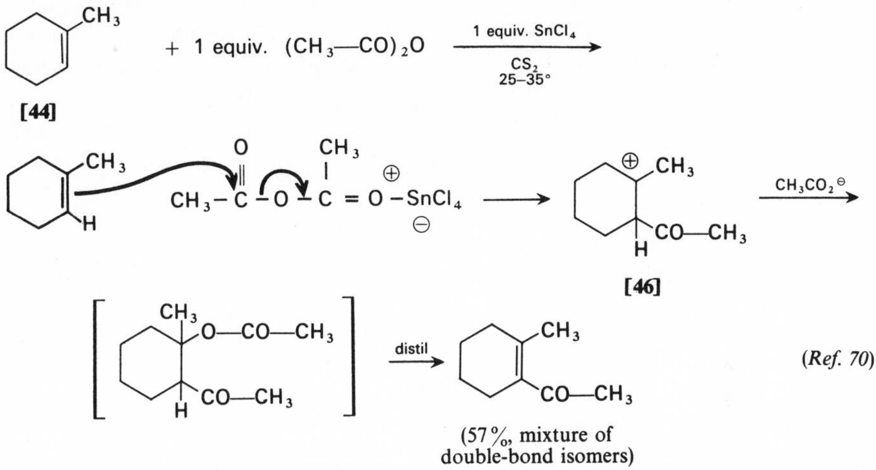

$$\text{[44] (1-methylcyclohexene, } CH_3\text{)} + 1\text{ equiv. } (CH_3{-}CO)_2O \xrightarrow[CS_2,\ 25\text{–}35°]{1\text{ equiv. } SnCl_4}$$

$$CH_3{-}\overset{O}{\overset{\|}{C}}{-}O{-}\overset{CH_3}{\overset{|}{C}}{=}\overset{\oplus}{O}{-}\overset{\ominus}{SnCl_4} \longrightarrow [46]\ (\oplus\ CH_3,\ H,\ CO{-}CH_3) \xrightarrow{CH_3CO_2^{\ominus}}$$

$$\left[\ CH_3,\ O{-}CO{-}CH_3,\ H,\ CO{-}CH_3\ \right] \xrightarrow{\text{distil}} CH_3,\ CO{-}CH_3$$

(57%, mixture of double-bond isomers) (*Ref.* 70)

presence of stannic chloride [68c,70] and the preparation of solutions of acid chloride–aluminum chloride complexes in methylene

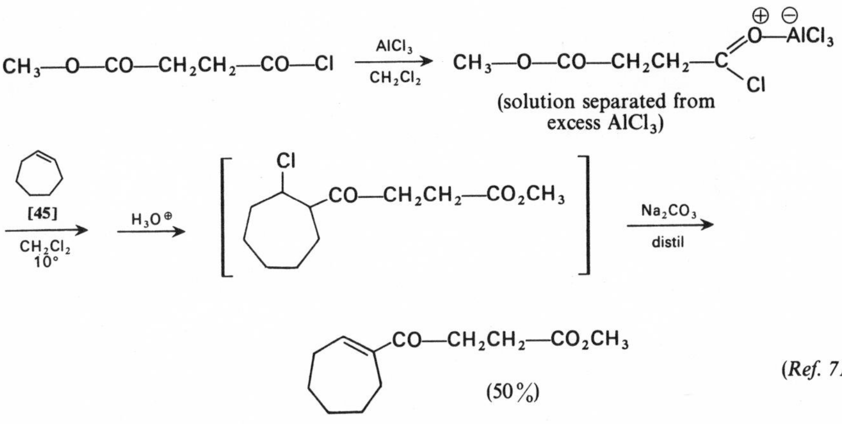

$$CH_3{-}O{-}CO{-}CH_2CH_2{-}CO{-}Cl \xrightarrow[CH_2Cl_2]{AlCl_3} CH_3{-}O{-}CO{-}CH_2CH_2{-}C(Cl){=}\overset{\oplus}{O}{-}\overset{\ominus}{AlCl_3}$$

(solution separated from excess $AlCl_3$)

$$\xrightarrow[CH_2Cl_2,\ 10°]{[45]} \xrightarrow{H_3O^{\oplus}} \left[\ Cl,\ CO{-}CH_2CH_2{-}CO_2CH_3\ \right] \xrightarrow[\text{distil}]{Na_2CO_3} CO{-}CH_2CH_2{-}CO_2CH_3$$

(50%) (*Ref.* 71*f*)

(70) (a) E. E. Royals and C. M. Hendry, *ibid.*, **15**, 1147 (1950); (b) H. O. House and W. F. Gilmore, *J. Am. Chem. Soc.*, **83**, 3980 (1961).

(71) (a) G. Baddeley, H. T. Taylor, and W. Pickles, *J. Chem. Soc.*, **1953**, 124; (b) H. T. Taylor, *ibid.*, **1958**, 3922; (c) N. Jones and H. T. Taylor, *ibid.*, **1959**, 4017; (d) N. Jones and H. T. Taylor, *ibid.*, **1961**, 1345; (e) N. Jones, H. T. Taylor, and E. Rudd, *ibid.*, **1961**, 1342; (f) N. Jones, E. J. Rudd, and H. T. Taylor, *ibid.*, **1963**, 2354.

chloride followed by treatment of these complexes with the olefin (e.g., **[45]**) to be acylated.[71] It will be noted that the position of acylation of the olefin **[44]** corresponds to the production of the more stable tertiary carbonium ion intermediate **[46]**.

Olefin acylation has also been achieved by reaction with carboxylic acids in polyphosphoric acid.[72] When α,β-unsaturated acids (e.g., **[47]**) are employed, cyclization of the intermediate acylation product (e.g., **[48]**) leads to a cyclopentenone derivative.

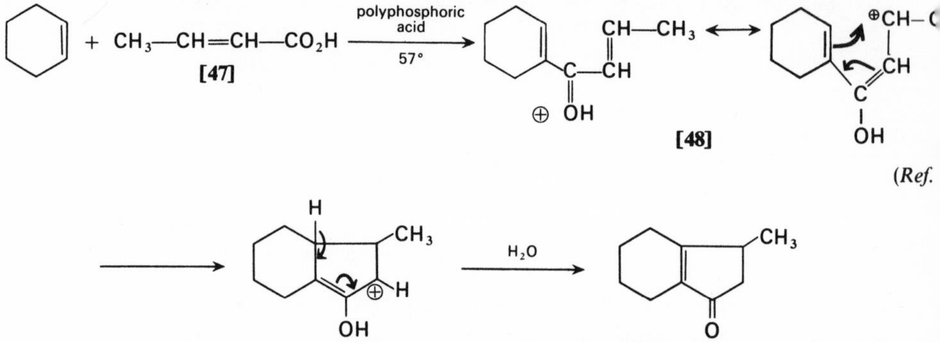

+ CH_3—CH=CH—CO_2H **[47]** —polyphosphoric acid, 57°→ CH—CH_3, C—CH, ⊕ OH **[48]** ⟷ ⊕CH—C, CH, C, OH

(*Ref.*

—→ H, CH_3, ⊕, H, OH —H_2O→ CH_3, O (60%)

Reactions of γ-lactones (e.g., **[49]**) and δ-lactones with polyphosphoric acid or phosphorous pentoxide have similarly been found to yield cyclopentenones, presumably via intramolecular acylation of the intermediate unsaturated acids. The acylation of olefins as well as of aromatic systems by reaction with carboxylic acids and

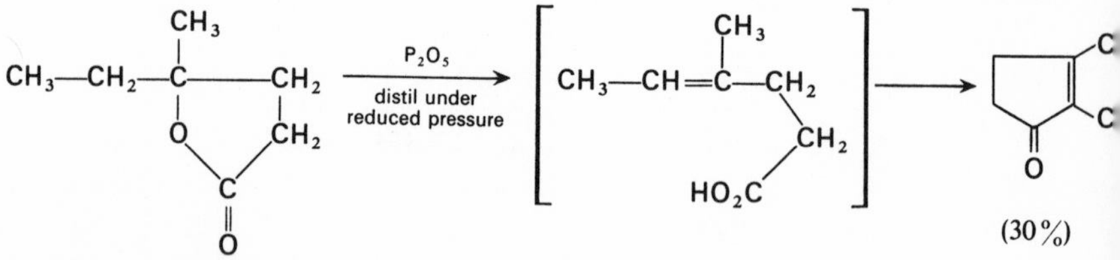

CH_3—CH_2—C(CH_3)—CH_2—CH_2—C(=O)—O **[49]** —P_2O_5, distil under reduced pressure→ [CH_3—CH=C(CH_3)—CH_2—CH_2—HO_2C] —→ O (30%)

(*Ref.* 7

(72) S. Dev, *J. Indian Chem. Soc.*, **32**, 255, 403 (1955); **33**, 703 (1956); **34**, 169 (1957).

(73) (a) R. L. Frank, R. Armstrong, J. Kwiatek, and H. A. Price, *J. Am. Chem. Soc.*, **70**, 1379 (1948); (b) S. Dev and C. Rai, *J. Indian Chem. Soc.*, **34**, 178, 266 (1957); (c) see also M. F. Ansell and M. H. Palmer, *Quart. Rev.* (*London*), **18**, 211 (1964).

$$CH_3CH_2—CH_2—C(CH_3)(—O—C(=O)—CH_2—CH_2—) \xrightarrow[97°]{\text{polyphosphoric acid}} \xrightarrow{H_2O} \text{3-methyl-2-ethylcyclopent-2-enone}$$ (Ref. 73b)

(90–92%)

trifluoroacetic anhydride has also been realized. As illustrated in the accompanying equations, this reaction is believed to involve acylation by the mixed anhydride (e.g., **[50]**), catalyzed by trifluoroacetic acid. Application of the same reaction to acetylenes (e.g., **[51]**) offers a synthetic route to 1,3-dicarbonyl compounds.

$$\text{cyclohexene} + n\text{-}C_3H_7—CO_2H \xrightarrow[\text{ca. } 25°]{(CF_3CO)_2O} \text{cyclohexene} + n\text{-}C_3H_7—C(=O)—O—C(=O)—CF_3 \;(H^{\oplus}) \longrightarrow$$

[50] (Ref. 74)

$$\text{2-}(CO—C_3H_7\text{-}n)\text{-1-}(O—CO—CF_3)\text{cyclohexane} \xrightarrow[H_2O]{Na_2CO_3} \text{1-}(CO—C_3H_7\text{-}n)\text{cyclohexene}$$

(51%)

$$n\text{-}C_4H_9—C{\equiv}CH \;\textbf{[51]} \xrightarrow[(CF_3CO)_2O,\ 27°]{CH_3CO_2H} n\text{-}C_4H_9—C(O—CO—CF_3){=}CH—CO—CH_3$$

$$\xrightarrow[\text{reflux}]{CH_3OH} n\text{-}C_4H_9—CO—CH_2—CO—CH_3$$ (Ref. 74)

(20%)

Some typical Friedel-Crafts acylations of aromatic systems are described in the equations below. As indicated in the first of these, reaction of an acid anhydride with aluminum chloride is thought to yield an acid chloride which is the actual acylating agent. Subsequent electrophilic attack of the Lewis acid–acid chloride complex (e.g., **[52]**) on the aromatic system, followed by loss of a proton from the intermediate ion (e.g., **[53]**) or sigma complex (see Chapter 6), leads to formation of the ketone, present in the reaction mixture as its conjugate acid. It will be noted that

(74) A. L. Henne and J. M. Tedder, *J. Chem. Soc.*, **1953**, 3628.

two equivalents of aluminum chloride are required in this sequence with acid anhydrides. Several of the examples illustrate the mild

$$C_6H_5{-}Br + (CH_3{-}CO)_2O \xrightarrow[CS_2,\ \text{reflux}]{(2.8\ \text{equiv.})\ AlCl_3} CH_3{-}CO{-}O{-}AlCl_2 + CH_3{-}CO{-}Cl$$

(1 equiv.)

$$\xrightarrow{AlCl_3} CH_3{-}\overset{Cl}{C}{=}\overset{\oplus}{O}{-}\overset{\ominus}{AlCl_3}\ [52] + C_6H_5Br \longrightarrow [53] \xrightarrow{-HCl}$$

[52] [53]

$$Br{-}C_6H_4{-}C(CH_3){=}\overset{\oplus}{O}{-}\overset{\ominus}{AlCl_3} \xrightarrow[H_2O]{HCl} Br{-}C_6H_4{-}CO{-}CH_3$$

(69–79%) (*Ref.* 75)

$$\text{acenaphthene} + \begin{array}{l} CH_2{-}CO \\ CH_2{-}CO \end{array}\!\!>O \xrightarrow[C_6H_5NO_2,\ 0\text{–}5^\circ]{(2\ \text{equiv.})\ AlCl_3} \xrightarrow[H_2O]{HCl}$$

(1 equiv.)

5-(CO—CH₂CH₂—CO₂H)acenaphthene (81%) + 3-(CO—CH₂CH₂—CO₂H)acenaphthene (5%) (*Ref.* 76)

$$C_6H_5{-}NH{-}CO{-}CH_3 + Cl{-}CH_2{-}CO{-}Cl \xrightarrow[CS_2,\ \text{reflux}]{(3\ \text{equiv.})\ AlCl_3}$$

(1 equiv.) (1.7 equiv.)

$$\xrightarrow[H_2O]{HCl} CH_3{-}CO{-}NH{-}C_6H_4{-}CO{-}CH_2{-}Cl$$

(79–83%) (*Ref.* 77)

(75) (a) R. Adams and C. R. Noller, *Org. Syn.*, **Coll. Vol. 1**, 109 (1944); see also (b) F. E. Ray and G. Rieveschl, Jr., *Org. Syn.*, **Coll. Vol. 3**, 23 (1955).

(76) (a) L. F. Fieser, *ibid.*, **Coll. Vol. 3**, 6 (1955); see also (b) O. Grummitt, E. I. Becker, and C. Miesse, *ibid.*, **Coll. Vol. 3**, 109 (1955); (c) L. F. Fieser, *Org. Syn.*, **Coll. Vol. 1**, 517 (1944); (d) L. F. Somerville and C. F. H. Allen, *Org. Syn.*, **Coll. Vol. 2**, 81 (1943).

(77) (a) J. L. Leiserson and A. Weissberger, *Org. Syn.*, **Coll. Vol. 3**, 183 (1955); see also (b) C. F. H. Allen, *Org. Syn.*, **Coll. Vol. 2**, 3 (1943); (c) W. Minnis, *ibid.*, **Coll. Vol. 2**, 520 (1943).

$$o\text{-}(CO{-}Cl)C_6H_4\text{-}NH{-}SO_2{-}C_6H_4{-}CH_3\text{-}p \xrightarrow[C_6H_6,\ 80\text{–}90°]{(4.4\text{ equiv.})\ AlCl_3} \xrightarrow[H_2O]{HCl} o\text{-}(CO{-}C_6H_5)C_6H_4\text{-}NH{-}SO_2{-}C_6H_4{-}CH_3\text{-}p \xrightarrow{H_2SO_4,\ 100°}$$

(1 equiv.)

$$\xrightarrow[H_2O]{NH_4OH} o\text{-}(CO{-}C_6H_5)C_6H_4\text{-}NH_2$$

(54%) (*Ref. 78*)

$$Cl{-}CO{-}(CH_2)_4{-}CO{-}Cl \xrightarrow[C_6H_6,\ 0\text{–}25°]{(2.3\text{ equiv.})\ AlCl_3} \xrightarrow[H_2O]{HCl} C_6H_5{-}CO{-}(CH_2)_4{-}CO{-}C_6H_5$$

(1 equiv.) (75–81%) (*Ref. 79*)

$$\text{thiophene} + CH_3{-}CO{-}Cl \xrightarrow[C_6H_6,\ 0°]{(1\text{ equiv.})\ SnCl_4} \xrightarrow[H_2O]{HCl} \text{2-thienyl}{-}CO{-}CH_3$$

(1 equiv.) (79–83%) (*Ref. 80*)

$$m\text{-}C_6H_4(OH)_2 + CH_3{-}CO_2H \xrightarrow[152\text{–}159°]{ZnCl_2} \xrightarrow[H_2O]{HCl} HO{-}C_6H_3(OH){-}CO{-}CH_3$$

(61–65%) (*Ref. 81*)

$$\text{thiophene} + (CH_3{-}CO)_2O \xrightarrow[\text{reflux}]{(\text{cat. amt.})\ H_3PO_4} \text{2-thienyl}{-}CO{-}CH_3$$

(74–79%) (*Ref. 82*)

conditions (zinc chloride, stannic chloride, or aluminum chloride in nitrobenzene) required for reactive aromatic nuclei.

Other procedures that result in acylation of reactive aromatic nuclei include acid-catalyzed condensation with nitriles (e.g., [**54**]),

(78) (a) H. J. Scheifele, Jr., and D. F. DeTar, *Org. Syn.*, **Coll. Vol. 4**, 34 (1963); see also (b) C. F. H. Allen and W. E. Barker, *Org. Syn.*, **Coll. Vol. 2**, 156 (1943); (c) F. J. Villani and M. S. King, *Org. Syn.*, **Coll. Vol. 4**, 88 (1963).

(79) (a) R. C. Fuson and J. T. Walker, *Org. Syn.*, **Coll. Vol. 2**, 169 (1943); see also (b) R. E. Lutz, *Org. Syn.*, **Coll. Vol. 3**, 248 (1955).

(80) J. R. Johnson and G. E. May, *Org. Syn.*, **Coll. Vol. 2**, 8 (1943).

(81) (a) S. R. Cooper, *Org. Syn.*, **Coll. Vol. 3**, 761 (1955); see also (b) I. C. Badhwar and K. Venkataraman, *Org. Syn.*, **Coll. Vol. 2**, 304 (1943).

(82) A. I. Kosak and H. D. Hartough, *Org. Syn.*, **Coll. Vol. 3**, 14 (1955).

called the Hoesch reaction,[83] and acid-catalyzed condensation with

$$\text{1,3,5-}(HO)_3C_6H_3 + CH_3{-}C{\equiv}N \ \textbf{[54]} \xrightarrow[(C_2H_5)_2O,\ 0^\circ]{HCl,\ ZnCl_2} 2,4,6\text{-}(HO)_3C_6H_2{-}C(CH_3){=}\overset{\oplus}{N}H_2\ Cl^{\ominus}$$

(*Ref. 84*)

$$\xrightarrow[\text{reflux}]{H_2O} 2,4,6\text{-}(HO)_3C_6H_2{-}CO{-}CH_3 \quad (74\text{–}87\%)$$

amides (e.g., **[55]**). The related reaction of N,N-disubstituted amides with aromatic systems in the presence of phosphorous

$$C_6H_5{-}N(CH_3)_2 + C_6H_5{-}CO{-}NH{-}C_6H_5 \ \textbf{[55]} \xrightarrow[100\text{–}125^\circ]{POCl_3} (CH_3)_2N{-}C_6H_4{-}C(C_6H_5){=}N{-}C_6H_5$$

$$\xrightarrow[H_2O]{HCl} (CH_3)_2N{-}C_6H_4{-}CO{-}C_6H_5 \quad (72\text{–}77\%)$$

(*Ref. 85*)

oxychloride, known as the Vilsmeier reaction, has proved especially valuable.[86] Its use to introduce the formyl group is illustrated in the following equations. The reaction is thought [86c,d] to involve a salt such as **[56]** as an electrophilic intermediate. Introduction of formyl groups has also been effected by reaction of aromatic systems (e.g., **[57]** and **[58]**) either with hydrogen cyanide and hydrogen

(83) (a) P. E. Spoerri and A. S. DuBois, *Org. Reactions*, **5**, 387 (1949); (b) for examples of the intramolecular acylation of olefins with nitriles in the presence of polyphosphoric acid, see R. K. Hill and R. T. Conley, *J. Am. Chem. Soc.*, **82**, 645 (1960).

(84) K. C. Gulati, S. R. Seth, and K. Venkataraman, *Org. Syn.*, **Coll. Vol. 2**, 522 (1943).

(85) C. D. Hurd and C. N. Webb, *Org. Syn.*, **Coll. Vol. 1**, 217 (1944).

(86) (a) M. R. de Maheas, *Bull. Soc. Chim. France*, **1962**, 1989; (b) K. Hafner and co-workers, *Angew. Chem., Intern. Ed. Engl.*, **2**, 123 (1963); (c) Z. Arnold and A. Holy, *Collection Czech. Chem. Commun.*, **27**, 2886 (1962); (d) G. Martin and M. Martin, *Bull. Soc. Chim. France*, **1963**, 1637; (e) for the application of the Vilsmeier reaction to enol ethers, see D. Burn and co-workers, *Tetrahedron*, **20**, 597 (1964).

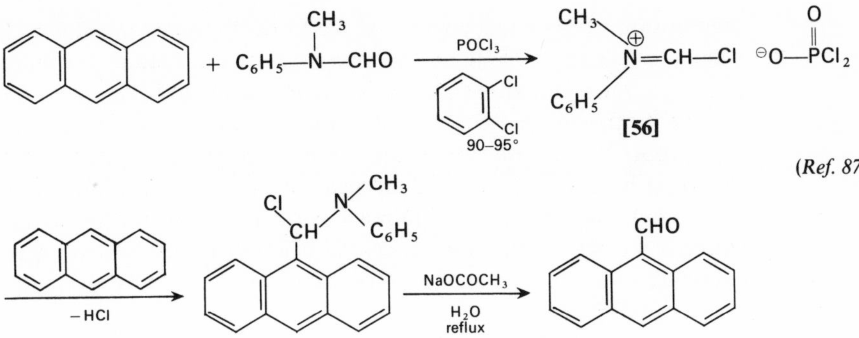

$C_6H_5N(CH_3)CHO \xrightarrow[\text{o-dichlorobenzene, 90–95°}]{POCl_3} [C_6H_5(CH_3)N^{\oplus}{=}CH{-}Cl]\ {}^{\ominus}O{-}P(O)Cl_2$ **[56]**

(*Ref. 87*)

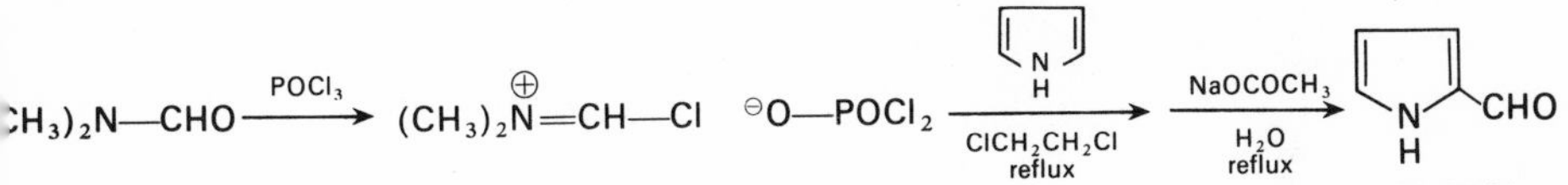

$\xrightarrow[-HCl]{\text{anthracene}}$ 9-[CH(Cl)N(CH_3)C_6H_5]anthracene $\xrightarrow[H_2O,\ \text{reflux}]{NaOCOCH_3}$ 9-anthraldehyde (77–84%)

$(CH_3)_2N{-}CHO \xrightarrow{POCl_3} (CH_3)_2N^{\oplus}{=}CH{-}Cl\ \ {}^{\ominus}O{-}POCl_2 \xrightarrow[ClCH_2CH_2Cl,\ \text{reflux}]{\text{pyrrole}} \xrightarrow[H_2O,\ \text{reflux}]{NaOCOCH_3}$ pyrrole-2-carboxaldehyde (78–79%)

(*Ref. 88*)

chloride or with carbon monoxide and hydrogen chloride, procedures developed by Gattermann.[89] An alternative method for the

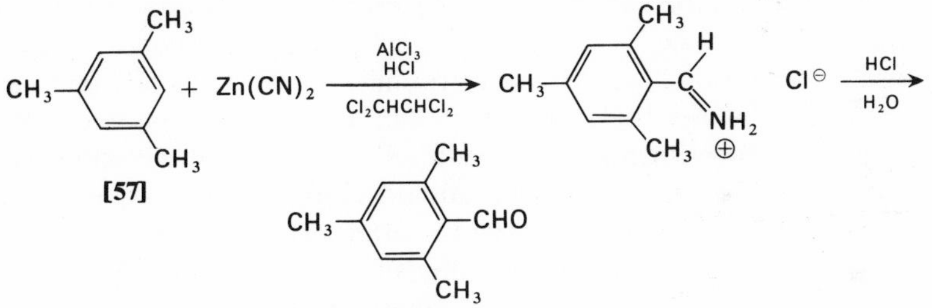

mesitylene **[57]** $+ Zn(CN)_2 \xrightarrow[Cl_2CHCHCl_2]{AlCl_3,\ HCl}$ $2,4,6-(CH_3)_3C_6H_2{-}CH{=}NH_2^{\oplus}\ Cl^{\ominus} \xrightarrow[H_2O]{HCl}$ $2,4,6-(CH_3)_3C_6H_2{-}CHO$ (75–81%)

(*Ref. 90*)

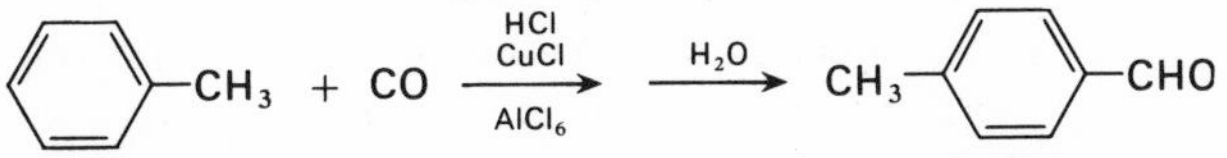

toluene **[58]** $+ CO \xrightarrow[AlCl_6]{HCl,\ CuCl} \xrightarrow{H_2O} CH_3{-}C_6H_4{-}CHO$ (46–51%)

(*Ref. 91*)

(87) L. F. Fieser, J. L. Hartwell, and J. E. Jones, *Org. Syn.*, **Coll. Vol. 3**, 98 (1955).

(88) (a) R. M. Silverstein, E. E. Ryskiewicz, and C. Willard, *Org. Syn.*, **Coll. Vol. 4**, 831 (1963); see also (b) P. N. James and H. R. Snyder, *ibid.*, **Coll. Vol. 4**, 539 (1963); (c) A. W. Weston and R. J. Michaels, Jr., *ibid.*, **Coll. Vol. 4**, 915 (1963).

(89) W. E. Truce, *Org. Reactions*, **9**, 37 (1957).

(90) R. C. Fuson, E. C. Horning, S. P. Rowland, and M. L. Ward, *Org. Syn.*, **Coll. Vol. 3**, 549 (1955).

(91) G. H. Coleman and D. Craig, *Org. Syn.*, **Coll. Vol. 2**, 583 (1943).

preparation of acylated phenols is based on the rearrangement of phenyl esters (e.g., **[59]**) in the presence of aluminum chloride. This reaction, known as the Fries rearrangement,[92] appears to involve both intermolecular and intramolecular transfer of the acyl group.[92c] The intermolecular transfer presumably occurs by electrophilic attack of an acid chloride or an acyl cation on either the phenyl ester or the aluminum alkoxide derived from the phenol whereas the intramolecular process is believed to proceed via a pi complex.

$$C_6H_5{-}O{-}CO{-}CH_2{-}CH_3 \xrightarrow[\text{CS}_2,\ \text{reflux}]{\text{(1.1 equiv.) AlCl}_3} [CH_3{-}CH_2{-}\overset{\oplus}{C}O + C_6H_5{-}O{-}\overset{\ominus}{Al}Cl_3] \xrightarrow[140\text{–}150^\circ]{}$$

(1 equiv.) **[59]**

$$\xrightarrow[H_2O]{HCl} p\text{-}HO{-}C_6H_4{-}CO{-}CH_2{-}CH_3 + o\text{-}HO{-}C_6H_4{-}CO{-}CH_2{-}CH_3$$

(45–50%) (32–35%) (*Ref. 93*)

From a number of the preceding examples, it is apparent that the position taken by an entering acyl group corresponds to the usual orientation observed in electrophilic substitutions of aromatic systems. The reactivity of the system is enhanced by electron-donating substituents and reduced by electron-withdrawing substituents. In fact, Friedel-Crafts acylations of benzene derivatives containing powerful electron-withdrawing substituents (e.g., nitro or carbonyl functions) usually fail making possible the use of nitrobenzene as a solvent for aromatic acylation reactions. The orientation resulting from a Friedel-Crafts acylation is unusually susceptible to steric effects, as is evidenced by the relatively high proportion of *para* to *ortho* isomer obtained in acylations of monosubstituted benzene derivatives. This steric influence is obvious in the acetylation of *p*-cymene **[60]**, where the acetyl group is introduced *ortho* to the smaller alkyl group. The use of nitrobenzene as a solvent not only reduces the activity of aluminum

(92) (a) A. H. Blatt, *Org. Reactions,* **1**, 342 (1942); (b) C. R. Hauser and E. H. Man, *J. Org. Chem.*, **17**, 390 (1952); (c) Y. Ogata and H. Tabuchi, *Tetrahedron*, **20**, 1661 (1964).

(93) (a) E. Miller and W. H. Hartung, *Org. Syn.,* **Coll. Vol. 2**, 543 (1943); see also (b) G. C. Amin and N. M. Shah, *Org. Syn.,* **Coll. Vol. 3**, 280 (1955); (c) A. Russel and J. R. Frye, *ibid.*, **Coll. Vol. 3**, 281 (1955).

$$p\text{-}CH_3C_6H_4CH(CH_3)_2\ [60] + CH_3\!-\!CO\!-\!Cl \xrightarrow[CS_2,\ 0\text{–}5°]{AlCl_3} \xrightarrow[H_2O]{HCl} 2\text{-}CH_3CO\text{-}4\text{-}CH(CH_3)_2\text{-}C_6H_3CH_3\ (50\text{–}55\%)$$ (*Ref. 77b*)

chloride as a Lewis acid but also appears to increase the effective steric bulk of the acylating agent, presumably because the nitrobenzene becomes associated with the aluminum chloride–acid chloride complex. The change in product orientation that results when naphthalene acylation is carried out in its presence rather than in its absence (see accompanying equations) has been suggested to reflect the differing steric sizes of the acylating agents in the two cases. Alternatively, it has been suggested that the acylation is reversible and leads to the formation of the thermodynamically more stable β-acyl derivative when a less reactive

$$\underset{(1\ \text{equiv.})}{CH_3\!-\!CO\!-\!Cl} \xrightarrow[ClCH_2CH_2Cl]{(1\ \text{equiv.})\ AlCl_3} \text{solution of complex} \xrightarrow[ClCH_2CH_2Cl,\ 35°]{\text{naphthalene}}$$

1-acetylnaphthalene (98% of product) + 2-acetylnaphthalene (2% of product) (93%) (*Ref. 94*)

$$\underset{(1\ \text{equiv.})}{CH_3\!-\!CO\!-\!Cl} + \underset{(1\ \text{equiv.})}{C_6H_5\!-\!NO_2} \xrightarrow[ClCH_2CH_2Cl]{(1\ \text{equiv.})\ AlCl_3} \text{solution of complex} \xrightarrow[ClCH_2CH_2Cl,\ 35°]{\text{naphthalene}}$$

1-acetylnaphthalene (40% of product) + 2-acetylnaphthalene (60% of product) (82%) (*Ref. 94*)

(94) G. Baddeley, *J. Chem. Soc.*, **1949**, S99.

acylating agent is used.[60a] Steric effects are also observed in acylation reactions employing α-substituted succinic anhydrides[60d]; in such cases, the aromatic system is usually acylated predominantly by the less sterically hindered carbonyl function.

The accompanying equations illustrate the application of intramolecular Friedel-Crafts acylations to the preparation of cyclic ketones. The synthesis of the eight-membered-ring ketone **[62]** from the acid chloride **[61]** requires high-dilution conditions. A similar cyclic ketone has been prepared without high dilution by cyclization

$C_6H_5CH_2CH_2CH_2—CO—Cl$ → (1.1 equiv.) $AlCl_3$, CS_2, reflux → HCl, H_2O → (74–91%) (*Ref.* 95)

CO_2H, CO, CH_3 → SO_3, H_2SO_4, 100° → H_2O → CH_3 (81–90%) (*Ref.* 96)

$C_6H_5CH_2CH_2—CO_2H$ → polyphosphoric acid, 70° → H_2O → (94%) (*Ref.* 97)

$C_6H_5(CH_2)_5—CO—Cl$ **[61]** → $AlCl_3$, CS_2, high-dilution conditions, 25° → **[62]** (67%) (*Ref.* 98)

(95) (a) E. L. Martin and L. F. Fieser, *Org. Syn.*, **Coll. Vol. 2**, 569 (1943); see also (b) H. R. Snyder and F. X. Werber, *Org. Syn.*, **Coll. Vol. 3**, 798 (1955); (c) G. D. Johnson *Org. Syn.*, **Coll. Vol. 4**, 900 (1963).

(96) L. F. Fieser, *Org. Syn.*, **Coll. Vol. 1**, 353 (1944).

(97) J. Koo, *J. Am. Chem. Soc.*, **75**, 1891 (1953).

(98) (a) W. M. Schubert, W. A. Sweeney, and H. K. Latourette, *ibid.*, **76**, 5462 (1954); (b) G. D. Hedden and W. G. Brown, *ibid.*, **75**, 3744 (1953).

$$\text{[63]} \xrightarrow[\text{Cl}_2\text{CHCHCl}_2,\ 0°]{\text{AlCl}_3} \xrightarrow[\text{H}_2\text{O}]{\text{HCl}} (49\%)$$ (*Ref. 99a*)

$$\text{C}_{10}\text{H}_7\text{–(CH}_2)_9\text{–CO–Cl} \xrightarrow[\text{high-dilution conditions}]{\text{AlCl}_3,\ \text{CS}_2} \text{(33\% of mixture)}$$ (*Ref. 99b*)

$$\text{C}_6\text{H}_5\text{–(CH}_2)_4\text{–CO}_2\text{CH}_3 \xrightarrow[95°]{\text{polyphosphoric acid}} (90\%)$$ (*Ref. 100*)

of the acid chloride **[63]**; however, closure of the next higher homolog to form a nine-membered ring failed.[99a] With longer side chains, cyclization under high-dilution conditions has occurred at positions other than the *ortho* position to produce cyclic ketones.[99b] In the absence of opposing steric interactions, the ease of ring closure in intramolecular acylations follows the order 6-membered > 5-membered > 7-membered.[60c] This generalization is exemplified by the cyclizations of the diacids **[64]** and **[65]**. However, the preference for six-membered-ring formation is sufficiently small that it may be altered by opposing steric interactions.

$$\text{C}_6\text{H}_5\text{–CH}_2\text{–CH(CO}_2\text{H)–CH}_2\text{CH}_2\text{–CO}_2\text{H} \xrightarrow[20°]{\text{HF}} \text{(indanone)–CH}_2\text{CH}_2\text{–CO}_2\text{H}$$

[64] (81%) (*Ref. 101*)

(99) (a) H. Stetter, B. Schäfer, and H. Spangenberger, *Chem. Ber.*, **89**, 1620 (1956); (b) R. Huisgen and U. Rietz, *Tetrahedron*, **2**, 271 (1958) and references therein.
(100) (a) R. C. Gilmore, Jr., *J. Am. Chem. Soc.*, **73**, 5879 (1951); (b) R. C. Gilmore, Jr., and W. J. Horton, *ibid.*, **73**, 1411 (1951).
(101) M. F. Ansell and D. H. Hey, *J. Chem. Soc.*, **1950**, 2874.

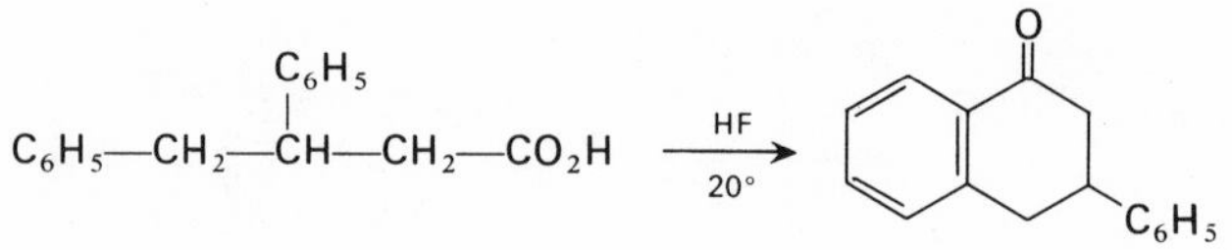

$C_6H_5-CH_2-CH(C_6H_5)-CH_2-CO_2H \xrightarrow[20°]{HF}$ 3-phenyl-1-tetralone (*Ref. 102*)

[65] (66%)

For example, the acid [**66**] produces predominantly the indanone [**68**] under conditions where the diastereoisomeric acid [**67**] forms predominantly the tetralone [**69**]. In each case that ring closure is

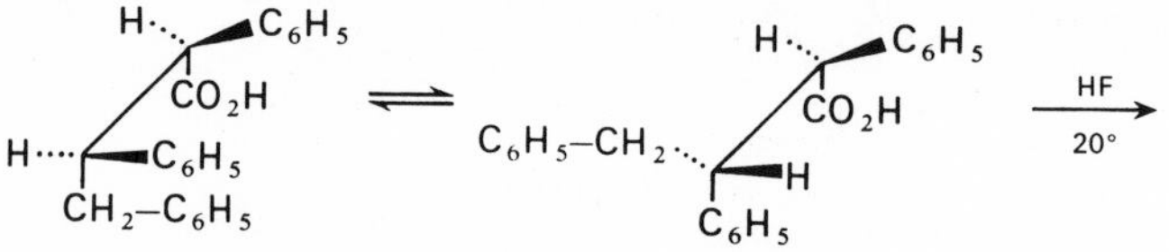

[66a] ⇌ [66b] $\xrightarrow[20°]{HF}$ (*Ref. 102*)

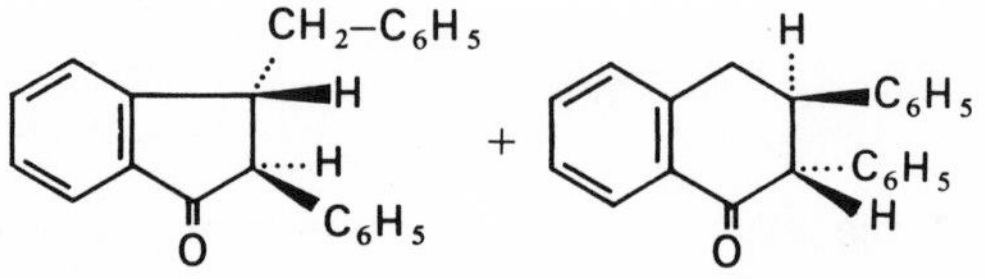

[68] (ca. 67% of mixture) + [69] (ca. 33% of mixture, apparently formed by cyclization and subsequent epimerization)

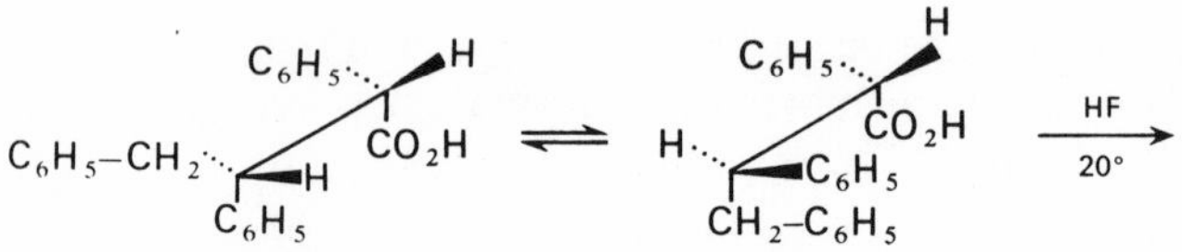

[67a] ⇌ [67b] $\xrightarrow[20°]{HF}$

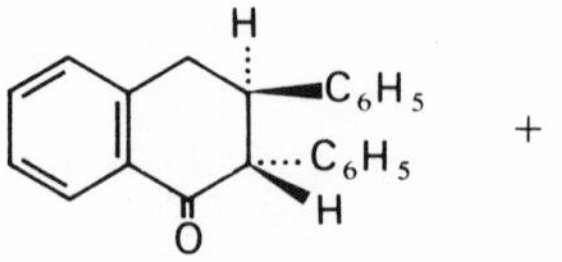

[69] (ca. 75% of mixture) + an indanone believed to be [**68**] or its C-2 epimer (ca. 25% of mixture) (*Ref. 102*)

(102) D. Lednicer and C. R. Hauser, *J. Am. Chem. Soc.*, **80**, 3409, 6364 (1958).

favored which avoids eclipsing the two large substituents in the transition state. Configuration about a double bond will also control the direction of cyclization, as shown by the closure of the unsaturated acid **[70]** to form a seven-membered rather than a

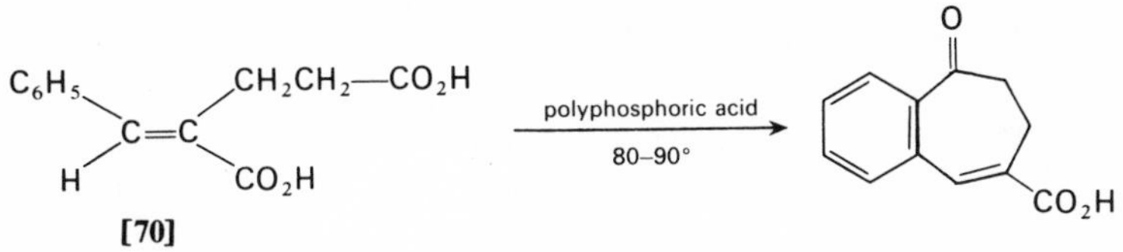

$C_6H_5(H)C{=}C(CO_2H)CH_2CH_2{-}CO_2H$ **[70]** —polyphosphoric acid, 80–90°→ (*Ref. 103*)

five-membered ring. This fact has been used to assign configurations to the isomeric α-arylidenesuccinic acids (e.g., **[71]** and **[72]**) obtained from the Stobbe condensation (see Chapter 8).[104] It should be noted that cyclization of the unsaturated acid **[72]**

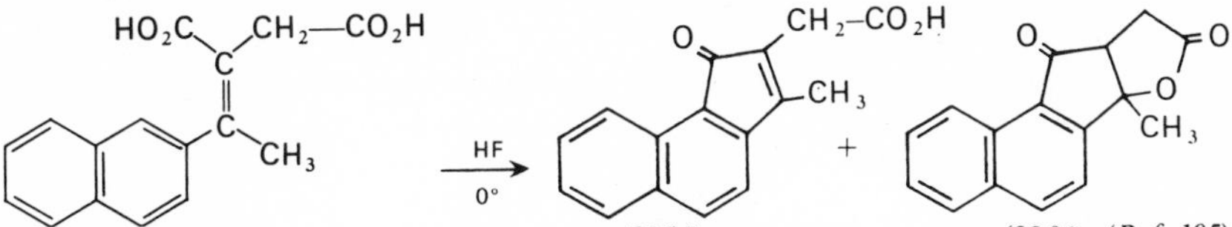

[71] —HF, 0°→ (31%) + (39%) (*Ref. 105*)

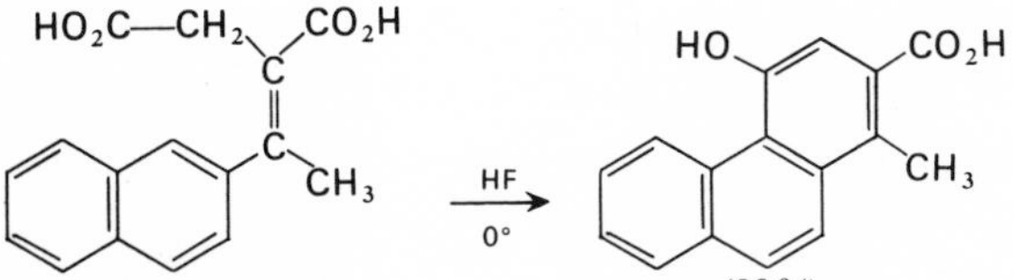

[72] —HF, 0°→ (82%) (*Ref. 105*)

leads to isolation of a phenol derivative rather than of the thermodynamically less stable unsaturated ketone.

Normally, configuration at an asymmetric center not adjacent to the carbonyl function is not altered by the conditions of the Friedel-Crafts acylation, as illustrated by the cyclization of the diastereoisomeric acids **[73]** and **[74]**. However, if one of the centers of asymmetry is adjacent to the carbonyl function, epimerization of the initial product to a more stable stereoisomer may be observed. For example, addition of aluminum chloride to the *trans*-acid chloride **[75]** leads to formation of the more stable *cis*-ketone **[76]**. The same type of epimerization is seen in the previously mentioned

(103) H. O. House, V. Paragamian, R. S. Ro, and D. J. Wluka, *ibid.*, **82**, 1452 (1960).

(104) W. S. Johnson and G. H. Daub, *Org. Reactions*, **6**, 1 (1951).

(105) W. S. Johnson and A. Goldman, *J. Am. Chem. Soc.*, **66**, 1030 (1944).

[73] $\xrightarrow[20°]{HF}$ (*Ref. 106*)

[74] $\xrightarrow[20°]{HF}$ (92%) (*Ref. 106*)

cyclization of the acid [**66**] to the ketone [**69**]. Interestingly, the reverse procedure, in which the acid chloride [**75**] is added to excess aluminum chloride, produces the less stable *trans* isomer [**77**]. In both cases, the initial product is believed to be the conjugate acid [**78**] of the *trans*-ketone. The formation of the conjugate acid [**78**] in the presence of excess acid chloride (which can serve as a base: see Chapter 6) allows enolization to occur and, consequently permits epimerization of the asymmetric center adjacent to the carbonyl function. However, in the reaction where aluminum chloride is always in excess, no base is present to abstract a proton from the conjugate acid [**78**] and epimerization is not observed.

[**75**] (1 equiv.) → (1.1 equiv.) $AlCl_3$, CS_2 (acid chloride added to $AlCl_3$) → H_2O → [**77**] (86%) (*Ref. 68c*)

[**75**] → 1.1 equiv. $AlCl_3$, CS_2 ($AlCl_3$ added to acid chloride) → [**78**] (base, $AlCl_3$) → $-Cl^{\ominus}$ → $OAlCl_2$ enolate → H_2O → [**76**] (74%) (*Refs. 68c, 106*)

(106) (a) C. D. Gutsche, *ibid.*, **73**, 786 (1951); (b) C. D. Gutsche and W. S. Johnson, *ibid.*, **68**, 2239 (1946).

INDEX